Ontario's Health System:

Key Insights for Engaged Citizens, Professionals and Policymakers

John N. Lavis, Editor

McMaster University   McMaster HEALTH FORUM

The publisher of this book is the McMaster Health Forum, 1280 Main St. West, MML-417, Hamilton, ON, Canada L8S 4L6. The McMaster Health Forum welcomes corrections, updates and feedback, as well as suggestions for conditions, treatments and populations that are not covered in the book, so that they can be considered for incorporation in a future eBook and in future print editions of the book. Any corrections, updates, feedback and suggestions provided do not certify authorship. Please send your comments to mhf@mcmaster.ca.

The appropriate citation for this book is: Lavis JN (editor), Ontario's health system: Key insights for engaged citizens, professionals and policymakers. Hamilton: McMaster Health Forum; 2016.

ISBN 978-1-927565-11-7 (Print)
ISBN 978-1-927565-12-4 (Online)

Contents

List of tables and figures

Tables

Figures

Biographies

Amanda C. Hammill is Lead, Evaluations, at the McMaster Health Forum, and Research Co-ordinator in the Forum's Impact Lab. She earned her Master's degree in Social Welfare Policy and a graduate diploma in Health Services and Policy Research at McMaster University.

John N. Lavis is the Director of the McMaster Health Forum. He holds the Tier 1 Canada Research Chair in Evidence-Informed Health Systems. He is the Co-director of the World Health Organization Collaborating Centre on Evidence-Informed Policy, Associate Director of the Centre for Health Economics and Policy Analysis, Professor in the Department of Health Evidence and Impact, and Associate Member of the Department of Political Science at McMaster University. He holds an MD from Queen's University, an M.Sc. from the London School of Economics and Political Science, and a PhD in Health Policy from Harvard University.

Cristina A. Mattison is Co-Lead, Evidence Synthesis, at the McMaster Health Forum, and Research Coordinator in the Forum's Impact Lab. She holds an M.Sc. in Global Health and is completing her PhD in Health Policy at McMaster University.

Kaelan A. Moat is the Scientific Lead, Health Systems Evidence and Learning, at the McMaster Health Forum, and an Investigator with the Forum's Impact Lab. He is a Member of the Centre for Health Economics and Policy Analysis and an Assistant Professor (part time) in the Department of Health Evidence and Impact at McMaster University. He holds an M.Sc. from the London School of Economics and Political Science, and a PhD in Health Policy from McMaster University.

Kody Doxtater was an Indigenous Undergraduate Summer Research Scholar with the McMaster Health Forum at the time he contributed to the book. He is from Six Nations of the Grand River, has worked as a paramedic, and holds an honours specialization in First Nations Studies and a major in Health Sciences from Western University. He is now an MPH student at the University of Victoria.

Michael G. Wilson is the Assistant Director of the McMaster Health Forum, and an Investigator with the Forum's Impact Lab. He is a Member of the Centre for Health Economics and Policy Analysis and an Assistant Professor in the Department of Health Evidence and Impact at McMaster University. He holds a B.H.Sc. (Honours) from McMaster University, completed course requirements in the M.Sc. Health Research Methodology program before transferring directly to the PhD program, and studied political science at the University of Toronto. He completed his PhD in Health Research Methodology and graduate diploma in Health Services and Policy Research at McMaster University.

Preface

John N. Lavis

Ontario's health system is complex (which can make it hard to navigate) and has features that many simply take for granted as the way things are done (which can make it hard to transform). The primary goal in writing this book was to help make the system more understandable to the citizens who pay for it and are served by it, the professionals who work in it (and future professionals who will one day work in it), and the policymakers who govern it. The secondary goal was to highlight the taken-for-granted nature of the system's features so that citizens, professionals and policy-makers can appreciate that some of these features do not need to be that way. Our goal was not to provide a navigational aid that any given citizen can use to address a particular health problem, although the book provides important context to those navigating the system.

Some key word choices warrant consideration up front. By citizens we mean the taxpayers who finance much of the system, the patients who receive care in the system, and the family and other caregivers who support patients receiving care in the system. We do not mean just those who hold Canadian citizenship and reside in Ontario. In specific sections of the book, such as Chapter 6, we use the terms most commonly used in particular sectors (e.g., clients in the home and community care sector, patients in the primary and specialty care sectors, both clients and patients in the rehabilitation care sector, and residents in the long-term care sector). By professionals we mean the nurses, physicians and other members of the health workforce who provide care to patients. And by policymakers we mean the democratically elected politicians who make tough decisions about the system on our collective behalf, their political advisors, the public servants who provide politicians with impartial advice and who implement their decisions, as well as the staff of the government agencies and other organizations who make many other decisions that influence how the system operates.

In writing key messages for each of these three groups (citizens, professionals and policymakers), we focused on what someone moving up their learning curve would need to know and the 'angle' that would most interest them. For professionals, someone moving up their learning curve about Ontario's health system might include an individual still in an educational or training program (e.g., a nursing student or medical resident) or a health professional who has just moved to the province or into a new clinical area. For policymakers, someone moving up their learning curve might include a director or policy analyst who has just moved to a new part of the Ministry of Health and Long-Term Care. An experienced health professional or policymaker who has worked in a clinical or policy area for some time will likely find nothing new in the key messages, and will want to dig into the details in the chapter right away.

Returning to the issue of word choices, some do not do justice to the reality of Ontario's health system, but they are perhaps the best we have. Some would question whether we have a system per se or whether it is a healthcare system (i.e., one focused on treating disease) and not a health system (i.e., one focused on promoting health and both preventing and treating disease). Although parts of it may not seem connected to the whole and large parts of it are focused on treating diseases that could have been prevented, policymakers are increasingly taking steps to address fragmentation and to position population-based approaches to disease prevention and health promotion more centrally in the system. Others would question the use of the phrase 'providing care' as the focus of the system. Although 'delivering programs, services and drugs' (including population-based programs) or more tangibly 'getting the right mix of programs, services and drugs to the people who need them' may be more accurate in some ways, something gets lost when using that language. Still others would question why we have a *Public Hospitals Act, 1990* that regulates private not-for-profit hospitals and a *Private Hospitals Act, 1990* that regulates the province's very few private-for-profit hospitals (which existed before the introduction of hospital insurance and thus were 'grandfathered' into our current system). We have called them by the more descriptive label and not by the name implied by the act that governs them.

The initial impetus for writing this book was the recognition that those who want to learn about and from the Ontario health system are not fully served by attempts to profile the Canadian health 'system,' which generalize across the very different provincial and territorial health systems that make up the ill-named 'Canadian' health system (or Medicare as it is sometimes called). As we note above in describing our goal in writing this book, those interested in learning *about* the Ontario health system – citizens, professionals and policymakers – are our primary target audience. But given the importance of considering the local applicability of synthesized research evidence to a particular health system, those interested in learning *from* the approaches being used in the Ontario health system (ideally from rigorous evaluations that are put alongside all other comparable evaluations in the systematic reviews contained in Health Systems Evidence – www.healthsystemsevidence.org) are our secondary target audience.

The staff at the McMaster Health Forum who worked part time for two years to create the tables and figures in this book and to draft the text were financially supported by several sources, including my Tier 1 Canada Research Chair in Evidence-Informed Health Systems and McMaster University's Labarge Optimal Aging Initiative. Much of the content of the book drew on the outputs of the McMaster Health Forum, including Health Systems Evidence (and the Ontario health system documents contained within it), the rapid syntheses the Forum has prepared at the request of health-system policymakers and stakeholders, the stakeholder dialogues and citizen panels convened by the Forum (and the evidence briefs and citizen briefs prepared to inform them), and Health Systems Learning (and the course materials that comprise it). The McMaster Health Forum receives both financial and in-kind support from McMaster University.

We thank the policymakers, stakeholders and researchers who reviewed chapters or sections of chapters, including: Adalsteinn Brown (Chapter 2), Alina Gildiner ('rehabilitation care' section of Chapter 6), Carlos Quiñonez ('dental services' section of Chapter 8), Emile Tompa ('work-related injuries and diseases' section of Chapter 7), Gail Donner ('home and community care' section of Chapter 6), Heather Boon ('complementary and alternative therapies' section of Chapter 8), Ian Johnson ('public health' section of Chapter 6), Janet Durbin ('mental health and addictions' section of Chapter 7), Jennifer Walker (Chapter 9), Jennifer Zelmer (Chapter 4), José Pereira ('end-of-life' section of Chapter 7), Michael Hillmer (Chapter 1),

Nancy Cooper ('long-term care' section of Chapter 6), Paul Grootendorst ('prescription and over-the-counter drugs' section of Chapter 8), Raisa Deber (Chapter 3), Sharon Johnston (Chapter 11), Simon Rabinovitch ('specialty care' section of Chapter 6), Terry Sullivan ('cancer' section of Chapter 7, as well as Chapter 10), and Wayne Warry (Chapter 9), as well as two anonymous reviewers (Chapter 5 and the 'primary care' section of Chapter 6).

We also thank the McMaster students who worked with Amanda, Cristina and myself on the tables and figures (Ben Li, Carolyne Wang, Lucas Gallo and Matthew Hughsam), Tommaso D'Ovidio who coordinated the review of chapters and sections of chapters, Nancy Johnson and Sue Johnston who copy-edited the book, Ileana Ciurea who participated in the final 'read through,' Jenn Belanger and Caitlin O'Connell who designed the book, Kerry Waddell who coordinated the review of page proofs, our colleagues at McMaster who provided feedback on the book through extensive discussions of many chapters at monthly 'Polinomics' sessions, and our colleagues at McMaster who reviewed chapters or sections of chapters, including: Andrew Costa ('long-term care' section of Chapter 6), Anne Holbrook ('prescription and over-the-counter drugs' section of Chapter 8), Anne Snider ('cancer' section of Chapter 7), Arthur Sweetman (Chapter 5), Christina Hackett (Chapter 9), David Price ('primary care' section of Chapter 6), Fran Scott ('dental services' section of Chapter 8), Glen Randall (Chapter 10), Heather Bullock ('mental health and addictions' section of Chapter 7), Hsien Seow (Chapter 11), Jeremiah Hurley (Chapters 1 and 3), Joy MacDermid ('work-related injuries and diseases' section of Chapter 7), Julia Abelson (Chapter 2), Julie Richardson ('rehabilitation care' section of Chapter 6), Liz Alvarez ('complementary and alternative therapies' section of Chapter 8), Maureen Markle-Reid ('home and community care' section of Chapter 6), Michel Grignon (Chapter 4), Michelle Howard ('end-of-life' section of Chapter 7), Mitch Levine ('specialty care' section of Chapter 6), and M. Mustafa Hirji ('public health' section of Chapter 6).

The views expressed in the book are the views of the authors and should not be taken to represent the views of the book's or the McMaster Health Forum's funders or the views of the 41 policymakers, stakeholders and researchers who reviewed chapters or sections of chapters. The information presented in the book was drawn from publicly available information. We did not pay for customized data analyses or for proprietary reports.

We apologize for any errors in the text, tables or figures that escaped our scrutiny.

We welcome corrections, updates and feedback, as well as suggestions for conditions, treatments and populations that we do not cover in the book, so that we can incorporate them when we create an eBook (which we plan to do in 2017) and when we update the print version of the book (which we plan to do periodically). Indeed we ask you the same question we asked our 41 reviewers:

1) do the key messages appropriately highlight what each of engaged citizens, engaged professionals and engaged policymakers need to know (and if not, what would you recommend changing)?
2) do we get the 'big picture' right (and if not, what would you recommend emphasizing or de-emphasizing)?
3) do we get any of the details wrong (and if so, what would you recommend correcting and, if applicable, what citation(s) would you recommend be used to support the corrected content)?
4) do we present material in a fair and balanced way (and if not, what content or wording would you recommend be changed)?
5) do we use language that is appropriate for an audience comprised of engaged citizens, professionals and policymakers?

Please send your comments to mhf@mcmaster.ca.

1. Introduction and overview

John N. Lavis and Cristina A. Mattison

Key messages for citizens

- The health system is largely the responsibility of the provincial government, albeit within certain broad rules set by the federal government.
- Care is increasingly being organized by region, with each region overseen by a Local Health Integration Network.
- The care provided in hospitals or by physicians is free to patients at the point of use, and more money is now spent on prescription drugs (which are far from free for most patients) than is spent on physicians.
- The money spent on the health system each year ($5,877 on average per Ontarian in 2013) comes from government (two thirds) and private sources like employers or out-of-pocket charges (one third).
- Ontarians (especially women) tend to live long lives, with cancer and heart disease the most common causes of lives being cut short, but many factors beyond the health system contribute to long life expectancy.

Key messages for health professionals

- The provincial government has a big say in how the health system functions, whereas the federal government's role is either less visible (e.g., financial contributions to the provincial government) or more focused (e.g., care for First Nations populations living on reserve).
- The province is divided into 14 regions and most types of care (besides physician-provided care and prescription drugs) are planned and funded by regional bodies (Local Health Integration Networks) that can be sensitive to unique regional needs.
- Patients cannot be charged for medically necessary care provided in hospital or by a physician, but they can be (and are) charged for many other types of care, most notably prescription drugs.
- Long life expectancies mean that health professionals deal with lots of elderly patients, many of whom will die from cancer or heart disease.

Key messages for policymakers

- The provincial government has constitutional responsibility for health-care, but it intersects with the federal government in areas where the latter has responsibility (e.g., First Nations) or sets broad terms under which financial transfers are provided.

- While two thirds of the system's total costs are paid for by government, the government's share is particularly high for hospital-based and physician-provided care, even if the province's private not-for-profit hospitals and physicians working in private practice operate quite autonomously from government.

- Given that 43 cents of every dollar the government spends goes to healthcare, relatively little money is available for the many other areas where the government needs to act.

- Ontario's generally good health status indicators overall mask significant differences in these indicators across socio-economic and other groups.

. . .

Like all health systems, Ontario's health system operates within a historical, geographic and socio-demographic context, a current political and economic context, and a particular context in terms of the health status of Ontarians. This chapter describes that context and concludes with a brief overview of the book.

Historical context

Decisions made in the past about the health system shape it in profound ways today. Some of the key features of this historical context, particularly those relating to governance and financial arrangements that involve federal/provincial relations (and the hospital-based or physician-provided care that have been the main focus of these relations), include:

1) an early effort (in 1945) failed to introduce a national health-insurance plan that would have covered many types of care for Ontarians (not just hospital-based and physician-provided care);

2) hospital-based care started being paid for by the Government of Ontario in 1957 and physician-provided care followed suit in 1969 (both

of which were preceded by Saskatchewan, in 1947 and 1962, respectively, and supported financially by the federal government), however, hospitals remained independent and private not-for-profit entities and physicians remained working in independent private practice;

3) hospital-care insurance and medical-care insurance were combined programmatically under the Ontario Health Insurance Plan (OHIP) in 1972, and OHIP is administered under the terms of the *Canada Health Act, 1984*, which combined separate pieces of federal legislation in 1984, formally banned any form of user fee for medically necessary hospital-based and physician-provided care, and led to an unsuccessful strike by Ontario's physicians;

4) the federal government began in 1995 to reduce its financial support for the health system in Ontario (and in other provinces and territories), but dramatically increased its support through health accords in 2003 and 2004 in return for action in particular areas (e.g., wait times) and public reporting about progress;

5) the provincial government created Local Health Integration Networks in 2006 to plan, integrate and fund care (including hospital-based care) in their respective regions; and

6) the *Excellent Care for All Act, 2010* created an agency (Health Quality Ontario) and a set of mechanisms (e.g., mandatory Quality Improvement Plans) to support quality improvement in the health system.

For a detailed list of major milestones in the evolution of Ontario's health system, see Table 1.1.

Table 1.1: Major milestones in the health system's evolution

Year	Jurisdiction	Milestone
1945	Canada	Government of Canada fails in its attempt to introduce a national health-insurance plan for family physician-provided care, visiting nurse-provided care, and hospital-based care, and (in late stages) medical specialist-provided care, other nurse-provided care, prescription drugs, laboratory services, and dental services (15)
1948	Canada	National Health Grants Program begins providing grants to provinces and territories to support health initiatives, including hospital construction, public health, professional training, provincial surveys, and public health research (15)
1955	Ontario	Government of Ontario announces its willingness to introduce public payment for hospital and diagnostic services if the federal government shares the cost (and the Government of Canada agrees in principle in 1956) (15)
1957	Canada	Government of Canada passes the *Hospital Insurance and Diagnostic Services Act*, which sets out the conditions for provinces and territories to receive shared-cost financing for hospital-based care (16)
	Ontario	Ontario Hospital Services Commission is created to administer the hospital-insurance plan (15)

Continued on next page

Year	Jurisdiction	Milestone
1959	Ontario	Ontario Hospital Insurance Plan becomes the new name of the Ontario Hospital Services Commission (15)
1964	Canada	Royal Commission on Health Services (Hall Commission) recommends the expansion of provincial health-insurance plans to include physician-provided care (15)
1966	Canada	Canada Assistance Plan begins cost-sharing (between federal and provincial governments) for social services (16)
		Government of Canada passes the *Medical Care Act*, which sets out the conditions for provinces and territories to receive shared-cost financing for physician-provided care (16)
	Ontario	Ontario Medical Services Insurance Plan is created to pay for physician-provided care for those who cannot afford private medical insurance because of age, health status, employment status or ability to pay (15)
1969	Ontario	Government of Ontario creates a health-insurance plan that covers physician-provided care for all Ontarians (16)
1971	Ontario	Department of Health becomes the Ministry of Health
1972	Ontario	Ontario Health Insurance Plan (OHIP) is created to administer a health-insurance plan covering both hospital-based and physician-provided care (15)
1977	Canada	Government of Canada passes the *Federal-Provincial Fiscal Arrangements and Established Programs Financing Act*, which shifts its contributions from a cost-sharing model to a block-funding model (17)
1980	Canada	Health Services Review recommends ending user fees and extra-billing and setting national standards for provincial health-insurance plans in the areas of public administration, comprehensiveness, universality, portability and accessibility (18)
1981	Canada	A provincial/territorial reciprocal billing agreement is reached for inpatient hospital care that is provided to a person travelling outside their home province or territory (16)
1984	Canada	Government of Canada passes the *Canada Health Act*,(19) which combines previous acts related to hospital and medical insurance, bans user fees and extra-billing, and sets the conditions and criteria (related to public administration, comprehensiveness, universality, portability and accessibility) for receiving money from the federal government for provincial health-insurance plans
		The provincial/territorial reciprocal billing agreement is expanded to include outpatient hospital care (16)
1987	Ontario	Ontario Health Review Panel recommends strengthening the role of the individual in personal healthcare and adopting new funding approaches and organizational arrangements to encourage the use of outpatient and community-based health programs (as alternatives to hospital-based care) (20)
1988	Canada	A provincial/territorial reciprocal billing agreement is reached by all provinces (except Quebec) for care provided by a physician to a person travelling outside their home province or territory (16)
1990	Ontario	Ministry of Health becomes the Ministry of Health and Long-Term Care (21)
		Government of Ontario passes the *Independent Health Facilities Act*,(22) which introduces a licensing and funding mechanism for community-based specialty clinics providing care that had been historically provided in hospitals (23)
1995	Canada	Government of Canada effectively merges the Canada Assistance Plan and the Established Programs Financing plan in creating the Canada Health and Social Transfer to support healthcare, social services and post-secondary education, and simultaneously reduces transfer payments to provincial governments (24)
1999	Canada	Federal, provincial and territorial governments (except Quebec) agree to a Social Union Framework Agreement, which provides a collective approach to social (including health) policy and program development (25)

Continued on next page

Year	Jurisdiction	Milestone
2000	Canada	First Ministers' Meeting Communiqué on Health confirms First Ministers' commitment to strengthening and renewing Canada's publicly funded healthcare services through partnership and collaboration, and outlines the vision, principles and action plan for health-system renewal (26)
		The action plan includes collaboration on specific priorities such as access to care; health promotion and wellness; supply of physicians, nurses and other health personnel; home and community care; pharmaceuticals management; health information and communication technology; and health equipment and infrastructure (26)
2002	Canada	Standing Senate Committee on Social Affairs, Science and Technology (Kirby committee) publishes its recommendations for reforming health systems in Canada (27)
		Commission on the Future of Health Care in Canada (Romanow commission) publishes its recommendations (28)
2003	Canada	First Ministers announce the First Ministers Accord on Healthcare Renewal (29)
		Health Council of Canada is established to monitor and report on progress of accord-related reforms (16)
2004	Canada	Government of Canada splits the Canada Health and Social Transfer into the Canada Health Transfer and the Canada Social Transfer.(16) First Ministers announce a 10-year plan to strengthen healthcare (16)
	Ontario	Government of Ontario passes the *Commitment to the Future of Medicare Act,*(30) which reaffirms its commitment to the principles of the *Canada Health Act, 1984*
2005	Ontario	Government of Ontario, as part of its commitments related to the accord, publishes its Wait Time Strategy, which provides increased funding for hip and knee joint replacements, cataract, cardiac and cancer surgeries, and extended MRI hours of operation; and provides for the development of a 'wait times' website and a surgical registry for the five key areas (31)
		Government of Ontario announces the creation of the Ministry of Health Promotion to focus on programs dedicated to healthy lifestyles (and to operate alongside the Ministry of Health and Long-Term Care), although this ministry was later re-absorbed into the Ministry of Health and Long-Term Care
2007	Canada	Federal, provincial and territorial governments, as part of their commitments to the accord, introduce the Patient Wait Times Guarantees initiative (31)
2007	Ontario	Government of Ontario passes the *Local Health Integration Act,*(32) which creates 14 Local Health Integration Networks (LHINs) to plan, integrate and fund local health services, including hospital services (but leaving hospital boards of directors intact)
2010	Ontario	Government of Ontario passes the *Excellent Care for All Act* (33) to support system-wide quality improvement (with an initial focus on hospitals) and through which Health Quality Ontario is established (34; 35)
		Government of Ontario passes the *Broader Public Sector Accountability Act,*(36) which establishes new rules and higher accountability standards for LHINs, hospitals, and broader public-sector organizations (and the LHINs then apply similar standards to the organizations they fund)
2012	Ontario	Commission on the Reform of Ontario's Public Services publishes its recommendations for extensive spending reductions in Ontario, including capping annual increases in healthcare spending at 2.5%, providing more home-based care, and using less expensive health workers (e.g., nurse practitioners) (37)
		Health system funding reform changes funding for hospitals and Community Care Access Centres (38)
2014	Canada	Health Council of Canada ceases to function
2016	Canada	Supreme Court of Canada extends the federal government's fiduciary relationship from status First Nations peoples to include Métis and non-status Indigenous peoples (39)

Sources: 15-42

Four of the most consequential impacts of these decisions for how the health system is experienced by citizens and professionals are:

1) Ontarians have their own health system, not a 'Canadian health system' (although provisions allow for them to be covered under another health-insurance plan if they move to another province or territory);

2) the health system provides medically necessary care for free at the point of use (i.e., with no out-of-pocket charges) to patients if the care is provided in a hospital or by a physician, but not (necessarily) for care provided in other settings or by other regulated health professionals;

3) many physicians see themselves as small-business owners who happen to have customers whose bills are paid by the government; and

4) care is increasingly organized on a regional basis, albeit with a strong stewardship role for government and for government agencies like Health Quality Ontario.

These past decisions also shape decisions about the health system's future in many notable ways, perhaps most noticeably in how efforts to achieve the 'triple aim' – improve the patient experience and population health, and keep per capita costs manageable (which we return to in Chapter 11) – shy away from changes to the independence of the province's physicians and (to a lesser extent) hospitals. Past decisions have channelled resources and created incentives in ways that supported the emergence of large, well-resourced hospital and medical associations that can act as a countervailing power to the government that pays their bills. Past decisions have also changed how professionals and citizens think about the system. For example, many physicians receive payment as individual 'medicine professional corporations,' not as members of interdisciplinary teams or as staff of a primary-care or other organization, and many citizens accept dramatic differences in the way the health system deals with hospital-based and physician-provided care, which is free for patients, and prescription drugs, which are largely paid for by patients or their private insurance plans.

Geographic and socio-demographic context

Ontario has a very large land mass, which complicates access to care in large parts of the province. Since 2007, the province has been divided into 14 regions (Figure 1.1), each overseen by an administrative body called a Local Health Integration Network (LHIN), to enable the planning,

Figure 1.1: Province[1] and its 14 regions, each of which is overseen by a Local Health Integration Network

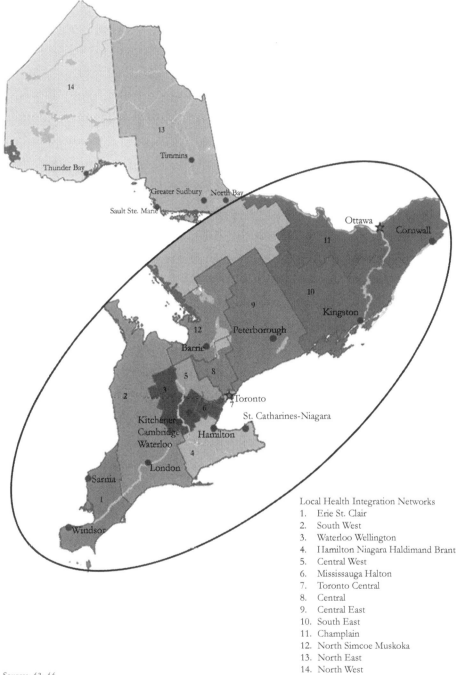

Local Health Integration Networks
1. Erie St. Clair
2. South West
3. Waterloo Wellington
4. Hamilton Niagara Haldimand Brant
5. Central West
6. Mississauga Halton
7. Toronto Central
8. Central
9. Central East
10. South East
11. Champlain
12. North Simcoe Muskoka
13. North East
14. North West

Sources: 43; 44

Note:
[1] The part of the province shown within the oval has been magnified to show an appropriate level of detail.

integration and funding of care to be adapted to regional needs (ethnocultural or linguistic diversity, transportation, etc.). Some of the regions have a population centre anchoring it (e.g., South West is anchored by London), whereas some population centres straddle multiple regions (e.g., Toronto contains one entire LHIN and parts of three other LHINs). Increasingly care is organized along regional lines, particularly for care like home care, some of which is funded by Community Care Access Centres (one per region, although this function will be taken on by LHINs in 2017),(1) and for care like cancer care, much of which is provided in and supported by regional cancer centres.

A list of the province's main population centres (defined as having more than 200,000 residents) is dominated by Toronto, surrounding centres (Mississauga, Brampton, Markham and Vaughan) and other nearby centres (Hamilton and Kitchener), leaving only a few main population centres (Ottawa, London and Windsor) more than a short drive away from Toronto (Table 1.2). The biggest growth in population over the 2001-11 period

Table 1.2: Main population centres, their corresponding Local Health Integration Network, and their population, 2001 and 2011

Jurisdiction	Local Health Integration Network	Population		
		2001	2011	10-year percentage change
Toronto	Toronto Central (7) and parts of Central West (5), Central (8) and Central East (9)	2,481,494	2,615,060	5%
Ottawa	Champlain (11)	774,072	883,391	14%
Mississauga	Mississauga Halton (6)	612,925	713,443	16%
Brampton	Central West (5)	325,428	523,911	61%
Hamilton	Hamilton Niagra Haldimand Brant (4)	490,268	519,949	6%
London	South West (2)	336,539	366,151	9%
Markham	Central (8)	208,615	301,709	45%
Vaughan	Central (8)	182,022	288,301	58%
Kitchener	Waterloo Wellington (3)	190,399	219,153	15%
Windsor	Erie St.Clair (1)	209,218	210,891	1%
Ontario		11,410,046	12,851,821	13%
Canada		30,007,094	33,476,688	12%

Sources: 45-47

has been in Toronto's surrounding centres, particularly Brampton (61%), Vaughan (58%), and Markham (45%), which have required significant investments in infrastructure and a large inflow of health professionals. These main population centres frequently provide care to those living in rural communities, which are defined as those with a population of less than 30,000 that are more than 30 minutes away from a community with a population of more than 30,000.(2)

Smaller population centres, such as Greater Sudbury, Thunder Bay, Sault Ste. Marie, North Bay and Timmins, serve as key hubs for healthcare in northern Ontario, which is comprised of 145 municipalities in an area covering over 800,000 square kilometres (starting near Parry Sound in the south and ending with Hudson Bay in the north) and representing nearly 90% of Ontario's land mass. This area includes many remote communities, which are mostly Indigenous communities and defined as those lacking year-round road access, relying on a third party (e.g., ferry, train or airplane) for transportation to a larger centre, or both.(2)

Ontario is an ethnoculturally diverse province. In 2011, foreign-born persons living in the province accounted for 30% of the population.(3) The two main population centres with the largest percentage of people born outside the country are Toronto (46%) and Ottawa-Gatineau (19%).(3) Just over a quarter of the province's population (26%) belongs to a visible minority.(3) This percentage is projected to double by 2031.(4) The largest visible minority groups are south Asian (8% of Ontario population) followed by Chinese (5%), southeast Asian (5%), and black (4%).(5) Ontario's visible-minority populations are largely concentrated in the Toronto metropolitan census area, including the municipalities of Markham (where visible minorities account for 72% of its population), Brampton (66%), Mississauga (54%), and the city of Toronto (49%).(3) Indigenous peoples, mostly of First Nations and Métis descent, account for 2% of the population (which we return to in Chapter 9).(3)

Ontario has two official languages (English and French) and no official religion. Just under 5% of Ontarians speak French at home.(6) Almost a third of the population (31%) speak one of many other non-official languages, the most widely spoken being Italian, Spanish, Punjabi and Cantonese.(5) Nearly two thirds of Ontarians (64%) report an affiliation with a Christian religion – of whom nearly two fifths (39%) specifically report an affiliation with the Roman Catholic church, the sponsor of many private not-for-profit hospitals in Ontario – and 23% report having no religious affiliation.(3) Non-Christian religious affiliations include Muslim (5% of the population), Hindu (3%), Jewish (2%), Sikh (1%) and Buddhist (1%), with the greatest concentrations of these religious affiliations in the metropolitan Toronto area.(3)

Ontarians have relatively high socio-economic status on average but face significant inequality. As we return to later in the chapter, the average gross domestic product (GDP) per capita in 2013 was $51,340 (compared to $53,868 in Canada as a whole) in 2013 dollars (as opposed to the 2002 dollars used as the reference in a later table). However, more than a tenth (12%) of the Ontario population is living in poverty, with these individuals and families concentrated in larger census metropolitan areas such as Windsor and Toronto (18% and 15% of the population living in poverty, respectively).(5; 7; 8) Also, the employment rate in Ontario is 61%.(9) Ontario has the highest percentage (29%) of university-degree holders of all Canadian provinces and a higher proportion than the national average (26%).(10) Nearly one quarter (24%) of the adult population has a high-school diploma as their highest educational attainment, and more than one in 10 (11%) have no certificate, diploma or degree qualifications.(5)

Political context

Ontario shares many features of the current political context for its health system with other provinces, including:

1) healthcare is the provincial government's constitutional responsibility;
2) the provincial government is bound by the public administration, comprehensiveness, universality, portability and accessibility principles of the federal government's *Canada Health Act, 1984*, namely: a) the provincial health insurance plan (OHIP) must be publicly administered, b) all medically necessary hospital-based and physician-provided care must be covered through the plan, c) all eligible Ontario residents must be covered by the plan, d) Ontarians moving to other provinces must be covered by the plan (currently for two months) after they become a resident in a new province, and e) Ontarians must not be charged fees for medically necessary hospital-based and physician-provided care (in contrast, there are no provisions as to whether or how the provincial

government must treat care provided outside hospitals or by health professionals other than physicians, which includes prescription drugs (provided outside hospital), home care, rehabilitation care, and long-term care); and

3) the 'core bargain' that the government effectively struck with hospitals in the 1950s and with physicians in the 1960s maintained a private delivery model when the payment mechanism was changed from private to public.

This core bargain has left the province with a legacy of private-practice physicians and private not-for-profit hospitals (the latter being the case despite the legislation governing these hospitals being called the *Public Hospitals Act, 1990*).

On the other hand, some features of the political context for the health system take a particular form in or are unique to Ontario. Examples of this include:

1) the current (Liberal) majority government effectively faces no veto points and can make changes to the system as it wishes, provided that the *Canada Health Act, 1984* provisions are adhered to, although in practice Ontario governments have been particularly hesitant to introduce reforms that would impinge on physicians' private practices (and to a lesser extent on the autonomy of the boards of directors governing hospitals), but quicker to introduce or permit reforms in other areas (e.g., the privatization of the rehabilitation sector);(11)

2) the Ontario Medical Association is in a particularly powerful role compared to other professions because the Physicians Services Committee gives them a more direct 'policy participation' role than other professionals enjoy (although this has been sorely tested by the government's recent fee cuts and by the government's and association's inability to agree on a new Physician Services Agreement, which has led the association to curtail its involvement in government-organized or co-organized activities);

3) additional vocal interests include other professional associations (e.g., Registered Nurses' Association of Ontario) and organizational associations (e.g., Ontario Hospital Association), and to a lesser extent citizen groups (e.g., Ontario Health Coalition, which is dominated by trade unions); and

4) media attention over the contracting practices of the government agency (eHealth Ontario) charged with supporting the introduction

and use of information and communication technology (e.g., ICT such as electronic health records) in the province (in 2009), and over challenges in addressing severe acute respiratory syndrome or SARS, (in 2003) have led to a climate of fear around contracting and concerns around ICT and public-health emergency preparedness.

These features of the political context for Ontario's health system can be understood in relation to four groups of factors – institutions, interests, ideas and factors external to the system – that help to explain why policy-making processes unfold in the way that they do (Table 1.3). We provide more details about how and why such factors matter in an online course, offered through Health Systems Learning, entitled 'Setting Agendas and Developing and Implementing Policies.' A one-page summary of the course is available on the McMaster Health Forum website (see 'About us' then 'Our resources').

Table 1.3: Political context

Notable examples and their implications
Institutions (policy legacies)

British North America Act, 1867
- Healthcare is the constitutional responsibility of provincial governments, while other domains (e.g., defence, relations with Indigenous peoples) are the responsibility of the federal government
- As a result, Canada has 14 health systems (or 13 systems plus a set of programs):
  - 10 provincial health systems (with Ontario's being one of them)
  - three territorial health systems
  - a set of federal government-supported health programs that cover First Nations peoples and Inuit, Canadian Armed Forces, eligible veterans, Royal Canadian Mounted Police, inmates of federal penitentiaries, and some refugee claimants (48)

Canada Health Act, 1984
- The Government of Ontario must adhere to the five principles of public administration, comprehensiveness, universality, portability and accessibility to receive federal government support for healthcare
  - In 2015-16 the Government of Ontario received $21.3 billion in transfers from the federal government (Canada Health Transfer $13.9 billion, Canada Social Transfer $5.1 billion, and equalization $2.3 billion) (49)
- The initial 'core bargain' that brought hospitals and then physicians into a public payment model left the delivery of care 'private':
  - private not-for-profit hospitals deliver care with first-dollar, one-tier public payment
  - private-practice physicians deliver care with first-dollar, one-tier public (often fee-for-service) payment

Continued on next page

Institutions (government structures)

Government of Ontario:(50)
- Liberal majority government
- Unicameral legislature
  - Seat distribution in the Legislative Assembly of Ontario: 58 Liberal, 29 Progressive Conservative, and 20 New Democrat
- Effectively no veto points

Federal government:(51)
- Liberal majority government
- Bicameral legislature
  - Seat distribution in the House of Commons: 182 Liberal, 97 Conservative, 44 New Democrat, 10 Bloc Québécois, one Green, one independent, and three vacant seats
  - Seat distribution in the Senate: 42 non-affiliated, 41 Conservative, 21 independent Liberal, and one vacant seat
- Weak veto point with the Senate

Court system:(52)
- Ontario Court of Justice (General Division and Provincial Division)
- Court of Appeal
- Supreme Court of Canada

Institutions (policy networks)

Policy networks in the health system are pluralist, with fragmented state authority coupled with poorly developed organized interests (compared to some other countries)
- Most policy networks are considered pressure pluralist, whereby the government or government agency is autonomous and organized interests assume policy advocacy roles
- The Ontario Medical Association is arguably in a clientele pluralist network and it typically assumes a policy participation role on issues pertaining to physicians (through the Physician Services Committee)

Interests

Main healthcare interest groups (see Figure 2.3 for a more extensive list):
- professional associations (e.g., Ontario Medical Association, Ontario Nurses' Association and Registered Nurses' Association of Ontario)
- institution-based interest groups (e.g., Ontario Hospital Association)
- citizen-based interest groups (e.g., Ontario Health Coalition)

Ideas

Values (53)
- With regard to traditional domains of hospital-based and physician-provided services, Canadians have historically valued a 'one-tier, no user fee' system
- Canadians are more open to two-tier care and for-profit delivery in areas such as home care and high-tech care

Knowledge
- Applied research centres conducting health policy research

External factors

"Have not province"
- Ontario was a "have province" (i.e., a province that does not receive 'equalization' payments from the federal government to equalize its ability to generate tax revenues) until the 2009-10 fiscal year when it received its first equalization payment and since which it has continued to receive yearly payments ($347 million in 2009-10 and $2 billion in 2014-15) (49)

Commission on the Reform of Ontario's Public Services (i.e., Drummond report)
- A 2012 report advising the Government of Ontario on deficit reduction in the public service (37)

eHealth Ontario
- Established in 2008 to create and maintain electronic health records
- Ontario Auditor General's 2009 report identified the mismanagemnet of funds (54)

Continued on next page

Severe acute respiratory syndrome (SARS) outbreak
  • Ontario was the hardest-hit Canadian province in the 2003 outbreak, with the majority of the country's SARS cases concentrated in Toronto (55)

Strong investigative journalism and experienced journalists
  • e.g., The Toronto Star, André Picard from The Globe and Mail

Sources: 15; 37; 48-56

Economic context

A key point of background to the current economic context for Ontario's health system is the public/private mix in spending on the system. Public expenditures (i.e., expenditures by government) account for roughly two thirds of all spending, whereas private expenditures (i.e., by employers or by citizens paying insurance premiums or making out-of-pocket payments, etc.) account for the remaining one third (Figure 1.2). However, this generalization masks differences between care covered by the 'core bargain' (care provided in hospitals and by physicians), which is 85-99% paid for by government, versus care not covered by the core bargain (e.g., prescription drugs and care provided in other settings or by other health professionals), which is more likely to be paid for by private sources (e.g., 65% for prescription drugs and 93% for other health professionals). A second key point of background is that more money (from public and private sources combined) is now spent on prescription drugs than on physicians.

In 2013, $5,877 was spent per person on care, which in 2002 dollars was the equivalent to spending $4,869 per person on care (on GDP per capita of $41,740, so roughly 12%) (Table 1.4). Of this total amount, $3,296 was paid for by government and $1,572 privately, in 2002 dollars. The percentage of total spending from government (68%) was more than in the U.S. (47%), slightly less than the percentage in Canada as a whole (71%), and less than in the U.K. (84%) in the same year.(12)

In the 2014-15 fiscal year, the provincial government spent 43 cents of each dollar of revenue (not counting borrowing) on the health system ($40 billion/$94 billion in 2002 dollars) (Table 1.5). Interest on the government's debt is the equivalent of 20% of the amount spent on the health system ($8 billion/$40 billion in 2002 dollars). The provincial government debt amounted to $15,388 in 2002 dollars for every Ontarian (or 40% of the

Figure 1.2: Public/private mix in spending on the health system, 2013

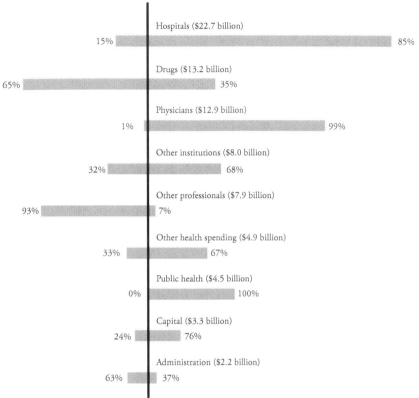

Health-system expenditures
($79.6 billion)

Private sector 32% ($25.7 billion)   Public sector 68% ($53.9 billion)

Hospitals ($22.7 billion)
15% — 85%

Drugs ($13.2 billion)
65% — 35%

Physicians ($12.9 billion)
1% — 99%

Other institutions ($8.0 billion)
32% — 68%

Other professionals ($7.9 billion)
93% — 7%

Other health spending ($4.9 billion)
33% — 67%

Public health ($4.5 billion)
0% — 100%

Capital ($3.3 billion)
24% — 76%

Administration ($2.2 billion)
63% — 37%

Sources: 57-61

Table 1.4: Key economic indicators, 2000 to 2013

Economic indicator	Ontario			Canada
	2000	2010	2013	2013
Gross domestic product (GDP)[1] (millions)	472,302	540,343	565,614	1,539,641
GDP per capita[1]	40,426	41,137	41,740	43,795
Total health spending[2] (millions)	41,008	63,113	65,977	173,536
Total health spending[2] ($ per capita)	3,509	4,805	4,869	4,936
Total health spending as percentage of GDP[2]	9%	12%	11%	11%
Public-sector health spending[2] (millions)	27,266	43,060	44,669	122,737
Public-sector health spending[2] ($ per capita)	2,333	3,278	3,296	3,491
Public-sector health spending as a proportion of total health spending[2]	67%	68%	68%	71%

Continued on next page

30   Ontario's health system

Economic indicator	Ontario			Canada
	2000	2010	2013	2013
Private-sector health spending[2] (millions)	13,742	20,068	21,308	50,799
Private-sector health spending[2] ($ per capita)	1,176	1,527	1,572	1,445
Private-sector health spending as a proportion of total health spending[2]	34%	32%	32%	29%

Sources: 14; 59; 61-71

Note:
[1] Inflation adjusted to 2002, according to Statistics Canada's Consumer Price Index (all items), CANSIM 326-0020: value x (CPI 2002/CPIi) = value (2002) where i = year
[2] Inflation adjusted to 2002, according to Statistics Canada's Consumer Price Index (healthcare), CANSIM 326-0020: value x (CPI 2002/CPIi) = value (2002) where i = year

Table 1.5: Government financial overview, 2000-01 to 2014-15[1]

	2000-01	2010-11	2014-15
Revenue ($ billions)			
Taxation	52	61	65
Government of Canada	6	20	17
Income from government business enterprises	4	4	4
Other non-tax revenue	6	7	7
Total revenue	68	92	94
Expense ($ billions)			
Health	24	38	40
Education	11	19	20
Post-secondary education/training	—	6	6
Children's and social services	—	11	12
Justice	3	4	3
Other programs	—	17	13
Total program expense	65	95	94
Interest on debt to revenues	—	8	8
Total expense	—	104	102
Reserve	0	0	0
Annual deficit	—	(12)	(8)
Indicators of financial condition			
Interest on debt to revenues	—	9%	8%
Net debt-to-GDP	—	35%	40%
Total spending-to-GDP	—	19.3%	17.9%
Net debt per capita	—	13,938	15,388
Tangible capital assets per capita	—	4,544	5,592

Sources: 14; 72-74

Note:
[1] Data not available for the specific reference period are denoted by —. Inflation adjusted to 2002, according to Statistics Canada's Consumer Price Index (healthcare), CANSIM 326-0020: value x (CPI 2002/CPIi) = value (2002) where i = year

province's GDP). These data suggest that the government has little room to manoeuvre in terms of how much more it can spend on the health system, and that any additional spending likely comes at the cost of spending on education, children and social services, and other areas of government responsibility, unless the government finds other sources of revenue.

Health status of the population

Given that many factors beyond the health system contribute to life expectancy and mortality rates, such data about the health status of the population are typically a better reflection of the context for the health system than indicators of its performance. Ontarians can boast generally good health status on average, however, some Ontarians (e.g., those with lower incomes, Indigenous peoples) have worse health status. We return to the health status of Indigenous peoples in Chapter 9.

On average, Ontarians born between 2009 and 2011 can expect to live to age 82, and if they survive to age 65, they can expect to live until 86, all of which is roughly comparable to the rest of Canada (Table 1.6). Ontario women live roughly four years longer than Ontario men. This gender dif-ferential narrows when one considers years of life lived in good health; in 2005-07, health-adjusted life expectancy for women in Ontario was 1.5 years longer than for men (70.5 versus 69).(13) In the province, 4.6 infants (i.e., children under one year of age) die for every 1,000 live births, which is also roughly comparable to the situation in Canada as a whole (Table 1.7). On the other hand, the rate of mortality (death) per 100,000 population, both among those younger than age 75 (premature mortality) and for potentially avoidable mortality (whether prevented among those still without a condition, among those with a condition but at risk of it getting worse or suffering from complications, or both), is typically a bit lower in Ontario than in Canada taken as a whole (Table 1.8). The number of potential years of life lost due to premature or potentially avoidable mortality is small compared to many other countries in the world, but still striking (e.g., 2,831 years of life were lost from potentially avoidable mor-tality for every 100,000 Ontarians). The top two leading causes of death in Ontario are cancer (malignant neoplasms) and heart disease (Table 1.9).

Table 1.6: Life expectancy at birth and at age 65, 2000-02 and 2009-11[1]

| | Ontario | | Canada |
	2000-02	2009-11	2009-11
Life expectancy at birth, females	82.1	83.9	83.6
Life expectancy at birth, males	77.4	79.8	79.3
Life expectancy at birth, total population	79.8	81.9	81.5
Life expectancy at age 65, females	20.4	21.9	21.7
Life expectancy at age 65, males	17.2	19.0	18.8
Life expectancy at age 65, total population	18.9	20.5	20.3

Sources: 75; 76

Note:
[1] Life expectancy is calculated using three years of data and is the number of years a person would be expected to live (starting at birth or at age 65).

Table 1.7: Infant, perinatal and maternal mortality indicators for 2000, 2010 and 2011

| | Ontario | | | Canada |
	2000	2010	2011	2011
Infant mortality rate[1] (deaths per 1,000 total births)	5.3	5.0	4.6	4.8
Perinatal mortality rate[2] (deaths per 1,000 total births)	6.7	5.9	5.9	6.0
Maternal mortality[3] (age-standardized mortality rate per 1,000 population)	0.1	0.1	0.1	0.1

Sources: 77-79

Notes:
[1] Death of a child under one year of age, with stillbirths excluded
[2] Death of a child under one week of age or a stillbirth (>28 weeks of gestation)
[3] Taken from leading causes of death based on 2011 World Health Organization, International Statistical Classification of Diseases and Related Health Problems, 10th Revision (ICD-10): pregnancy, childbirth and the puerperium

Table 1.8: Premature and potentially avoidable mortality, by number of deaths and as age-standardized rates per 100,000 population for 2000, 2010 and 2011

| | Ontario | | | Canada |
	2000	2010	2011	2011
Mortality (and age-standardized rate per 100,000 population)				
Premature mortality[1]	33,789 (287.9)	33,474 (229.0)	33,231 (221.2)	91,901 (233.3)
Potentially avoidable mortality[2]	24,301 (207.4)	24,373 (167.1)	23,880 (159.1)	66,194 (168.5)
Mortality from preventable causes[3]	14,885 (126.6)	15,532 (105.7)	15,178 (100.5)	43,118 (109.5)
Mortality from treatable causes[4]	9,416 (80.9)	8,842 (61.4)	8,702 (58.6)	23,076 (59.0)
Potential years of life lost[5] (and age-standardized rate per 100,000 population)				
Premature mortality	533,950 (4,724.5)	544,006 (3,970.2)	528,442 (3,777.1)	1,478,962 (4,087.1)

Continued on next page

	Ontario			Canada
	2000	2010	2011	2011
Potential years of life lost[5] (and age-standardized rate per 100,000 population) – continued				
Potentially avoidable mortality	389,684 (3,464.6)	411,178 (3,026.6)	393,339 (2,831.0)	1,109,416 (3,094.4)
Mortality from preventable causes	233,324 (2,027.1)	252,488 (1,793.1)	241,221 (1,676.5)	707,117 (1,930.1)
Mortality from treatable causes	156,360 (1,437.5)	158,689 (1,233.5)	152,119 (1,154.5)	402,299 (1,164.3)

Source: 80

Notes:
[1] Deaths of individuals younger than age 75
[2] Premature deaths that could potentially have been avoided through all levels of prevention (primary, secondary, tertiary)
[3] Premature deaths that could potentially have been prevented through primary prevention efforts
[4] Premature deaths that could potentially have been avoided through secondary or tertiary prevention
[5] Number of years of potential life not lived when a person dies 'prematurely' (i.e., before age 75)

Table 1.9: Leading causes of death, by number of deaths and as age-standardized rates per 100,000 population for 2000, 2010 and 2011[1]

Leading causes of death (ICD-10)	Ontario			Canada
	2000	2010	2011	2011
Malignant neoplasms	23,253 (177.3)	26,628 (152.3)	26,842 (149.0)	72,476 (154.1)
Disease of the heart	20,926 (154.3)	17,983 (93.4)	17,614 (88.3)	47,627 (91.0)
Cerebrovascular disease	6,149 (44.7)	5,315 (27.0)	4,930 (24.0)	13,283 (24.8)
Accidents (unintentional injuries)	2,842 (22.3)	4,283 (25.0)	4,203 (23.8)	11,184 (22.1)
Chronic lower respiratory diseases	3,393 (25.0)	3,684 (19.6)	3,800 (19.6)	10,716 (24.2)
Diabetes mellitus	2,830 (21.2)	2,873 (15.6)	2,867 (15.1)	7,194 (14.5)

Source: 79

Note:
[1] Based on 2011 World Health Organization, International Statistical Classification of Diseases and Related Health Problems, 10th Revision (ICD-10)

Overview of the book

The bulk of the book is organized into three parts, the first of which is 'the building blocks of the system.' The 'building blocks' include governance arrangements (i.e., who can make what types of decisions); financial arrangements (i.e., how revenue is raised to pay for care and how organizations are funded, professionals remunerated, products and services purchased, and consumers incentivized); and delivery arrangements (i.e., where and with what supports care is provided and by whom care is provided). The latter building block has been divided into two parts: infrastructure and workforce. There are parallels to the World Health Organization's 'building blocks,' but our experience in coding all of the systematic reviews and economic evaluations in the world about strengthening health systems (for inclusion in Health Systems Evidence – www.healthsystemsevidence.org – a free online resource) have led us to use governance, financial and delivery arrangements as building blocks.

The second part of the book – 'using the building blocks to provide care' – has been organized into 'care by sector' (i.e., home and community care, primary care, specialty care, rehabilitation care, long-term care and public health, which we use as an organizing framework throughout the book); care for select conditions (where we focus on four conditions or groupings of conditions that are handled in unique ways in the health system, namely mental health and addictions, work-related injuries and diseases, cancer, and end of life); care using select treatments (where we focus on three types of treatment that are handled in unique ways in the health system, namely prescription and over-the-counter drugs, complementary and alternative therapies, and dental services); and care for a select population (where we focus on Indigenous peoples, whose historical relationship to, and treatment by, government has created a unique patchwork of care and a political imperative to right past wrongs). We explain our rationale for singling out select conditions and treatments and a select population in more detail in the corresponding chapters.

To explain 'care by sector' a little more, home and community care includes both the nursing care provided at home after hospital discharge and the care provided by community-based organizations (e.g., assisted living in supportive housing). Primary care has historically meant a family physician, but increasingly means interprofessional teams of physicians, nurses and other professionals. Specialty care includes hospitals (and their outpatient clinics), condition-specific facilities (e.g., for cancer or mental health and addictions), and a mix of other types of facilities (such as Independent Health Facilities and Out of Hospital Premises, and private laboratories). Long-term care includes places like long-term care homes and complex continuing care facilities (or units within hospitals). Public health is typically focused on population-based interventions, but in Ontario it sometimes also involves direct service provision to individuals, albeit usually with more of a prevention focus than a treatment focus.

In this (second) part of the book we repeatedly use a figure that shares column and row headers to highlight similarities and differences. The key column headers include five of the six sectors listed above (with rehabilitation care excluded because it is an element of most of the other sectors), and these are bracketed by column headers for 'technology' provision (prescription and over-the-counter drugs, medical and assistive devices, diagnostics, and vaccinations) and for any key federal government or national organization involvement. The row headers include policies (e.g., acts); programs (e.g., Ontario Health Insurance Plan and Ontario Drug Benefit Program); places (e.g., primary-care clinics, laboratories, pharmacies, hospital emergency rooms, and long-term care homes); and people (both professionals like nurses and citizens like people living with diabetes, as well as the organizations that regulate or represent them). We call it the sector4P figure for short (Figure 1.3).

The third part of the book – change and progress – has been divided into health-system reforms (where the focus is an analysis of reforms introduced since 2000) and assessment of the health systems (where the focus is what formal evaluations of the system tell us about whether it is achieving its objectives). The book ends with a brief conclusion.

To facilitate comparisons across health systems, parts of the general structure of the book and the focus and organization of some of the tables and figures follow the approach used by published books on national health systems (e.g., Health Systems in Transition series coordinated by the European Observatory on Health Systems and Policies), or by published or planned books on other provincial/territorial health systems (e.g., Nunavut and Saskatchewan). These books can be identified through Health Systems Evidence, by selecting 'health-system descriptions' as the document type and the name of the country in the 'advanced search.' For example, Chapters 1-5 and 10-12 are broadly comparable to chapters appearing in these published or planned books, and the approach to providing Ontario data for the year 2000, year 2010 and the most recent year for which data are available, as well as data for the country as a whole whenever possible, is comparable to the planned books. That said, we have also departed significantly from these books in a number of ways, including expanding what would have been Chapter 6 into four separate chapters (Chapters 6-9), which we felt was necessary to do justice to the complexity of how care is provided in Ontario, and introducing the sector4P figures, which highlight key features of a sector or other part of the health system 'at-a-glance.'

To facilitate comparisons over time, tables or figures that present financial data for multiple years have been adjusted for inflation using Statistics Canada's Consumer Price Index (2002 = 100). Specifically, we applied the Consumer Price Index for Ontario using the 'healthcare' component (e.g., 2002 = 100 and 2015 = 124).(14) Given the sometimes significant difference between forecasts of financial data and the actual financial data that are eventually published, we typically do not present forecasts. While this decision can leave the impression that some of our data are 'old,' they are in fact the most recently published data.

To facilitate more in-depth examination of the issues raised in the book, we have added all of the key documents cited in the book to Health Systems Evidence (provided they meet its eligibility criteria). These documents can be identified and accessed (again through hyperlinks when freely available) by selecting 'Ontario's health system documents' as the type of complementary content and then using additional filters (e.g., 'primary care' as the sector), or by simply copying and pasting the title of the document into the 'open search' box.

Lastly, to make our descriptions readable by a diverse audience and to make comparisons possible across health systems and over time, we have effectively disaggregated a complex health system into its component parts (both its governance, financial and delivery arrangements, and the ways that care is provided in different sectors, for select conditions, using select treatments, and for a select population), while recognizing that these parts interact with one another in dynamic ways and that these parts individually and collectively adapt to events like a system reform.

Figure 1.3: Structure of the figure used in select chapters in the book

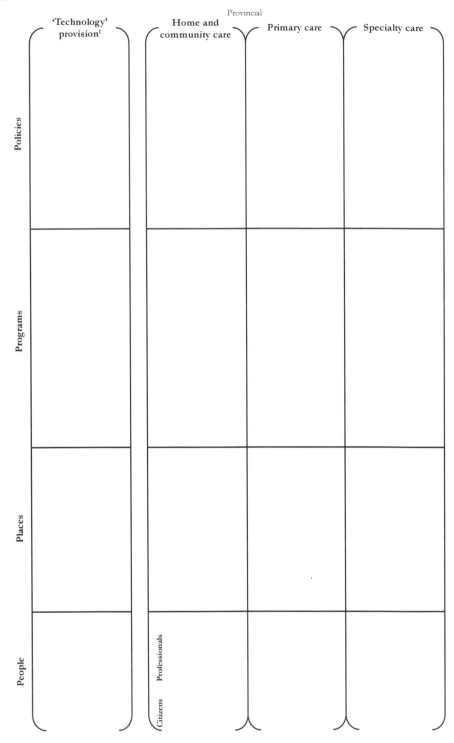

Provincial   Federal

Long-term care   Public health

Policies

Programs

Places

People

Note:
[1]Includes drugs, vaccines,
devices, diagnostics and
surgeries

References

1. Ministry of Health and Long-Term Care. Patients first: Action plan for health care. Toronto: Queen's Printer for Ontario; 2015. http://www.health.gov.on.ca/en/ms/ecfa/healthy_change/docs/rep_patientsfirst.pdf (accessed 25 August 2016).

2. Ministry of Health and Long-Term Care. Rural and northern health care framework. Stage 1 report. Toronto: Queen's Printer for Ontario; 2011.

3. Statistics Canada. Immigration and ethnocultural diversity in Canada, catalogue no. 99-010-X2011001 (National Household Survey, 2011). Ottawa: Statistics Canada; 2013. http://www12.statcan.gc.ca/nhs-enm/2011/as-sa/99-010-x/99-010-x2011001-eng.pdf (accessed 26 August 2016).

4. Statistics Canada. Canada year book 2012. Chapter 13: Ethnic diversity and immigration. Ottawa: Statistics Canada; 2012. http://www.statcan.gc.ca/pub/11-402-x/2012000/pdf/ethnic-ethnique-eng.pdf (accessed 24 August 2016).

5. Statistics Canada. Ontario (Code 35) (table). National Household Survey (NHS) Profile. 2011 National Household Survey. Statistics Canada Catalogue no. 99-004-XWE. Ottawa: Statistics Canada; 2013. https://www12.statcan.gc.ca/nhs-enm/2011/dp-pd/prof/index.cfm?Lang=E (accessed 26 August 2016).

6. Statistics Canada. Census program. Table 4 - Number of people and proportion of the population reporting French by selected language characteristic, New Brunswick and Ontario, 2006 and 2011. Ottawa: Statistics Canada; 2015. https://www12.statcan.gc.ca/census-recensement/2011/as-sa/98-314-x/2011003/tbl/tbl3_1-4-eng.cfm (accessed 2 November 2016).

7. Statistics Canada. Table 202-0802 - Persons in low income families, annual, CANSIM (database). Ottawa: Statistics Canada; 2013. http://www5.statcan.gc.ca/cansim/a26?lang=eng&retrLang=eng&id=2020802&&pattern=&stByVal=1&p1=1&p2=-1&tabMode=dataTable&csid= (accessed 25 August 2016).

8. Statistics Canada. Windsor, CMA, Ontario (Code 559) (table). National Household Survey (NHS) Profile. 2011 National Household Survey. Statistics Canada Catalogue no. 99-004-XWE. Ottawa: Statistics Canada; 2013. http://www12.statcan.gc.ca/nhs-enm/2011/dp-pd/prof/index.cfm?Lang=E (accessed 26 August 2016).

9. Statistics Canada. Labour force characteristics, seasonally adjusted, by province (monthly) (Quebec, Ontario, Manitoba). Ottawa: Statistics Canada; 2016. http://www.statcan.gc.ca/tables-tableaux/sum-som/l01/cst01/lfss01b-eng.htm (accessed 24 August 2016).

10. Statistics Canada. Education in Canada: Attainment, field of study and location of study. National Household Survey, 2011. Catalogue no. 99-012-X2011001. Ottawa: Statistics Canada; 2013. http://www12.statcan.gc.ca/nhs-enm/2011/as-sa/99-012-x/99-012-x2011001-eng.pdf (accessed 26 August 2016).

11. Gildiner A. What's past is prologue: A historical-institutionalist analysis of public-private change in Ontario's rehabilitation health sector, 1985-1999 [PhD dissertation]. Toronto: University of Toronto; 2001.

12. World Bank. Health expenditure, public (% of total health expenditure). Washington: World Bank Group; 2015. http://data.worldbank.org/indicator/SH.XPD.PUBL (accessed 26 August 2016).

13. Statistics Canada. Table 102-0122 - Health-adjusted life expectancy, at birth and at age 65, by sex and income, Canada and provinces, occasional (years), CANSIM (database). Ottawa: Statistics Canada; 2012. http://www5.statcan.gc.ca/cansim/a26?lang=eng&id=1020122 (accessed 25 August 2016).

14. Statistics Canada. Table 326-0020 - Consumer Price Index, monthly (2002=100 unless otherwise noted), CANSIM (database). Ottawa: Statistics Canada; 2016. http://www5.statcan.gc.ca/cansim/a26?id=3260020 (accessed 24 August 2016).

15. Lavis JN, Arcus K, Forest P-G, Abelson J, Mendelsohn M. Commissioning a new political bargain for Canada's health-care system. Hamilton: Program in Policy Decision-Making; 2002.

16. Health Canada. Canada's health care system. Ottawa: Health Canada; 2014. http://www.hc-sc.gc.ca/hcs-sss/pubs/system-regime/2011-hcs-sss/index-eng.php - a3 (accessed 25 August 2016).

17. Canada Parliament House of Commons. Federal-Provincial Fiscal Arrangements Act (R.S.C., 1985, c. F-8). Ottawa: Canada Parliament House of Commons; 1985. http://laws.justice.gc.ca/PDF/F-8.pdf (accessed 26 August 2016).

18. Hall E. Health Services Review '79. Canada's National-Provincial Health Program for the 1980's: A Commitment for Renewal. Ottawa: Health and Welfare; 1980.

19. Canada Parliament House of Commons. Canada Health Act (R.S.C., 1985, c. C-6). Ottawa: Canada Parliament House of Commons; 1985. http://laws-lois.justice.gc.ca/eng/acts/C-6/FullText.html (accessed 26 August 2016).

20. Evans J. Toward a shared direction for health in Ontario: Report of the Ontario Health Review Panel. Toronto: The Ontario Health Review Panel; 1987.

21. Legislative Assembly of Ontario. Ministry of Health and Long-Term Care Act, 1990, R.S.O. 1990, c. M.26. Toronto: Queen's Printer for Ontario; 1990. http://www.e-Laws.gov.on.ca/html/statutes/english/elaws_statutes_90m26_e.htm (accessed 25 August 2016).

22. Legislative Assembly of Ontario. Independent Health Facilities Act, 1990, R.S.O. 1990, c. I.3. Toronto: Queen's Printer for Ontario; 1990. http://www.e-Laws.gov.on.ca/html/statutes/english/elaws_statutes_90i03_e.htm (accessed 25 August 2016).

23. Ministry of Health and Long-Term Care. Independent Health Facilities fact sheet. Toronto: Queen's Printer for Ontario; 2014. http://www.health.gov.on.ca/en/public/programs/ihf/docs/ihf_fact.pdf (accessed 25 August 2016).

24. Madore O. The Canada Health and Social Transfer: Operation and possible repercussions on the health care sector. Current Issues Review. Ottawa: Government of Canada; 2003.

25. Canadian Intergovernmental Conference Secretariat. Social Union Framework Agreement (SUFA). Ottawa: Government of Canada; 1999. http://www.scics.gc.ca/english/conferences.asp?a=viewdocument&id=638 (accessed 24 August 2016).

26. Canadian Intergovernmental Conference Secretariat. News release - First Ministers' meeting communique on health, September 11, 2000. Ottawa: Canadian Intergovernmental Conference Secretariat; 2000. http://www.scics.gc.ca/english/conferences.asp?a=viewdocument&id=1144 (accessed 25 August 2016).

27. Standing Senate Committee on Social Affairs Science and Technology. The health of Canadians – the federal role. Final report. Volume six: Recommendations for reform. Ottawa: Parliament of Canada; 2002. http://www.parl.gc.ca/content/sen/committee/372/soci/rep/repoct02vol6-e.htm (accessed 24 August 2016).

28. Romanow R. Building on values: The future of health care in Canada. Ottawa: Privy Council. Commission on the Future of Health Care in Canada; 2002.

29. Canadian Intergovernmental Conference Secretariat. 2003 First Ministers' accord on healthcare renewal. Ottawa: Canadian Intergovernmental Conference Secretariat; 2003. http://www.scics.gc.ca/CMFiles/800039004_e1GTC-352011-6102.pdf (accessed 24 August 2016).

30. Legislative Assembly of Ontario. Commitment to the Future of Medicare Act, 2004 (S.O. 2004). Toronto: Queen's Printer for Ontario; 2004. http://www.e-Laws.gov.on.ca/html/statutes/english/elaws_statutes_04c05_e.htm (accessed 25 August 2016).

31. Government of Ontario. Ontario's wait time strategy. 2005. https://news.ontario.ca/opo/en/2005/05/ontarios-wait-time-strategy.html (accessed 25 August 2016).

32. Legislative Assembly of Ontario. Local Health System Integration Act, 2006, S.O. 2006, c. 4. Toronto: Queen's Printer for Ontario; 2010. http://www.e-laws.gov.on.ca/html/statutes/english/elaws_statutes_06l04_e.htm (accessed 25 August 2016).

33. Legislative Assembly of Ontario. Excellent Care for All Act, 2010, S.O. 2010, c. 14. Toronto: Queen's Printer for Ontario; 2010. https://www.ontario.ca/laws/statute/10e14 - BK0 (accessed 24 August 2016).

34. Ministry of Health and Long-Term Care. About the Excellent Care for All Act. Toronto: Queen's Printer for Ontario; 2013. http://health.gov.on.ca/en/pro/programs/ecfa/legislation/act.aspx (accessed 26 August 2016).

35. Ministry of Health and Long-Term Care. About Excellent Care for All regulations. Toronto: Queen's Printer for Ontario; 2016. http://www.health.gov.on.ca/en/pro/programs/ecfa/legislation/act_regs.aspx (accessed 25 August 2016).

36. Legislative Assembly of Ontario. The Broader Public Sector Accountability Act, 2010, S.O. 2010, c. 25. Toronto: Queen's Printer for Ontario; 2010. http://www.ontla.on.ca/web/bills/bills_detail.do?locale=en&BillID=2420&detailPage=bills_detail_the_bill (accessed 24 August 2016).

37. Ontario Financing Authority. Commission on the reform of Ontario's public services. Toronto: Queen's Printer for Ontario; 2012.

38. Ministry of Health and Long-Term Care. Health system funding reform (HSFR). Toronto: Queen's Printer for Ontario; 2014. http://www.health.gov.on.ca/en/pro/programs/ecfa/funding/hs_funding.aspx (accessed 25 August 2016).

39. Supreme Court of Canada. Daniels v. Canada (Indian Affairs and Northern Development). Ottawa: Supreme Court of Canada; 2016. http://scc-csc.lexum.com/scc-csc/scc-csc/en/item/15858/index.do (accessed 24 August 2016).

40. Commission on the Reform of Ontario's Public Services. Public services for Ontarians: A path to sustainability and excellence. Toronto: Queen's Printer for Ontario; 2012.

41. Legislative Assembly of Ontario. Health Insurance Act (R.S.O. 1990, c. H.6). Last amendment: 2009, c. 33, Sched. 18, ss. 11, 17 (2). Toronto: Queen's Printer for Ontario; 2009. http://www.e-laws.gov.on.ca/html/statutes/english/elaws_statutes_90h06_e.htm (accessed 25 August 2016).

42. Parliament of Canada. Canada's federal and provincial health care inquiries: 1940s to 2003. Library of Parliament; 2003. http://www.lop.parl.gc.ca/content/lop/ResearchPublications/tips/tip95-e.htm (accessed 29 September 2016).

43. Local Health Integration Network. Local Health Integration Networks. Toronto: Queen's Printer for Ontario; 2005.

44. Statistics Canada. Health regions: Boundaries and correspondence with census geography, catalogue no. 82-403-X. Geography Division for the Health Statistics Division. Ottawa: Statistics Canada; 2013.

45. Statistics Canada. Population and dwelling counts, for Canada, provinces and territories, and census subdivisions (municipalities), 2011 and 2006 censuses. Ottawa: Statistics Canada; 2011.

46. Statistics Canada. Population and dwelling counts, for Canada, provinces and territories, and census subdivisions (Municipalities), 2001 and 1996 censuses - 100% data. Ottawa: Statistics Canada; 2001.

47. Statistics Canada. Population and dwelling counts, for Canada, provinces and territories, 1991 and 1996 censuses - 100% data. Ottawa: Statistics Canada; 1996.

48. Government of Canada. The federal role in health and healthcare. Ottawa: Government of Canada; 2005. http://www.lop.parl.gc.ca/content/lop/researchpublications/prb0858-e.pdf (accessed 26 August 2016).

49. Department of Finance. Federal support to provinces and territories. Federal support to Ontario. Ottawa: Government of Canada; 2015. http://www.fin.gc.ca/fedprov/mtp-eng.asp - Ontario (accessed 25 August 2016).

50. Legislative Assembly of Ontario. Branches of government. Toronto: Queen's Printer for Ontario; 2014. http://educationportal.ontla.on.ca/en/about-parliament/how-parliament-works/parliamentary-traditions/what-parliament/branches-government (accessed 26 August 2016).

51. Parliament of Canada. Forty-second, party standings in the House of Commons. Ottawa: Parliament of Canada; 2015. http://www.parl.gc.ca/parlinfo/Files/Parliament.aspx?Item=b67c82bf-0106-42e5-9be1-46ecb5feaf60&Language=E&MenuID=Lists.Parliament.aspx&MenuQuery=http%3A%2F%2Fwww.parl.gc.ca%2Fparlinfo%2Flists%2FParliament.aspx (accessed 24 August 2016).

52. Ministry of the Attorney General. Current structure of the Ontario courts. Toronto: Queen's printer for Ontario; 2010. http://www.attorneygeneral.jus.gov.on.ca/english/about/pubs/cjr/firstreport/courts.asp (accessed 28 August 2016).

53. Abelson J, Mendelsohn M, Lavis JN, Morgan SG, Forest P-G, Swinton M. Canadians confront health care reform. Health Affairs 2004;23(3): 186-193.

54. Office of the Auditor General of Ontario. Special report: Ontario's electronic health records initiative. Toronto: Office of the Auditor General of Ontario; 2009.

55. Health Canada. Learning from SARS. Renewal of public health in Canada. A report of the National Advisory Committee on SARS and public health. Ottawa: Health Canada; 2003.

56. Lavis JN. Studying health-care reforms. In: Lazar H, Lavis JN, Forest P-G, Church J, editors. Paradigm freeze: Why it is so hard to reform health care in Canada. Kingston: McGill-Queen's University Press; 2013.

57. CIHI. National health expenditure trends, 1975 to 2015. Series B, table B.1.1, Total health expenditure, by province/territory and Canada, 1975 to 2015—current dollars. Ottawa: Canadian Institute for Health Information; 2015.

58. CIHI. National health expenditure trends, 1975 to 2015. Series B, table B.2.1, Private sector health expenditure, by province/territory and Canada, 1975 to 2015—current dollars. Ottawa: Canadian Institute for Health Information; 2015.

59. CIHI. National health expenditure trends, 1975 to 2015. Series B, table B.2.3, Private sector health expenditure as a proportion of total health expenditure, by province/territory and Canada, 1975 to 2015—current dollars. Ottawa: Canadian Institute for Health Information; 2015.

60. CIHI. National health expenditure trends, 1975 to 2015. Series B, table B.3.1, Public sector health expenditure, by province/territory and Canada, 1975 to 2015—current dollars. Ottawa: Canadian Institute for Health Information; 2015.

61. CIHI. National health expenditure trends, 1975 to 2015. Series B, table B.3.3, Public sector health expenditure as a proportion of total health expenditure, by province/territory and Canada, 1975 to 2015—current dollars. Ottawa: Canadian Institute for Health Information; 2015.

62. CIHI. National Health Expenditure Trends, 1975 to 2015. Series A, table A24, total health expenditure by source of finance, Canada, 1975 to 2015—constant dollars. Ottawa: CIHI; 2015.

63. CIHI. National Health Expenditure Trends, 1975 to 2015. Series A, table A25, total health expenditure by source of finance, Canada, 1975 to 2015—constant dollars. Ottawa: CIHI; 2015.

64. CIHI. National health expenditure trends, 1975 to 2015. Series B, table B.1.4, total health expenditure, by province/territory and Canada, 1975 to 2015—constant dollars. Ottawa: Canadian Institute for Health Information; 2015.

65. CIHI. National health expenditure trends, 1975 to 2015. Series B, table B.3.5, public sector health expenditure, per capita, by province/territory and Canada, 1975 to 2015—constant dollars. Ottawa: Canadian Institute for Health Information; 2015.

66. CIHI. National Health Expenditure Trends, 1975 to 2015. Series B, table B24, private sector health expenditure, by province/territory and Canada, 1975 to 2015—constant dollars. Ottawa: CIHI; 2015.

67. CIHI. National Health Expenditure Trends, 1975 to 2015. Series B, table B25, private sector health expenditure, by province/territory and Canada, 1975 to 2015—constant dollars. Ottawa: CIHI; 2015.

68. CIHI. National health expenditure trends, 1975 to 2015. Series B, table B.3.4, public sector health expenditure, by province/territory and Canada, 1975 to 2015—constant dollars. Ottawa: Canadian Institute for Health Information; 2015.

69. CIHI. National Health Expenditure Trends, 1975 to 2015. Series B, table B35, public sector health expenditure, by province/territory and Canada, 1975 to 2015—constant dollars. Ottawa: CIHI; 2015.

70. Statistics Canada. Table 384-00384 - Gross domestic product, expenditure-based, provincial and territorial, annual, CANSIM (database). Ottawa: Statistics Canada; 2014. http://www.statcan.gc.ca/tables-tableaux/sum-som/l01/cst01/econ15-eng.htm (accessed 24 August 2016).

71. Statistics Canada. Table 151-0001 - Estimates of population by age group and sex for July 1, Canada, provinces and territories. Ottawa: Statistics Canada; 2015. http://www5.statcan.gc.ca/cansim/a26?lang=eng&retrLang=eng&id=0510001&pattern=Estimates+of+population+by+age+group+and+sex+for+July+1%2C+Canada%2C+provinces+and+territories&tabMode=dataTable&srchLan=-1&p1=1&p2=-1 (accessed 25 August 2016).

72. Ministry of Finance. Public accounts of Ontario 2000-2001. Annual report and consolidated financial statements. Toronto: Queen's Printer for Ontario; 2001.

73. Ministry of Finance. Public accounts of Ontario 2009-2010. Annual report and consolidated financial statements. Toronto: Queen's Printer for Ontario; 2010.

74. Treasury Board Secretariat. Public accounts of Ontario 2014-2015. Annual report and consolidated financial statements Toronto: Treasury Board Secretariat; 2015.

75. Statistics Canada. Table 102-0512 - Life expectancy, at birth and at age 65, by sex, Canada, provinces and territories, annual (years), CANSIM (database). Ottawa: Statistics Canada; 2012. http://www5.statcan.gc.ca/cansim/a05?searchTypeByValue=1&lang=eng&id=1020512&pattern=1020512 (accessed 26 August 2016).

76. Statistics Canada. Table 84-537-X - Life tables, Canada, provinces and territories 2009 to 2011, CANSIM (database). Ottawa: Statistics Canada; 2013. http://www.statcan.gc.ca/pub/84-537-x/84-537-x2013005-eng.htm (accessed 24 August 2016).

77. Statistics Canada. Table 102-0504 - Deaths and mortality rates, by age group and sex, Canada, provinces and territories, annual, CANSIM (database). Ottawa: Statistics Canada; 2013. http://www.statcan.gc.ca/tables-tableaux/sum-som/l01/cst01/health21a-eng.htm (accessed 24 August 2016).

78. Statistics Canada. Table 102-0508 - Perinatal mortality (number and rates) and components, Canada, provinces and territories, annual, CANSIM (database). Ottawa: Statistics Canada; 2013. http://www5.statcan.gc.ca/cansim/a26?lang=eng&retr-Lang=eng&id=1020508&tabMode=dataTable&srchLan=-1&p1=-1&p2=9 (accessed 25 August 2016).

79. Statistics Canada. Table 102-0563 - Leading causes of death, total population, by sex, Canada, provinces and territories, annual, CANSIM (database). Ottawa: Statistics Canada; 2014. http://www5.statcan.gc.ca/cansim/a26?lang=eng&retr-Lang=eng&id=1020563&tabMode=dataTable&srchLan=-1&p1=-1&p2=9 (accessed 25 August 2016).

80. Statistics Canada. Table 102-4312 - Premature and potentially avoidable mortality, Canada, provinces and territories, annual, CANSIM (database). Ottawa: Statistics Canada; 2014. http://www5.statcan.gc.ca/cansim/pick-choisir?lang=eng&p2=33&id=1024312 (accessed 26 August 2016).

2. Governance arrangements

John N. Lavis and Amanda C. Hammill

Key messages for citizens

- The voice of citizens in their own care is protected through a requirement that they give their informed consent to treatment, and increasingly mechanisms are also in place for their voice to be heard in how programs and services are delivered, in how the system's performance is monitored, and in how policy and organizational decisions are made.

- The provincial government has the authority to make a number of decisions about how the system works, but they've also delegated some of this authority to other organizations, such as the ones that regulate what different types of professionals (e.g., nurses or physicians) can do, and the Local Health Integration Networks that plan, integrate and fund care in the province's 14 regions.

- Many of the organizations that provide care are private organizations – some not-for-profit (like most hospitals) and others for-profit (like community pharmacies and the facilities that perform blood tests and X-rays) – and they have a lot of discretion in how they operate.

Key messages for health professionals

- Nursing and medicine are self-regulating professions, which means that the government has established regulatory colleges (led by both members of the profession and the general public) to regulate practice in each profession (e.g., who can call themselves a physician, what a registered nurse is allowed to do).

- The provincial government makes many decisions about the health system (e.g., who is eligible for what prescription drugs as part of the Ontario Drug Benefit Program), but has also delegated some authority to Local Health Integration Networks and to provincial agencies like Cancer Care Ontario.

- The government also acts in a stewardship role for the many private organizations involved in providing care by, for example, setting performance targets and requiring public reporting against these targets, and it is supported in this role by these organizations' voluntary participation in processes like accreditation (organized by Accreditation Canada).

Key messages for policymakers

- The provincial government makes decisions in some areas and delegates decisions in other areas (e.g., to Local Health Integration Networks about planning, integrating and – with much less discretion – funding many types of care, to regulatory colleges about professional practice, and to government agencies about performance monitoring and in some cases performance management).

- The government's stewardship role is particularly important for the many private (for-profit and not-for-profit) organizations that provide care in the health system.

- The federal government plays an important role in setting limits about which prescription drugs a pharmaceutical company can sell in Canada, the maximum 'factory gate' price it can charge (not the wholesale price or the retail price charged by pharmacies), and whether it can advertise to patients, but the details about which drugs are paid for by government are set provincially.

. . .

In this first of four chapters focused on the building blocks of the health system, we focus on governance arrangements, which can be thought of simply as who can make what types of decisions. Governance arrangements include issues like policy authority (e.g., is policymaking decentralized or not?), organizational authority (e.g., are primary-care organizations governed by a community-based board of directors?), commercial authority (e.g., can pharmacies set any price for prescription drugs?), professional authority (e.g., can anyone call themselves a nurse?), and consumer and stakeholder involvement (e.g., are citizens given a voice in policymaking about the health system?). We address each of these types of authority in turn below.

Before doing so, however, it is important to note that governance arrangements can be considered to be the 'regulation' option available to the Government of Ontario as it responds to the differences between healthcare and other goods and services; the other options being public financing (which is addressed in Chapter 3) and information provision (which is relied on to a much lesser degree and addressed in Chapter 4).(1) Public provision of services is used in countries like the U.K. – with its National Health Service in each of England, Northern Ireland, Scotland, and Wales – but not really in Ontario (with the now historical exception of the provincial government-owned 'mental hospitals' and the current exception of some municipal government-owned long-term care homes). Income transfer is used in countries like Singapore – with its government-financed medical savings accounts – but not in Ontario.

Governance arrangements can also be considered to be the 'legal instruments' available as one of four broad types of policy instrument that the Government of Ontario can use to ensure the health system advances the public interest.(2) Legal instruments include acts and regulations, self-regulation regimes (as have been set up for the province's health professions) and performance-based regulations, the first two of which are widely used in Ontario and the focus of much of this chapter. Other policy instruments include economic instruments (e.g., taxes and fees, public expenditure and loans, public ownership, insurance schemes, and contracts, some of which are the focus of Chapter 3), as well as voluntary instruments (e.g., standards and guidelines and both formalized partnerships and less formalized networks) and information and education instruments (which are addressed in Chapter 4).

Policy authority

The Government of Ontario has the policy authority to establish, through acts and regulations, who can make what types of decisions, both within government (e.g., Ministry of Health and Long-Term Care) and among the organizations and professionals in the health system, and the citizens the system serves. These acts and regulations can apply across all sectors (e.g., *Regulated Health Professions Act, 1991* and the regulatory colleges created by the Act, which establish things like who can call themselves a nurse and what a physician can do) or to one or more sectors (e.g., *Local Health Systems Integration Act, 2006* which created the Local Health Integration Networks, or LHINs, that plan, integrate and fund care in the province's 14 regions) (see the 'policies' row of Figure 2.1, which provides a broad overview of the health system, particularly its five sectors and prescription drugs). Looking at it from a different perspective, the acts and regulations can apply across the entire system or to particular programs, places or people (professionals or citizens), and some federal government acts and regulations also apply to Ontario's health system. For a detailed list of the key acts that determine who can make what types of decision in the health system, see Table 2.1. Many of the acts use the acronym RSO, 1990, which stands for Revised States of Ontario, 1990, and reflects the fact that the last consolidation of all public statutes and all regulations occurred in 1990 and hence this is the starting point for e-Laws, which provide online access to official copies of Ontario's acts and regulations. The *Patients First Act, 2016* amended 20 existing acts, with key changes including an expansion of the role of the LHINs for planning and integrating primary care and home and community care.(3)

The government has retained policy authority to make decisions in some areas and decentralized that authority in other areas (if one considers such authority to include allocating budgets, developing strategies, and monitoring and reporting on performance or other related activities). It has retained policy authority in a number of key programmatic areas, including, for example, the Ontario Drug Benefit Program, which pays most of the cost of prescription drugs for select groups (see the 'programs' row of Figure 2.1). The government makes decisions about who is covered (e.g., those 65 and over and those receiving social assistance) and what they're covered for (e.g., drugs listed on an approved formulary), with the support of an advisory committee. On the other hand, the government has effectively decentralized some of its policy authority to LHINs (and has indicated that it will decentralize some of this authority further to as-yet-unnamed LHIN sub-regions)(4) and to regulatory colleges (e.g., College of Physicians and Surgeons of Ontario, which regulates the practice of medicine).

It has also decentralized some authority to government agencies, such as Cancer Care Ontario (CCO), eHealth Ontario, Health Quality Ontario (HQO), HealthForceOntario, Public Health Ontario, and Trillium Gift of Life Network, which play key roles in cancer care, electronic health records, evidence standards and quality improvement, supply and distribution of health professionals, public health, and organ and tissue donation, respectively (see the top two lines in the 'people' row of Figure 2.1). In a way, the government has shared some authority as well with the medical profession through the Physician Services Committee, which is comprised of representatives from the Ministry of Health and Long-Term Care and the Ontario Medical Association (OMA), and which addresses broad system issues that affect the profession (and under the terms of the Representation

Figure 2.1: Health-system overview

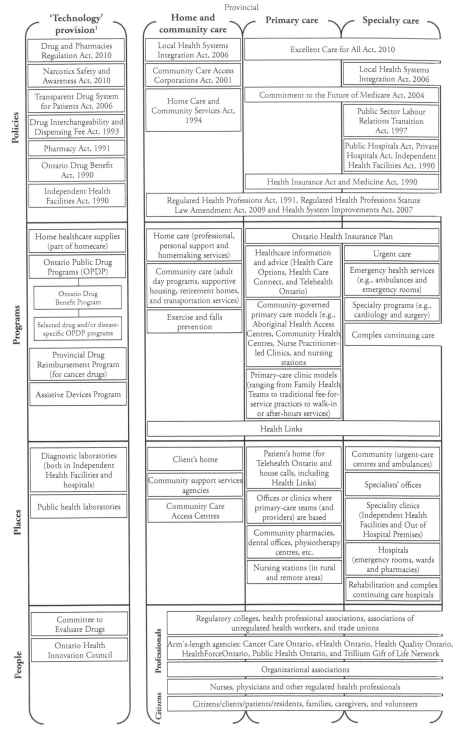

Provincial

	'Technology' provision[1]	Home and community care	Primary care	Specialty care
Policies	Drug and Pharmacies Regulation Act, 2010	Local Health Systems Integration Act, 2006	Excellent Care for All Act, 2010	
	Narcotics Safety and Awareness Act, 2010	Community Care Access Corporations Act, 2001		Local Health Systems Integration Act, 2006
	Transparent Drug System for Patients Act, 2006	Home Care and Community Services Act, 1994	Commitment to the Future of Medicare Act, 2004	
	Drug Interchangeability and Dispensing Fee Act, 1993			Public Sector Labour Relations Transition Act, 1997
	Pharmacy Act, 1991			Public Hospitals Act, Private Hospitals Act, Independent Health Facilities Act, 1990
	Ontario Drug Benefit Act, 1990		Health Insurance Act and Medicine Act, 1990	
	Independent Health Facilities Act, 1990	Regulated Health Professions Act, 1991, Regulated Health Professions Statute Law Amendment Act, 2009 and Health System Improvements Act, 2007		

Programs	Home healthcare supplies (part of homecare)	Home care (professional, personal support and homemaking services)	Ontario Health Insurance Plan	
	Ontario Public Drug Programs (OPDP)	Community care (adult day programs, supportive housing, retirement homes, and transportation services)	Healthcare information and advice (Health Care Options, Health Care Connect, and Telehealth Ontario)	Urgent care
	Ontario Drug Benefit Program			Emergency health services (e.g., ambulances and emergency rooms)
	Selected drug and/or disease-specific OPDP programs	Exercise and falls prevention	Community-governed primary care models (e.g., Aboriginal Health Access Centres, Community Health Centres, Nurse Practitioner-led Clinics, and nursing stations)	Specialty programs (e.g., cardiology and surgery)
	Provincial Drug Reimbursement Program (for cancer drugs)			Complex continuing care
	Assistive Devices Program		Primary-care clinic models (ranging from Family Health Teams to traditional fee-for-service practices to walk-in or after-hours services)	
		Health Links		

Places	Diagnostic laboratories (both in Independent Health Facilities and hospitals)	Client's home	Patient's home (for Telehealth Ontario and house calls, including Health Links)	Community (urgent-care centres and ambulances)
		Community support services agencies		Specialists' offices
	Public health laboratories	Community Care Access Centres	Offices or clinics where primary-care teams (and providers) are based	Speciality clinics (Independent Health Facilities and Out of Hospital Premises)
			Community pharmacies, dental offices, physiotherapy centres, etc.	Hospitals (emergency rooms, wards and pharmacies)
			Nursing stations (in rural and remote areas)	Rehabilitation and complex continuing care hospitals

People	Committee to Evaluate Drugs	**Professionals** — Regulatory colleges, health professional associations, associations of unregulated health workers, and trade unions		
	Ontario Health Innovation Council	Arm's-length agencies: Cancer Care Ontario, eHealth Ontario, Health Quality Ontario, HealthForceOntario, Public Health Ontario, and Trillium Gift of Life Network		
		Organizational associations		
		Citizens — Nurses, physicians and other regulated health professionals		
		Citizens/clients/patients/residents, families, caregivers, and volunteers		

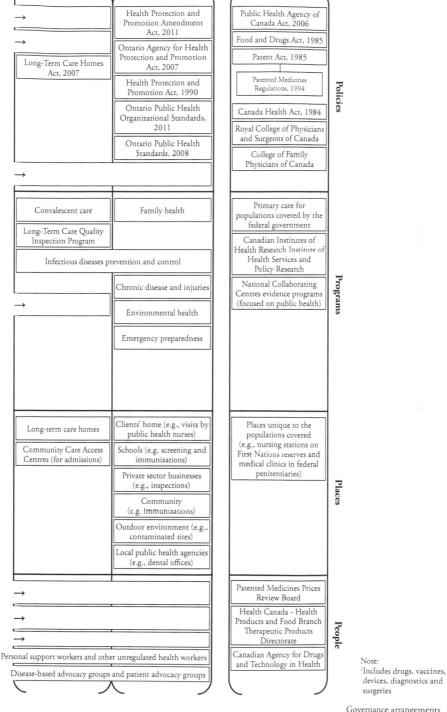

Note:
[1]Includes drugs, vaccines, devices, diagnostics and surgeries

Table 2.1: Key acts that determine who can make what types of decision in the health system

Legislation	Consequences
Federal	
British North America (BNA) Act, 1867 (Constitution Act, 1982)	Established healthcare as the constitutional responsibility of provincial governments, effectively leading to the creation of 14 different health systems in Canada – 10 provincial, three territorial, and one set of 'federal' (for Indigenous peoples, armed services personnel, etc.)
Canada Health Act, 1984	Established five criteria that provincial governments must adhere to in the design, delivery and funding of provincial health-insurance programs: public administration, comprehensiveness, universality, portability and accessibility
	Banned 'extra-billing' and thereby re-affirmed the 'core bargain' with hospitals and physicians: • private not-for-profit hospitals deliver care with first-dollar, one-tier public payment • private-practice physicians deliver care with first-dollar, one-tier public (fee-for-service) payment
Patent Act, 1985	Established the independent quasi-judicial Patented Medicines Prices Review Board to approve the entry of prescription drugs into the Canadian market, to ensure their prices are not excessive, and to report on research and development spending by patentees
Public Health Agency of Canada Act, 2006	Established the Public Health Agency of Canada and a Chief Medical Officer of Health to advise the Minister of Health and to coordinate federal efforts to identify and reduce public health risk factors (including measures relating to health protection and promotion, population health assessment, health surveillance, and disease and injury prevention), and to support public health emergency preparedness and response at the national level
Ontario - System	
Ministry of Health and Long-Term Care Act, 1990	The *Ministry of Health and Long-Term Care Act* set up the overall administrative structure of the Ontario health system with the minister presiding over and having charge of the ministry and all of its functions
Health Protection and Promotion Act, 1990	Established boards of health for all local public health agencies and the authorities of medical officers of health serving each board
	Required municipalities to cost-share the funding for all board activities
Mental Health Act, 1990	Established mental health as a subset of healthcare in Ontario, assigned the Minister of Health and Long-Term Care responsibility for designating psychiatric facilities, and governs how people may be involuntarily admitted to psychiatric facilities, how their mental health records are kept and accessed, how their financial affairs are handled, and how they can be released into the community
French Language Services Act, 1990	Guaranteed individuals the right to receive services in French from all provincial ministries and from government agencies in 26 designated areas across the province, as well as allowed hospitals to seek status as designated official French-language service providers (but does not require the 'active offer' of services in French, which means that if individuals do not request services in French there is no obligation to offer them even if French-language services might be highly valued

Continued on next page

Legislation	Consequences

Ontario - System – continued

Public Sector Labour Relations Transition Act, 1997

Established a framework to resolve labour relations issues arising from the amalgamation of municipalities and other decisions that affect collective agreements and collective-bargaining processes (e.g., requires specialty clinics to assume the terms of existing collective agreements and collective-bargaining processes when commitments to provide diagnostic and therapeutic procedures are transferred from hospitals to specialty clinics, whether or not they had any unionized staff at the time that they began providing the services)

Commitment to the Future of Medicare Act, 2004

Re-affirmed the government's commitment to the principles of public administration, comprehensiveness, universality, portability and accessibility as provided in the *Canada Health Act, 2004*, which includes the province's commitment to no user fees for medically necessary hospital-based and physician-provided care

Established an organization (that became what is now known as Health Quality Ontario (HQO) to publicly report on health-system performance and support continuous quality improvement

Local Health System Integration Act, 2006

Created 14 regional Local Health Integration Networks (LHINs) to plan, integrate and fund local health services, including home and community care, hospital care and much long-term care

Reduced the number of Community Care Access Centres (CCACs) from 43 to 14, aligned their boundaries with those of the LHINs, and established the LHINs as their funder

Health System Improvements Act, 2007

Amended and repealed a number of statutes administered by the Ministry of Health and Long-Term Care and added new legislation including the creation of the Ontario Agency for Health Protection and Promotion (renamed Public Health Ontario in 2011), the requirement for greater transparency for health regulatory colleges, and the establishment of new health profession colleges for naturopathy, homeopathy, kinesiology and psychotherapy

Excellent Care for All Act, 2010

Underpins the Excellent Care for All Strategy, linking quality and evidence-based care

Established a new payment mechanism (under the term 'health system funding reform') for hospitals

Consolidated several research and advisory bodies under one umbrella, namely HQO

Health Protection and Promotion Amendment Act, 2011

Established the authority for the provincial chief medical officer of health to direct boards of health and local medical officers of health to adopt policies or measures in cases of a pandemic, public health event and/or emergency with health impacts

Ontario - Programs

Health Insurance Act, 1990

Governs the administration and operation of the Ontario Health Insurance Plan, which provides insurance against the costs of insured (medically necessary) hospital-based and physician-provided services

Has been modified by two acts: the *Health Care Accessibility Act, 1990* (now repealed) and the *Commitment to the Future of Medicare Act, 2004*

Ontario Drug Benefit Act, 1990

Governs the Ontario Drug Benefit (ODB) Program (introduced in 1985), whereby the province reimburses pharmacies when they dispense prescription drugs at no charge to eligible persons – primarily seniors and persons on social assistance

For those with high prescription drug costs relative to household income, the Trillium Drug Program was added in 1995 to cover all ODB Program-approved drugs

Continued on next page

Legislation	Consequences

Ontario - Programs – continued

*Drug Interchange-
ability and
Dispensing Fee,
1990*

Introduced with the *Ontario Drug Benefit Act, 1990* to address rising drug prices and empowered the Executive Officer of the Ministry of Health and Long-Term Care to designate a generic drug as 'interchangeable' with a brand-name drug, and also limited the dispensing fees that pharmacies can charge private customers

*Transparent Drug
System for Patients
Act, 2006*

Amended the *Ontario Drug Benefit Act, 1990* and the *Drug Interchangeability and Dispensing Fee Act, 1990* to reform the ODB to improve patient access to drugs, ensure better value for money, reward innovation, and strengthen transparency

*Narcotics Safety
Awareness Act,
2010*

Underlies Ontario's Narcotics Strategy, promoting proper use and prescribing of prescription narcotics and other controlled substance medications through the introduction of a monitoring system

*Drug and
Pharmacies
Regulation Act,
2011*

Extended through a regulation in 2011, this act controls the sale of drugs in the province by requiring that they be sold only through registered pharmacists and licensed pharmacies

Ontario - Places

*Public Hospitals
Act, 1990*

Regulated the establishment of, and provided the operational framework for, private not-for-profit hospitals in Ontario (notwithstanding the name, which suggests incorrectly that these are public hospitals)

*Private Hospitals
Act, 1990*

Prohibits the operation of a for-profit hospital unless licensed as one prior to 29 October 1973

*Independent Health
Facilities Act, 1990*

Provided a funding and licensing mechanism for two types of community-based specialty clinics:
- diagnostic Independent Health Facilities (IHFs) to provide imaging (e.g., nuclear medicine and diagnostic radiology and ultrasound), sleep studies and pulmonary function tests
- ambulatory care IHFs to provide surgical and therapeutic procedures on an outpatient basis (e.g., cataract surgery)

Ontario Regulation 353/13 (effective January 2014) made every IHF within the meaning of the *Independent Health Facilities Act* a prescribed 'health service provider' for the purposes of the *Local Health System Integration Act, 2006*, which gave LHINs the same funding responsibility for IHFs as they have for hospitals

*Healing Arts
Radiation Protec-
tion Act, 1990*

Governs the use of radiation in hospitals and Independent Health Facilities

*Health Facilities
Special Orders Act,
1990*

Enables the minister of health to suspend services and facilities if deeming a facility as not operating according to regulation (applies only to laboratories, ambulance services, private hospitals and long-term care homes)

*Homes for Special
Care Act, 1990*

Established requirements for the housing and support services provided to people with serious mental illness as a 'non-institutional' (i.e., community living) alternative to care in psychiatric facilities

Continued on next page

Legislation	Consequences
Ontario - Places – continued	
Home Care and Community Services Act, 1994	Focused on the provision of an alternative to institutional care by ensuring a range of culturally appropriate services be available on a continuum of care to people in the home and in the community, including providing support and relief for caregivers
	Established clients' rights with regard to home and community care, the basket of covered services, the complaints and appeals process, and (through a regulation) the eligibility criteria for services and the maximum levels of nursing, personal support and homemaking services that can be provided to an individual
	Established what we now know as CCACs, although when they began operation in 1996 there were 43 across the province
Community Care Access Corporations Act, 2001	Established 43 CCACs as corporate entities (later reduced in number to 14 to match LHIN boundaries) and provides for the CCACs' mandate, governance and accountabilities
Long-Term Care Homes Act, 2007	Defined requirements for licensing and regulation, financing, staff training, services to be provided, and quality monitoring and reporting in long-term care homes, as well as established residents' right to a safe and secure environment and involvement in care planning
Broader Public Sector Accountability Act, 2010	Established a number of new requirements designed to improve accountability and transparency across the broader public sector
	In the hospital sector, the *Broader Public Sector Accountability Act* banned the practice of hiring lobbyists using public funds, legislated transparent processes for procurement, established new expense and perquisite rules for hospital employees, provided for the creation of reporting directives related to accountability provisions in the Act (e.g., annual reports to LHINs on consultant use, semi-annual public posting of executive and board member expenses), and brought hospitals under the *Freedom of Information and Protection of Privacy Act, 1990* (excepting quality-of-care information)
Ontario - Professionals	
Medicine Act, 1991	Confirmed physicians as self-regulating professionals, outlined the responsibilities of the College of Physicians and Surgeons of Ontario for governing the medical profession, and described the duties, scope of practice and authorized acts of physicians
Ontario Medical Association Dues Act, 1991	Financially strengthened the Ontario Medical Association (OMA) by requiring that every physician in Ontario (whether a member of the OMA or not), pay the association's dues and assessments (or an equivalent amount)
Regulated Health Professions Act, 1991	Provided the legislative framework for the self-governance of the now 28 regulated health professions[1] in Ontario by the now 26 health regulatory colleges[2]
Midwifery Act, 1991	Brought midwives under the *Regulated Health Professions Act, 1991* with the profession overseen and regulated by the College of Midwives of Ontario
Health System Improvements Act, 2007	Included the requirement for greater transparency for health regulatory colleges, and the establishment of new transitional health profession colleges – naturopathy, homeopathy, kinesiology, and psychotherapy

Continued on next page

Legislation	Consequences
Ontario - Professionals – continued	
Regulated Health Professions Statute Law Amendment Act, 2009	Expanded the scope of practice of many regulated health professionals (e.g., nurse practitioners, pharmacists, physiotherapists, dietitians, midwives and medical radiation technologists) and changed the rules related to various aspects of drug administration by select health professionals (nurse practitioners, pharmacists, midwives, chiropodists, podiatrists, dentists, and dental hygienists)
	Mandated that all regulated health professionals have professional liability insurance, health colleges make team-based care a key component of their quality-assurance programs, and health colleges with professions providing the same or similar services develop common standards for those services
Naturopathy Act, 2015	Brought naturopathy under the *Regulated Health Professions Act, 1991* with the profession overseen and regulated by the College of Naturopaths of Ontario
Ontario - Citizens	
Municipal Freedom of Information and Protection of Privacy Act, 1990	Increased protection of individual information and the right to access municipal government records, including general information and personal records
Substitute Decisions Act, 1992	Established provisions for the naming of powers of attorney and statutory guardians, for both personal care and property, for those found to be mentally incapable of personal care or managing property
Health Care Consent Act, 1996	Established rules with respect to consent to treatment (and situations of emergency treatment), admission to a care facility (including crisis admissions) and receipt of 'personal assistance' services, rules for when a person lacks the capacity to make decisions about such matters, and rules for such a person to contest a decision made for them to an independent provincial tribunal (Consent and Capacity Board)
Bill 68, Brian's Law (Mental Health Legislative Reform), 2000	Modified assessment and committal criteria for seriously mentally ill people to enable earlier intervention by their families and health professionals and to enable their treatment in the community rather than in a psychiatric facility
Personal Health Information Protection Act, 2004	Enshrined patient confidentiality as an individual right by outlining rules for collecting, using and disclosing personal information about individuals, that protect confidentiality while also providing effective healthcare
Bill 119, Health Information Protection Act, 2016	Amended the *Personal Health Information Protection Act, 2004* and other acts to establish a framework for electronic health records, and to provide increased accountability, transparency and privacy protection for personal health information
	Repealed and replaced the 2004 *Quality of Care Information Protection Act, 2004*, and set out rules for the disclosure and use of quality-of-care information

Sources: 6; 8-45

Notes:
[1] Audiology, chiropody, chiropractic, dental hygiene, dental technology, dentistry, denturism, dietetics, homeopathy, kinesiology, massage therapy, medical laboratory technology, medical radiation technology, medicine, midwifery, naturopathy, nursing, occupational therapy, opticianry, optometry, pharmacy, physiotherapy, podiatry, psychology, psychotherapy, respiratory therapy, speech-language pathology, traditional Chinese medicine
[2] Audiologists and speech-language pathologists are regulated by a single professional college as are chiropodists and podiatrists.

Rights Agreement this committee can continue to function despite the lack of a Physician Services Agreement).

The government also acts in a stewardship role for the many private organizations involved in providing care. Beyond its role in establishing who can do what, it may, for example, set performance targets and require public reporting against these targets (see the 'places' row of Figure 2.1). The health system is complex, with lots of moving parts, and most of us only experience select parts of it. But for a health system to perform well in improving the patient experience and population health and in keeping per capita costs manageable, policy authority is needed, even if it takes many forms (from hands-on government control to light-touch stewardship).

Not surprisingly, the government has developed a highly complex structure to determine who can make what types of decisions and to actually make decisions about the highly complex health system (Figure 2.2). While decisions about regulation and funding, among others, go to the democratically elected politicians who are members of cabinet (premier and ministers) or who direct other central agencies (Treasury Board Secretariat and Ministry of Finance), and some decisions (e.g., proposed acts) go to the legislature (where elected members of provincial parliament sit), the minister (also elected but appointed to a ministerial role by the Premier) and Ministry of Health and Long-Term Care have delegated policy authority for many decisions. The ministry itself is overseen by a deputy minister and divided up into many divisions, each headed by an assistant deputy minister and addressing particular aspects of the health system. The staff working in the ministry are (politically neutral) public servants who advise the minister and implement the minister's (or cabinet's or the legislature's) decisions (e.g., plan, budget, fund and administer programs, invest in infrastructure, monitor progress against action plans, convene expert groups, and manage stakeholders). Some ministry staff (e.g., Executive Officer of the Ontario Public Drug Programs and Chief Medical Officer of Health) have a dual accountability, and report both to the deputy minister and to the legislature. The minister also has a small number of political advisors who provide political advice. Increasingly the government convenes inter-ministerial groups to address issues that involve multiple ministries, such as the mental health of children and youth, and participates in inter-governmental groups (e.g., Council of the Federation and Conferences of Federal-Provincial-Territorial Ministers of Health) to

Figure 2.2: Key parts of government that determine who can make decisions and what types of decisions they can make

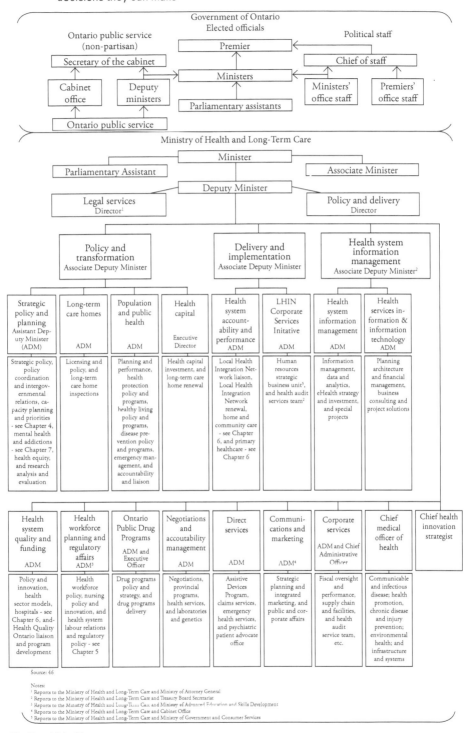

Source: 46

Notes:
1 Reports to the Ministry of Health and Long-Term Care and Ministry of Attorney General
2 Reports to the Ministry of Health and Long-Term Care and Treasury Board Secretariat
3 Reports to the Ministry of Health and Long-Term Care and Ministry of Advanced Education and Skills Development
4 Reports to the Ministry of Health and Long-Term Care and Cabinet Office
5 Reports to the Ministry of Health and Long-Term Care and Ministry of Government and Consumer Services

address issues that are national in scope, such as the health workforce.

Organizational authority

The corporate directors of the many private organizations involved in providing care have broad organizational authority to – either directly or through the management staff they hire – buy or lease space, recruit and employ staff, and organize how care is provided as long as they are operating within the rules set by relevant government acts and regulations or by regulatory college policies (e.g., having the president of the medical staff, chair of the medical advisory committee and chief nursing executive be non-voting members of hospital boards of directors). Some of the organizations are not-for-profit (e.g., most community-based mental health and addictions agencies, Community Health Centres, hospitals and rehabilitation clinics), others are for-profit (e.g., community pharmacies that are often owned by large chains, many Independent Health Facilities that provide diagnostic and therapeutic procedures, and a small number of hospitals that were functioning before hospital-care insurance was introduced), and a very small number are public (e.g., some municipal government-owned long-term care homes, and all local public health agencies). Many primary-care organizations are difficult to categorize because they range from a solo physician with an incorporated practice (who effectively functions as a small business owner) to a community-governed Family Health Team or Community Health Centre (which has community members, in addition to or instead of owners, on its board of directors). The solo physician's 'organization' (or practice) is not regulated per se, but the physician is regulated by the College of Physicians and Surgeons of Ontario.

These organizations are also subject to (what can be thought of as) institutions of independent accountability. For example, under the terms of the *Excellent Care for All Act, 2010*, four types of organizations (Community Care Access Centres, interprofessional team-based primary-care organizations, hospitals, and long-term care homes) must submit a Quality Improvement Plan annually to HQO.(5) Under the terms of legislation that assigns an independent accountability role to CCO and to the College of Physicians and Surgeons of Ontario, organizations providing colonoscopy, mammography and pathology services, which may otherwise 'fall through the cracks' between these two organizations' responsibilities, are subject to a quality-management program (organized by a partnership between CCO and the College of Physicians and Surgeons of Ontario) that provides evidence standards, supports quality improvement, and publicly reports on quality at the provincial, regional, organizational and professional levels (just as is done for, say, the regional cancer centres and Independent Health Facilities that are more directly under the single authority of CCO and the College of Physicians and Surgeons of Ontario, respectively).

Organizations may also be required, or voluntarily agree, to be subject to institutions of independent accountability, as many hospitals and other facilities do (for cardiac care) with the Cardiac Care Network of Ontario, and a broader range of organizations do (for all aspects of their functioning) with Accreditation Canada (a national organization).

Commercial authority

Commercial authority in the health system is particularly salient for technologies such as drugs (both prescription and over-the-counter), devices (both medical and assistive), diagnostics and vaccinations. Only some companies may be licensed to produce a given technology and limits may be placed on the length of their patents, the size of their profits, the prices they can charge, who can buy from them and how, the approaches they can use in marketing, the people they can involve in sales and dispensing, and how their commercial liability works. The most well established regime affecting commercial authority in the health system is likely for prescription drugs. As will be discussed in Chapter 8, the federal government plays a significant role here, by establishing which drugs can enter the market and with what 'factory gate' ceiling price (not the wholesale price or the retail price charged by pharmacies), and by banning direct-to-consumer advertising of prescription drugs (although with the province's U.S. neighbour being one of only two countries in the world that does not ban such advertising, Ontarians are still exposed to a fair amount of it).

Professional authority

Clear rules about professional authority bring order to what would otherwise be a 'wild west' of individuals calling themselves a physician (whether or not they had the necessary training or licence), working outside their scope of practice (such as a registered nurse prescribing drugs, although the government has signalled its intent to move in this direction), providing care in a setting that does not meet established standards (such as providing general anesthesia in a physician's office), not maintaining their competence or reasonable standards of safety and quality (through continuing professional development and appropriate facility protocols), and practising without professional-liability insurance (through the Canadian Medical Protective Association for physicians and comparable bodies for other professionals). Some professionals may be prohibited from engaging in strike/job action that could jeopardize human life.

Interestingly, the list of registered health professionals who can call themselves 'doctor' when providing (or offering to provide) health services to individuals includes physicians (medical doctors) as well as chiropractors, dentists, naturopaths (who must use the phrase 'naturopathic doctor' after their name), optometrists, practitioners of traditional Chinese medicine, and psychologists. Audiologists have initiated a Charter challenge to be able to do the same.(6) A pharmacist or other regulated health professional who also holds a PhD can call themselves doctor, but not when providing (or offering to provide) health services to individuals. Veterinarians can also call themselves doctor.

Most professional authority is established through the regulatory colleges, which were created by the *Regulated Health Professions Act, 1991* and its various amendments.(6) The 26 colleges' websites typically provide a list of the policies that apply to members of their respective professions. An example would be the policies that were developed by the College of Physicians and Surgeons of Ontario for all physicians who are members of the college: www.cpso.on.ca/policies-publications/policy. Some health workers' authority is not formally regulated (e.g., personal support workers).

Citizen and stakeholder involvement

A key aspect of the governance arrangements of the health system is whether, how and under what conditions citizens have a formally recognized voice in their own care (e.g., informed consent to care and shared decision-making in what that care entails), in care provision (e.g., how a particular program or service is delivered), in system monitoring (e.g., which performance indicators are the focus of data collection and public reporting), and in policy and organizational decisions (e.g., what values should drive decision-making about how primary care is organized). Also important is whether, how and under what conditions other stakeholders (e.g., professionals and managers) are given a voice in policy and organizational decisions. And while this chapter is focused on governance arrangements, citizens and other stakeholders can, of course, seek to influence decisions through advocacy, lobbying and other informal channels, and through voting in elections.

Citizens have a formally recognized voice in their own care through a requirement (specified in the *Health Care Consent Act, 1996*) that they give their informed consent to treatment and through a right (articulated in the *Freedom of Information and Protection of Privacy Act, 1990*) to access their own personal health information (and to have the privacy and confidentiality of their personal healthcare information respected) (Table 2.2). They also have to give their informed consent to participate in research, with the key foundation for such consent being the Tri-Council Policy Statement: Ethical Conduct for Research Involving Humans.(7) What is much less formalized is the voice of citizens in shared decision-making about their care more generally, which is made easier through resources like the Decision Aids Database (maintained by the Ottawa Hospital Research Institute and available both directly and through the McMaster Optimal Aging Portal). Their voice in shared decision-making may not be actively supported by all health professionals.

Citizens also have a formally recognized voice in care provision (e.g., how a particular program or service is delivered) in a number of care settings, but it is typically not systematically or transparently elicited. In some of these care settings, this may only be through provisions for a complaints process. When patients have a concern with a particular health professional, complaints are handled through the relevant regulatory college. For home,

Table 2.2: Governance arrangements underpinning citizen engagement in the health system

Relevant policies

Patient autonomy and choice

Health Care Consent Act, 1996 provides rules that apply consistently in all healthcare settings with respect to consent to treatment (focusing on communication, patient autonomy and decision-making capacity)
* Regulatory colleges have formal guidelines for obtaining informed consent relevant to their respective professional members

Patient rights

Freedom of Information and Protection of Privacy Act, 1990 provides individuals with the right to access their own personal health information

Personal Health Information Protection Act, 2004 (PHIPA) and the *Health Information Protection Act, 2016* place limitations on the collection and sharing of healthcare information, including in electronic form

The Information and Privacy Commissioner of Ontario resolves appeals and privacy complaints under PHIPA, publicly reports breaches of PHIPA, and provides healthcare professionals with information on how to protect private information

Patient engagement

Excellent Care for All Act, 2010 (ECFAA) mandates patient engagement as part of the Quality Improvement Plan process in all Ontario hospitals[1]

Local Health Systems Integration Act, 2006 formally mandates the Local Health Integration Networks to engage citizens in the planning, integrating and funding of local health services

Patient complaints

Regulated Health Professionals Act, 1991 mandates that all health professional colleges have patient relations and quality assurance programs, processes to monitor and report on their effectiveness, and disciplinary procedures

Home Care and Community Services Act, 1994 requires that all home and community care service agencies have processes for appeals and complaints in place

Long-Term Care Homes Act, 2007 and Ontario Regulation 79/10 under the act (2010) outlines long-term care home-related complaints procedures, and include a Residents' Bill of Rights articulating the right of residents to quality care

Public Sector and MPP Accountability and Transparency Act, 2014 mandates the appointment of a specialized provincial Patient Ombudsman to respond to patient complaints and conduct investigations against Community Care Access Centres (CCACs), hospitals, and long-term care homes

Public reporting

ECFAA mandates Health Quality Ontario to publicly report on the quality of the Ontario health system and, through related regulations, mandates CCACs, interprofessional team-based primary-care organizations, hospitals, and long-term care homes to measure and report publicly on key quality indicators on an annual basis (and for primary care and hospital settings this includes measures of patient and provider satisfaction)

Although not a current ECFAA requirement, voluntary initiatives to evaluate quality in primary care are ongoing[2]

Sources: 15; 18; 33; 43; 47-60

Notes:
[1] Citizens councils have also been established to engage citizens in healthcare delivery (e.g., the Ontario Citizens' Council was created to act as an advisory body to the Executive Officer of Ontario Public Drug Programs and the Minister of Health and Long-Term Care.(59)
[2] An example is the Primary Care Patient Experience Survey undertaken by Health Quality Ontario, Association of Ontario Health Centres, Ontario College of Family Physicians, Ontario Medical Association and the Association of Family Health Teams of Ontario. Health Quality Ontario has also developed Quality Improvement Plan indicators for CCACs and long-term care.

community, hospital and long-term care organizations, complaints are handled through the organization itself. Now, with any aspect of the health system, citizens may direct concerns to a Patient Ombudsman, who first assumed the role in July 2016 (Table 2.2). On a related point, citizens have a formally recognized voice in system (and hospital) monitoring through a requirement (in the *Excellent Care for All Act, 2010*) for public reporting on patient (and professional) satisfaction on an annual basis.

Whereas there is much activity but also much heterogeneity drawing on the voice of citizens in policy and organizational decisions, select citizens play a formal governance role on:
1) government boards that address citizen consent and capacity issues (Consent and Capacity Board), issues related to lack of criminal responsibility because of mental illness (Ontario Review Board), payment for patient services (Health Services Appeal and Review Board), physician-payment issues (Physician Payment Review Board), and professional practice issues (Health Professions Appeal and Review Board);
2) government committees that address cases of disputed Ontario Health Insurance Plan (OHIP) coverage for patients (Medical Eligibility Committee), financial assistance for those who contracted hepatitis C (Ontario Hepatitis C Assistance Plan Review Committee) and cases of disputed OHIP coverage for select (typically non-physician) health professionals (Review Committees); and
3) governing boards of professional regulatory bodies (e.g., College of Physicians and Surgeons of Ontario), LHINs, hospitals, community-governed primary-care clinic models (e.g., Community Health Centres), and other organizations.

LHINs are formally mandated by their governing legislation to engage citizens in planning, integrating and funding local health services. Also, select citizens play a legislatively mandated advisory role through the Ontario Citizens' Council (which provides advice on the values of Ontario's citizens about government drug policy), (8) and an informal advisory role through standing initiatives at the provincial level (e.g., Ministry of Health and Long-Term Care's Patient and Family Advisory Council, CCO's Patient and Family Advisory Council, and HQO's Patient, Family and Public Advisors Council), programmatic initiatives at the provincial level (e.g., McMaster Health Forum's citizen panels program), one-off initiatives at the provincial level (e.g., Citizens' Reference Panel on Health Services), and a variety of initiatives at the organizational level (e.g., patient councils at hospitals).

Stakeholders (e.g., organized groups of professionals) often have a voice in policy and organizational decisions but typically not in a systematic or transparent way. However, exceptions exist, such as with the Physicians Services Committee (which gives physicians a voice in policy decisions that affect their profession) and many of the government boards and committees and governing boards noted above, as well as with initiatives like the McMaster Health Forum's stakeholder dialogues (which convene a broad range of policymakers, stakeholders and researchers to address a health-system problem, options for addressing it, and key implementation considerations). It is perhaps not surprising that much stakeholder engagement is handled in an ad hoc and behind-closed-doors manner given the vast array of citizen and other stakeholder groups with personal, professional, financial and other interests in the health system.

Key citizen and stakeholder groups include (Figure 2.3):
1) regulatory colleges, which regulate professional practice, adjudicate patient complaints, and oversee quality in Independent Health Facilities and Out of Hospital Premises, among other roles (as such colleges would not be considered a stakeholder group by many, we have placed them in the 'policies' row);
2) organizational associations that represent everything from large, influential organizations (e.g., hospitals) to smaller, less well-resourced organizations (e.g., Family Health Teams);
3) professional associations that represent professions that can contribute to large programming and advocacy budgets (e.g., the OMA, which runs programs to support the use of electronic health records, among other objectives, and the Registered Nurses' Association of Ontario, which develops and supports the use of best-practice guidelines, among other programs);
4) trade unions that negotiate contracts (addressing wages, benefits and employment conditions), some of which focus on a profession (e.g., Ontario Nurses' Association), while others focus on a broad range of types of staff (e.g., Ontario Public Service Employees Union);
5) citizen/patient groups, which can vary from groups that are formally coordinated by government or government agencies as mentioned above (e.g., Ontario Citizens' Council) to groups that operate independently (e.g., Patients Canada); and

Figure 2.3: Citizen and stakeholder organizations involved in the health system

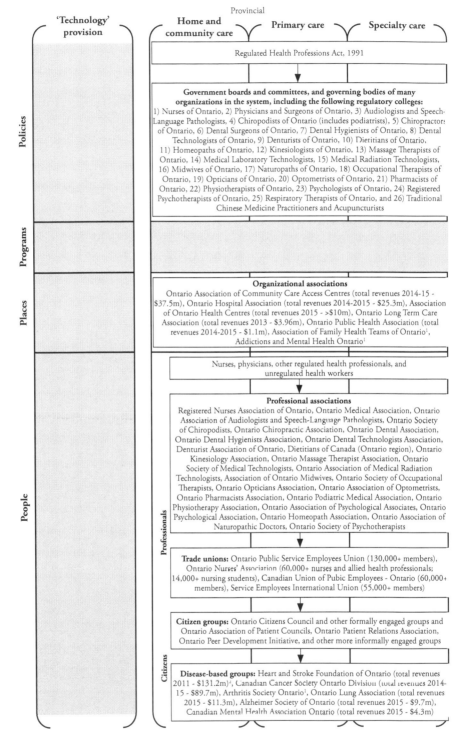

Provincial

'Technology' provision

Home and community care   **Primary care**   **Specialty care**

Policies

Regulated Health Professions Act, 1991

Government boards and committees, and governing bodies of many organizations in the system, including the following regulatory colleges:
1) Nurses of Ontario, 2) Physicians and Surgeons of Ontario, 3) Audiologists and Speech-Language Pathologists, 4) Chiropodists of Ontario (includes podiatrists), 5) Chiropractors of Ontario, 6) Dental Surgeons of Ontario, 7) Dental Hygienists of Ontario, 8) Dental Technologists of Ontario, 9) Denturists of Ontario, 10) Dietitians of Ontario, 11) Homeopaths of Ontario, 12) Kinesiologists of Ontario, 13) Massage Therapists of Ontario, 14) Medical Laboratory Technologists, 15) Medical Radiation Technologists, 16) Midwives of Ontario, 17) Naturopaths of Ontario, 18) Occupational Therapists of Ontario, 19) Opticians of Ontario, 20) Optometrists of Ontario, 21) Pharmacists of Ontario, 22) Physiotherapists of Ontario, 23) Psychologists of Ontario, 24) Registered Psychotherapists of Ontario, 25) Respiratory Therapists of Ontario, and 26) Traditional Chinese Medicine Practitioners and Acupuncturists

Programs

Places

Organizational associations
Ontario Association of Community Care Access Centres (total revenues 2014-15 - $37.5m), Ontario Hospital Association (total revenues 2014-2015 - $25.3m), Association of Ontario Health Centres (total revenues 2015 - >$10m), Ontario Long Term Care Association (total revenues 2013 - $3.96m), Ontario Public Health Association (total revenues 2014-2015 - $1.1m), Association of Family Health Teams of Ontario[1], Addictions and Mental Health Ontario[1]

Nurses, physicians, other regulated health professionals, and unregulated health workers

People

Professionals

Professional associations
Registered Nurses Association of Ontario, Ontario Medical Association, Ontario Association of Audiologists and Speech-Language Pathologists, Ontario Society of Chiropodists, Ontario Chiropractic Association, Ontario Dental Association, Ontario Dental Hygienists Association, Ontario Dental Technologists Association, Denturist Association of Ontario, Dietitians of Canada (Ontario region), Ontario Kinesiology Association, Ontario Massage Therapist Association, Ontario Society of Medical Technologists, Ontario Association of Medical Radiation Technologists, Association of Ontario Midwives, Ontario Society of Occupational Therapists, Ontario Opticians Association, Ontario Association of Optometrists, Ontario Pharmacists Association, Ontario Podiatric Medical Association, Ontario Physiotherapy Association, Ontario Association of Psychological Associates, Ontario Psychological Association, Ontario Homeopath Association, Ontario Association of Naturopathic Doctors, Ontario Society of Psychotherapists

Trade unions: Ontario Public Service Employees Union (130,000+ members), Ontario Nurses' Association (60,000+ nurses and allied health professionals; 14,000+ nursing students), Canadian Union of Pubic Employees - Ontario (60,000+ members), Service Employees International Union (55,000+ members)

Citizens

Citizen groups: Ontario Citizens Council and other formally engaged groups and Ontario Association of Patient Councils, Ontario Patient Relations Association, Ontario Peer Development Initiative, and other more informally engaged groups

Disease-based groups: Heart and Stroke Foundation of Ontario (total revenues 2011 - $131.2m)[2], Canadian Cancer Society Ontario Division (total revenues 2014-15 - $89.7m), Arthritis Society Ontario[1], Ontario Lung Association (total revenues 2015 - $11.3m), Alzheimer Society of Ontario (total revenues 2015 - $9.7m), Canadian Mental Health Association Ontario (total revenues 2015 - $4.3m)

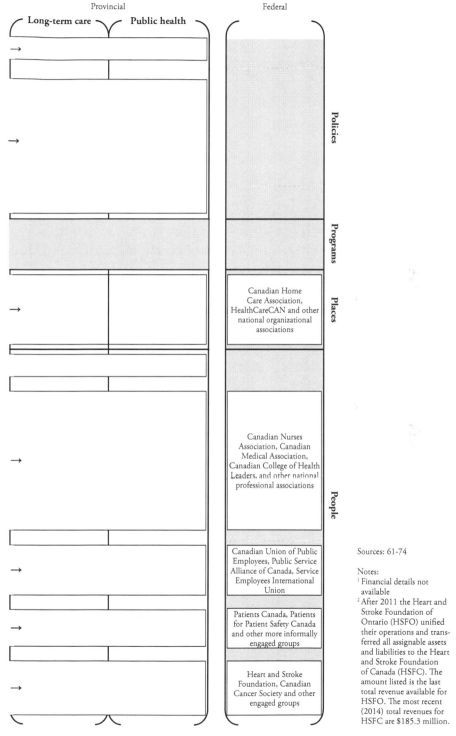

Provincial — Long-term care — Public health — Federal

Policies

Programs

Places

Canadian Home
Care Association,
HealthCareCAN and other
national organizational
associations

People

Canadian Nurses
Association, Canadian
Medical Association,
Canadian College of Health
Leaders, and other national
professional associations

Canadian Union of Public
Employees, Public Service
Alliance of Canada, Service
Employees International
Union

Patients Canada, Patients
for Patient Safety Canada
and other more informally
engaged groups

Heart and Stroke
Foundation, Canadian
Cancer Society and other
engaged groups

Sources: 61-74

Notes:
[1] Financial details not
available
[2] After 2011 the Heart and
Stroke Foundation of
Ontario (HSFO) unified
their operations and transferred all assignable assets
and liabilities to the Heart
and Stroke Foundation
of Canada (HSFC). The
amount listed is the last
total revenue available for
HSFO. The most recent
(2014) total revenues for
HSFC are $185.3 million.

6) disease-based groups, ranging from high-profile national health charities (e.g., Heart and Stroke Foundation of Ontario) to more grassroots organizations, the latter of which can sometimes receive significant funding from pharmaceutical/biotechnology companies (in which case they have been called 'astroturf' groups by some).

In Figure 2.3, these are typically listed in order of decreasing revenue or membership. Also, given the 'program' row was not needed, it was deleted in this sector4P figure.

Conclusion

The governance arrangements for the health system are complex and allow for innovation in some areas but constrain it in others. They comprise what some have called institutions of deliberation (e.g., legislature, citizens' councils), stewardship (e.g., Ministry of Health and Long-Term Care), and independent accountability (e.g., HQO). Increasingly governance arrangements are being rigorously studied and syntheses of the available research evidence on many key government arrangements can be identified by searching Health Systems Evidence (www.healthsystems evidence.org) and using the 'Governance arrangements' filter in the 'advanced search.' In Chapter 3 we will turn to financial arrangements, and what some have called the institutions of finance (e.g., OHIP, LHINs), and in Chapter 4 we will turn to delivery arrangements, including what some have called institutions for information (e.g., Institute for Clinical Evaluative Sciences, Statistics Canada) and normative institutions (e.g., HQO, with its evidence standards).

References

1. Barr N. The economics of the welfare state. Second Edition. Stanford: Stanford University Press; 1993.

2. Treasury Board of Canada Secretariat. Assessing, selecting, and implementing instruments for government action. Ottawa: Government of Canada; 2007.

3. Legislative Assembly of Ontario. Bill 41, Patients First Act, 2016. Toronto: Queen's Printer for Ontario; 2016. http://www.ontla. on.ca/web/bills/bills_detail.do?locale=en&Intranet=&BillID=4215 (accessed 7 October 2016).

4. Ministry of Health and Long-Term Care. Patients first: Action plan for health care. Toronto: Queen's Printer for Ontario; 2015. http://www.health.gov.on.ca/en/ms/ecfa/healthy_change/docs/rep_patientsfirst.pdf (accessed 25 August 2016).

5. Health Quality Ontario. Engaging with patients. Stories and successes from the 2015/2016 Quality Improvement Plans. Toronto: Health Quality Ontario; 2016. http://www.hqontario.ca/portals/0/documents/qi/qip/engaging-with-patients-en.pdf (accessed 7 October 2016).

6. Legislative Assembly of Ontario. Regulated Health Professions Act, 1994, S.O. 1991, c. 18, s.3. Toronto: Queen's Printer for Ontario; 1991. http://www.e-Laws.gov.on.ca/html/statutes/english/elaws_statutes_91r18_e.htm (accessed 25 August 2016).

7. Canadian Institutes of Health Research, Natural Sciences and Engineering Research Council of Canada, Social Sciences and Humanities Research Council of Canada. Tri-council policy statement: Ethical conduct for research involving humans, December 2014. Ottawa: Government of Canada; 2014. http://www.pre.ethics.gc.ca/pdf/eng/tcps2-2014/TCPS_2_FINAL_Web.pdf (accessed 11 October 2016).

8. Legislative Assembly of Ontario. Ontario Drug Benefit Act, 1990, Ontario Regulation 201/96. Toronto: Queen's Printer for Ontario; 1990. http://www.e-Laws.gov.on.ca/html/regs/english/elaws_regs_960201_e.htm (accessed 25 August 2016).

9. Canada Parliament House of Commons. Canada Health Act (R.S.C., 1985, c. C-6). Ottawa: Canada Parliament House of Commons; 1985. http://laws-lois.justice.gc.ca/eng/acts/C-6/FullText.html (accessed 26 August 2016).

10. Canada Parliament House of Commons. Patent Act, 1985, R.S.C., 1985, c. P-4. Ottawa: Canada Parliament House of Commons; 1985. http://www.laws-lois.justice.gc.ca/eng/acts/P-4/ (accessed 22 August 2016).

11. Canada Parliament House of Commons. Public Health Agency of Canada Act, S.C. 2006, c.5. Ottawa: Canada Parliament House of Commons; 2006. http://lois-laws.justice.gc.ca/eng/acts/P-29.5/ (accessed 11 October 2016).

12. Legislative Assembly of Ontario. Ministry of Health and Long-Term Care Act, 1990, R.S.O. 1990, c. M.26. Toronto: Queen's Printer for Ontario; 1990. http://www.e-Laws.gov.on.ca/html/statutes/english/elaws_statutes_90m26_e.htm (accessed 25 August 2016).

13. Legislative Assembly of Ontario. Health Protection and Promotion Act, R.S.O. 1990, c. H.7. Toronto: Queen's Printer for Ontario; 1990. http://www.e-Laws.gov.on.ca/html/statutes/english/elaws_statutes_90h07_e.htm (accessed 26 August 2016).

14. Legislative Assembly of Ontario. Mental Health Act R.S.O. 1990. Toronto: Queen's Printer for Ontario; 1990. http://www.e-Laws. gov.on.ca/html/statutes/english/elaws_statutes_90m07_e.htm (accessed 25 August 2016).

15. Legislative Assembly of Ontario. French Language Services Act, R.S.O. 1990, c. F.32. Toronto: Queen's Printer for Ontario; 2009. https://www.ontario.ca/laws/statute/90f32 (accessed 24 August 2016).

16. Commissariat aux services en français. Rapport spécial — L'offre active de services en français: La clé de voûte à l'atteinte des objectifs de la Loi sur les services en français de l'Ontario. Toronto: l'Assemblée législative de l'Ontario; 2016. http://csfontario.ca/ wp-content/uploads/2016/05/csf_rapport_special_2016.pdf (accessed 11 October 2016).

17. Legislative Assembly of Ontario. Public Sector Labour Relations Transition Act, 1997, S.O. 1997, c.21 Sched. B. Toronto: Queen's Printer for Ontario; 1997. http://www.e-Laws.gov.on.ca/html/statutes/english/elaws_statutes_97p21b_e.htm (accessed 25 August 2016).

18. Legislative Assembly of Ontario. Commitment to the Future of Medicare Act, 2004 (S.O. 2004). Toronto: Queen's Printer for Ontario; 2004. http://www.e-Laws.gov.on.ca/html/statutes/english/elaws_statutes_04c05_e.htm (accessed 25 August 2016).

19. Legislative Assembly of Ontario. Local Health System Integration Act, 2006, S.O. 2006, c. 4. Toronto: Queen's Printer for Ontario; 2010. http://www.e-laws.gov.on.ca/html/statutes/english/elaws_statutes_06l04_e.htm (accessed 25 August 2016).

20. Legislative Assembly of Ontario. Health System Improvements Act, S.O. 2007, c. 10 - Bill 171. Toronto: Queen's Printer for Ontario; 2007. https://www.ontario.ca/laws/statute/S07010 (accessed 11 October 2016).

21. Legislative Assembly of Ontario. Excellent Care for All Act, 2010, S.O. 2010, c. 14. Toronto: Queen's Printer for Ontario; 2010. https://www.ontario.ca/laws/statute/10e14 - BK0 (accessed 24 August 2016).

22. Legislative Assembly of Ontario. Health Protection and Promotion Amendment Act, 2011 S.O. 2011, c.7 - Bill 141. Toronto: Queen's Printer for Ontario; 2011. http://www.ontario.ca/laws/statute/s11007 (accessed 24 August 2016).

23. Legislative Assembly of Ontario. Drug Interchangeability and Dispensing Fee Act, 1990 (R.S.O. 1990, P.23). Toronto: Queen's Printer for Ontario; 1990. http://www.e-Laws.gov.on.ca/html/statutes/english/elaws_statutes_90p23_e.htm (accessed 25 August 2016).

24. Legislative Assembly of Ontario. Transparent Drug System for Patients Act, 2006, R.S.O. 2006, c. 14. Toronto: Queen's Printer for Ontario; 2006. http://www.ontla.on.ca/web/bills/bills_detail.do?locale=en&BillID=412 (accessed 24 August 2016).

25. Legislative Assembly of Ontario. Narcotics Safety and Awareness Act, 2010, Ontario Regulation 381/11. Toronto: Queen's Printer for Ontario; 2010. http://www.e-Laws.gov.on.ca/html/regs/english/elaws_regs_110381_e.htm (accessed 25 August 2016).

26. Legislative Assembly of Ontario. Drug and Pharmacies Regulation Act, 2011, Ontario regulation 58/11. Toronto: Queen's Printer for Ontario; 2011. http://www.ontario.ca/laws/regulation/r11058 (accessed 24 August 2016).

27. Legislative Assembly of Ontario. Public Hospitals Act, R.S.O. 1990, c. P.40. Toronto: Queen's Printer for Ontario; 1990. https://www.ontario.ca/laws/statute/90p40?search=public+hospitals+act (accessed 25 August 2016).

28. Legislative Assembly of Ontario. Private Hospitals Act, R.S.O. 1990, c. P.24. Toronto: Queen's Printer for Ontario; 1990. https://www.ontario.ca/laws/statute/90p24?search=private+hospitals+act (accessed 25 September 2016).

29. Legislative Assembly of Ontario. Independent Health Facilities Act, 1990, R.S.O. 1990, c. I.3. Toronto: Queen's Printer for Ontario; 1990. http://www.e-Laws.gov.on.ca/html/statutes/english/elaws_statutes_90i03_e.htm (accessed 25 August 2016).

30. Legislative Assembly of Ontario. Healing Arts Radiation Protection Act, R.S.O. 1990, c. H.2. Toronto: Queen's Printer for Ontario; 1990. https://www.ontario.ca/laws/statute/90h02 (accessed 11 October 2016).

31. Legislative Assembly of Ontario. Health Facilities Special Orders Act, 1990 (R.S.O. 1990, H.5). Toronto: Queen's Printer for Ontario; 1990. http://www.e-Laws.gov.on.ca/html/statutes/english/elaws_statutes_90h05_e.htm (accessed 25 August 2016).

32. Legislative Assembly of Ontario. Homes for Special Care Act, R.S.O. 1990, c.H.12. Toronto: Queen's Printer for Ontario; 1990. https://www.ontario.ca/laws/statute/90h12?search=homes+for+special+care (accessed 25 September 2016).

33. Legislative Assembly of Ontario. Home Care and Community Services Act, 1994, S.O. 1994, c. 26. Toronto: Queen's Printer for Ontario; 1994. http://www.e-Laws.gov.on.ca/html/statutes/english/elaws_statutes_94l26_e.htm (accessed 25 August 2016).

34. Legislative Assembly of Ontario. Community Care Access Corporations Act, 2001 (S.O. 2001, 33). Toronto: Queen's Printer for Ontario; 2001. https://www.ontario.ca/laws/statute/01c33 (accessed 26 August 2016).

35. Legislative Assembly of Ontario. Ontario regulation 79/10 made under the Long-term Care Homes Act, 2007. Toronto: Queen's Printer for Ontario; 2007. http://www.e-Laws.gov.on.ca/html/source/regs/english/2010/elaws_src_regs_r10079_e.htm (accessed 25 August 2016).

36. Legislative Assembly of Ontario. The Broader Public Sector Accountability Act, 2010, S.O. 2010, c. 25. Toronto: Queen's Printer for Ontario; 2010. http://www.ontla.on.ca/web/bills/bills_detail.do?locale=en&BillID=2420&detailPage=bills_detail_the_bill (accessed 24 August 2016).

37. Legislative Assembly of Ontario. Medicine Act, 1991. Loi de 1991 sur les médecins. Ontario Regulation 114/94. Toronto: Queen's Printer for Ontario; 1991. http://www.e-Laws.gov.on.ca/html/regs/english/elaws_regs_940114_e.htm (accessed 25 August 2016).

38. Legislative Assembly of Ontario. Ontario Medical Association Dues Act, 1991, S.O. 1991, c. 51. Toronto: Queen's Printer for Ontario; 1991. https://www.ontario.ca/laws/statute/91o51?search=medical+association+dues (accessed 25 August 2016).

39. Legislative Assembly of Ontario. Midwifery Act, S.O. 1991, c. 31. Ottawa: Queen's Printer for Ontario; 1991. https://www.ontario.ca/laws/statute/91m31?search=midwifery (accessed 25 August 2016).

40. Legislative Assembly of Ontario. Regulated Health Professions Statute Law Amendment Act, 2009, S.O. 2009, c. 26 - Bill 179. Toronto: Queen's Printer for Ontario; 2009. https://www.ontario.ca/laws/statute/s09026 (accessed 24 August 2016).

41. Legislative Assembly of Ontario. Naturopathy Act, 2007 (S.O. 2007, c.10, Sched. P.) Toronto: Queen's Printer for Ontario; 2015. http://www.ontario.ca/laws/statute/07n10 (accessed 24 August 2016).

42. Legislative Assembly of Ontario. Substitute Decisions Act, S.O. 1992, c. 30. Toronto: Queen's Printer for Ontario; 1992. https://www.ontario.ca/laws/statute/92s30?search=substitute+decisions+act (accessed 17 October 2016).

43. Legislative Assembly of Ontario. Health Care Consent Act, 1996 (S.O. 1996, c. 2 Sched. A). Toronto: Queen's Printer for Ontario; 1996. http://www.e-laws.gov.on.ca/html/statutes/english/elaws_statutes_96h02_e.htm (accessed 25 August 2016).

44. Legislative Assembly of Ontario. Personal Health Information Protection Act, 2004, S.O. 2004, c. 3, Sched. A. Toronto: Queen's Printer for Ontario; 2004. http://www.e-Laws.gov.on.ca/html/statutes/english/elaws_statutes_04p03_e.htm (accessed 25 August 2016).

45. Legislative Assembly of Ontario. Bill 119, Health Information Protection Act. Toronto: Queen's Printer for Ontario; 2016. http://www.ontla.on.ca/web/bills/bills_detail.do?locale=en&BillID=3438 (accessed 11 October 2016).

46. Ministry of Health and Long-Term Care. Ministry of Health and Long-Term Care organization chart. Toronto: Queen's Printer for Ontario; 2016. http://www.health.gov.on.ca/en/common/ministry/orgchart.pdf (accessed 25 August 2016).

47. Federation of Health Regulatory Colleges of Ontario. An inter-professional guide on the use of orders, directives and delegation for regulated health professionals of Ontario. Toronto: Federation of Health Regulatory Colleges of Ontario; 2007. http://mdguide.regulatedhealthprofessions.on.ca/why/default.asp (accessed 26 August 2016).

48. Health Quality Ontario. About Health Quality Ontario Toronto: Queen's Printer for Ontario; 2014. http://www.hqontario.ca/about-us (accessed 24 August 2016).

49. Health Quality Ontario. Patient experience survey. Toronto: Queen's Printer for Ontario; 2014. http://www.hqontario.ca/...care/primary-care-patient-experience-survey-faq-en.pdf (accessed 25 August 2016).

50. Information and Privacy Commissioner of Ontario. PHIPA. Toronto: Information and Privacy Commissioner of Ontario; 2014. http://www.ipc.on.ca/english/PHIPA/ (accessed 24 August 2016).

51. Legislative Assembly of Ontario. Health Insurance Act (R.S.O. 1990, c. H.6). Last amendment: 2009, c. 33, Sched. 18, ss. 11, 17 (2). Toronto: Queen's Printer for Ontario; 2009. http://www.e-laws.gov.on.ca/html/statutes/english/elaws_statutes_90h06_e.htm (accessed 25 August 2016).

52. CBCNews. Ontario votes. Seating chart of Ontario's Legislative Assembly. A schematic of party distribution of the seats in the assembly. 2014. http://www.cbc.ca/elections/ontariovotes2014/features/view/seating-chart-of-ontarios-legislative-assembly (accessed 25 August 2016).

53. Ministry of Health and Long-Term Care. Citizen's Council: About the Council. Toronto: Queen's Printer for Ontario; 2012. http://www.health.gov.on.ca/en/public/programs/drugs/councils/about.aspx (accessed 24 August 2016).

54. Ministry of Health and Long-Term Care. About Excellent Care for All Toronto: Queen's Printer for Ontario; 2014. http://www.health.gov.on.ca/en/pro/programs/ecfa/legislation/act_regs.aspx (accessed 25 August 2016).

55. Ministry of Health and Long-Term Care. A guide to the Long-Term Care Homes Act, 2007 and Regulation 79/10. Toronto: Queen's Printer for Ontario; 2014.

56. Ombudsman Ontario. Investigations. Toronto: Ombudsman Ontario; 2014. https://ombudsman.on.ca/Investigations.aspx (accessed 24 August 2016).

57. Ontario Hospital Association. Patient satisfaction. Toronto: Ontario Hospital Association; 2014. http://www.oha.com/knowledgecentre/library/healthreportsandprotocols/pages/patientsatisfaction.aspx (accessed 24 August 2016).

58. Ontario Medical Association Legal Services and Health Policy Departments. Responding to third-party requests for the sharing of patient data: Principles of Personal Health Protection Act apply. Toronto: Ontario Medical Association; 1996.

59. PricewaterhouseCoopers. About the Citizens' Reference Panel on Health Services. Toronto: PricewaterhouseCoopers; 2014. http://www.pwc.com/ca/en/healthcare/about-citizens-reference-panel.jhtml (accessed 24 August 2016).

60. Legislative Assembly of Ontario. Bill 119, Health Information Protection Act, 2016. Toronto: Queen's Printer for Ontario; 2016. http://www.ontla.on.ca/web/bills/bills_detail.do?locale=en&BillID=3438 (accessed 24 August 2016).

61. Ontario Public Health Association. Annual report 2014-2015. Toronto: Ontario Public Health Association; 2015.

62. Ontario Long Term Care Association. OLTCA annual report 2013. Shaping the future. Toronto: Ontario Long Term Care Association; 2013.

63. Ontario Hospital Association. Budget and operating plan. Toronto: Ontario Hospital Association; 2015.

64. PricewaterhouseCoopers. Ontario Association of Community Care Access Centres. Financial statements, March 31, 2015. Toronto: PricewaterhouseCoopers; 2015.

65. Thornton G. Financial statements of Canadian Cancer Society, Ontario Division (year ended January 31, 2015). Toronto: Grant Thornton Chartered Accountants; 2015.

66. Ontario Nurses' Association. Unions and the Ontario Nurses' Association. Toronto: Ontario Nurses Association; 2016. http://www.ona.org/faqs.html - f1 (accessed 24 August 2016).

67. CUPE SCFP Ontario. Health Care Workers Coordinating Committee (HCWCC). Markham: CUPE/SCFP Ontario; 2016. http://www.cupe.on.ca/s18/health-care (accessed 25 August 2016).

68. Service Employees International Union. SEIU Who we are. Toronto: SEIU; 2016. http://www.seiuhealthcare.ca/who-we-are/our-union (accessed 26 August 2016).

69. Heart and Stroke Foundation of Canada. Consolidated financial statement, August 31, 2013. Toronto: Pricewaterhouse Coopers; 2013. http://www.heartandstroke.com/site/c.ikIQLcMWJtE/b.5940253/k.6DC5/Financial_Statements.htm (accessed 24 August 2016).

70. Charity Intelligence Canada. Arthritis Society of Ontario. Toronto: Charity Intelligence Canada; 2015. http://charityintelligence.ca/charity-details/641-arthritis-society-ontario-division (accessed 26 August 2016).

71. BDO Canada. Alzheimer Society of Ontario financial statements for the year ended March 31, 2015. Mississauga: BDO Canada; 2015.

72. KPMG LLP. Financial statements of Ontario Lung Association year ended March 31, 2015. Toronto: KPMG LLP; 2015.

73. Canadian Mental Health Association. 2014/2015 annual report. Ottawa: CMHA; 2015. http://ontario.cmha.ca/files/2015/10/CMHA-2014-15-Annual-Report.pdf (accessed 26 August 2016).

74. Association of Ontario Health Centres. Leading transformative change: Report on the 2012-2015 AOHC strategic plan. Toronto: Association of Ontario Health Centres; 2015. https://issuu.com/aohc_acso/docs/aohc_2012-2015_report_-_english_-_f (accessed 24 August 2016).

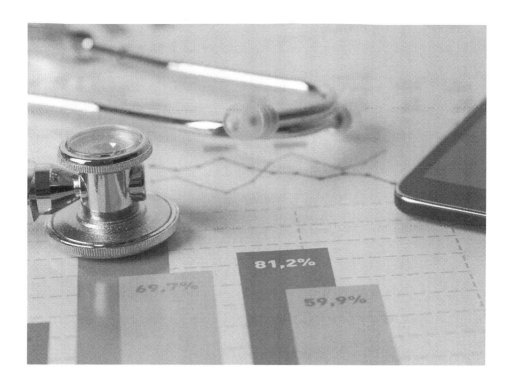

3. Financial arrangements

Kaelan A. Moat, Cristina A. Mattison and John N. Lavis

Key messages for citizens

- Public spending (i.e., government spending) on healthcare in Ontario is mostly financed through taxes, while private spending is mostly financed through direct out-of-pocket payments and premiums paid to private insurance plans.

- Many physicians are paid a set fee for each service they provide, but up to one third of all income received by physicians in Ontario is now paid to them in other ways (particularly in primary care). Other health professionals such as nurses are typically paid through salaries.

- While Ontarians are covered publicly for a wide range of necessary health products and services across all sectors, a number must be paid for out-of-pocket or through a private insurance plan (e.g., prescription drugs and dental services), which may result in citizens choosing not to access products and services that are not covered publicly.

Key messages for health professionals

- The largest portion of public revenues are allocated to Local Health Integration Networks to fund hospitals, home and community care agencies, and other organizations (in the case of hospitals through a combination of global budgets, the Health-Based Allocation Model and Quality-Based Procedures). The second-largest portion is allocated to the Ontario Health Insurance Plan, to pay for medically necessary services provided by physicians.

- Billing a set fee for each service is how most income is paid to Ontario's physicians, but other approaches are increasingly being used in primary care (e.g., payment for each enrolled patient in interprofessional models) and in academic hospital-based specialty care (e.g., payments to cover clinical research and teaching responsibilities). Non-physician health professionals, including most nurses, receive their income through salary arrangements.

- Medically necessary hospital-based and physician-provided services are fully covered for Ontarians, while public coverage of other products and services may depend on whether an individual is eligible for a public program (e.g., for prescription drugs) or a health professional prescribes or orders it (e.g., laboratory tests).

Key messages for policymakers

- An increasing proportion of total health spending in Ontario (32%) is financed privately through out-of-pocket payments or premiums paid to private insurance plans as the needs of Ontarians evolve beyond hospital-based and physician-provided services.

- Allocations of public revenues to Local Health Integration Networks and the Ontario Health Insurance Plan are the two largest government expenditures on the health system, and the ways this money is used to fund organizations and remunerate health professionals are periodically adjusted to align with health-system priorities (e.g., supporting inter-professional team-based primary care).

- Decisions about the products and services, populations and costs that are covered publicly may create disincentives for accessing care that is not covered.

. . .

In this second of four chapters focused on the building blocks of the health system, we explore financial arrangements, with a particular emphasis on how money flows through the system. When thinking about money within the context of Ontario's health system, many readers may default to thinking about the total amount spent on healthcare in Ontario (i.e., expenditures). This makes sense given the substantial sums involved, and given that total expenditures (both public and private) in Ontario increased by 61%, from $41 billion in 2000 to almost $66 billion in 2013, and the total amount spent per person increased by 39%, from roughly $3,500 per person in 2000 to approximately $4,900 per person in 2013 (all in 2002 dollars).(1-9)

While these numbers often attract attention in the media, they do not illuminate how money flows through the health system in Ontario, which is a key influence on how the system functions. Five inter-related categories of financial arrangements can be considered in order to provide a more comprehensive account of financial flows in the province: 1) financing the system (i.e., raising revenue); 2) funding organizations; 3) remunerating providers (both regulated health professionals and unregulated health workers); 4) purchasing products and services; and 5) incentivizing consumers.

This chapter is organized into sections that focus on each of these categories, which are depicted in Figure 3.1 as elements in the process of financial flows in the health system. While we separate the process into discrete elements to help explain the process in a clear way, in reality they are neither completely separate, nor sequential. The days of a simple contractual relationship between a service recipient (e.g., a patient paying for the care they want or need) and a service provider (e.g., a health professional providing that care) are long gone in most parts of most health systems around the world.(10) Today a variety of 'third parties' (e.g., government, private insurers, and workers' compensations boards) are involved in a web of relationships with providers that is often not visible to the service recipient (and sometimes not even to the provider).

The top left of Figure 3.1, the first element in the sequential representation of financial flows in Ontario's health system, depicts the primary source of revenue raised to pay for healthcare in the province: citizens. As we noted in the preface, we mean citizen in the broad sense of the term, not just those who hold Canadian citizenship and reside in Ontario (and we include permanent residents and refugees). Following the diagram in a counter-clockwise fashion, it shows that financial resources are collected from citizens through taxes and other means (e.g., insurance premiums) then move to government, private insurers and others (e.g., employers), where revenues are pooled. In this chapter, we refer to this process as 'financing the system.'

The second and third elements in the flow of financial resources through the health system in Ontario are depicted on the right side of Figure 3.1, and concern how pooled revenues become the money spent on care. The second element relates to how the revenues raised are allocated to the organizations responsible for providing programs, services and drugs to the citizens who need them, which we refer to as 'funding organizations' in this chapter. The third element relates to how the revenues raised are used to pay the individuals providing programs, services and drugs to the citizens who need them, which we refer to as 'remunerating providers' in this chapter. Some individuals may be remunerated directly by governments, private insurers, and others (e.g., physicians), while others may be remunerated by the organizations that are funded by governments, private insurers and others.

Figure 3.1: Financial arrangements, with a particular focus on the flow of money through the health system

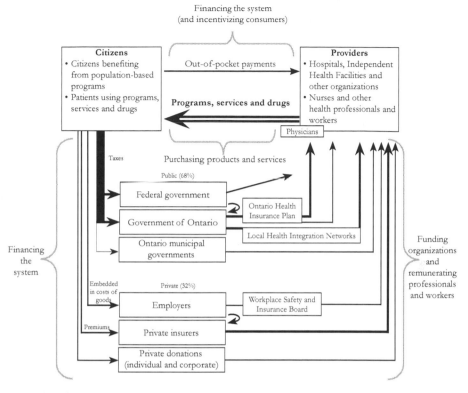

Sources: Adapted from: 65

The fourth element of health system financial flows is represented by the double arrow line at the top of Figure 3.1, and concerns the process through which the money spent on care translates into the programs, services and drugs used by the citizens of Ontario within the boundaries of a defined 'basket of services.' This is an ongoing process which we refer to in this chapter as 'purchasing products and services,' and relates to how decisions are made about the types of care paid for with public dollars (and therefore how much of the cost is covered for citizens). As Chapter 1 of this book already explained, at the most basic level, the health system in Ontario is defined by a 'core bargain' in which Ontarians have first-dollar coverage (i.e., 100% coverage with no deductible or cost-sharing) for all medically necessary hospital-based and physician-provided services – although as this chapter will highlight, there are many more nuances in the 'basket' of publicly funded programs, services and drugs. Perhaps more so with this element than any other discussed in this chapter, it is important to acknowledge that the sequence in which we have chosen to discuss the nature of purchasing products and services is to promote clarity in terms of understanding the 'big picture' of financial flows, and not necessarily the stage in the process where decisions are made. For example, in many instances the lists of covered programs, services and drugs are defined before organizations are funded and professionals are paid to deliver them to citizens.

The final element in the process, which is also represented by the top of Figure 3.1, is not really an element of a process in the traditional sense of the term. Specifically, what we refer to as 'incentivizing consumers' in this chapter relates to the consequences of the options adopted to finance the system. In discussing this, we focus on the ways in which approaches to healthcare financing, such as out-of-pocket payments, are used to encourage individual patients (or in this context, healthcare 'consumers') to interact with the health system in specific ways.

We now turn to detailed discussions of each of these categories, but suggest that readers periodically return to Figure 3.1 as a way to ensure the 'big picture' related to financial flows is kept in mind. For those interested in finding and using the best available synthesized research evidence about health-system financial arrangements, first understanding each of the categories below will be of great assistance. It is these categories that are used to index the full scope of systematic reviews, economic evaluations and policy documents on this topic in Health Systems Evidence (www.healthsystems-evidence.org), which is the world's most comprehensive free access point for research evidence about health-system arrangements, including financial arrangements.

Financing the system

The first element in the process of financial flows through any health system concerns where the money actually comes from to pay for care (represented in the top left corner of Figure 3.1). In any given health system, a number of options – both public and private – exist for financing the system, including raising revenue through:

1) taxation (general or earmarked taxation of individuals or corporations, with the latter meaning taxation that is designated specifically for

healthcare);

2) social health insurance (groupings of citizens, defined usually by occupation, make contributions, at least in part through income deductions);

3) community-based health insurance schemes (community-defined groups of citizens, such as those living in a particular geographic area, make contributions to insure community members against illness or injury);

4) community loan funds (community-defined groups of individuals establish a pool of funds that other community members can draw on for urgent healthcare needs);

5) private insurance (individuals, or their employers, make contributions to private insurers through premiums);

6) health savings accounts (individuals or employers make contributions to individual savings accounts earmarked for healthcare expenditures only);

7) user fees (out-of-pocket fees charged directly to patients to pay for products and services at the point of service delivery); and

8) fundraising (raising funds directly to support the construction or upgrading of infrastructure like buildings, the purchase of infrastructure like new technology, and the operating costs of healthcare clinics or organizations).

In general, most health systems are characterized by a mix of two or more of these options, and in Ontario the same is true. Specifically, as Figure 3.1 shows, the health system relies mostly on option 1 (both general and some earmarked) and to a lesser extent option 5 (private insurance premiums, many of which are part of employee benefits). However, there are some instances in which option 7 (e.g., paying out-of-pocket for the full price of uninsured products and services, user fees such as patient co-payments for prescription drugs or payments for home and community care above an assessed maximum) and option 8 (e.g., fundraising to pay for the construction of or upgrades to private not-for-profit hospitals) are also used as a mechanism to finance the health system.

Revenues

Details about the breakdown of total health expenditures in Ontario by both public and private sources have already been provided in Chapter 1 (e.g., see Figure 1.2, and Tables 1.4 and 1.5), but they are worth revisiting here as they are very relevant to the mechanisms through which revenues are raised to pay for healthcare in Ontario.

The first important consideration relates to the sources of public revenues used to finance the health system in Ontario, which account for 68% of total health expenditures in the province (Figure 1.2). The majority of the public revenues spent on healthcare in Ontario are generated through provincial taxation, which accounts for nearly 80% of all public sources of revenue.(11) The main sources for these public revenues are personal income tax (which accounts for 37%), sales tax (26%), and corporate tax (14%), with the remainder coming from other sources of taxation such as the education component of property tax, employer health tax, gas and fuel taxes, and the Ontario health premium.(11) Transfers from the federal government to the province make up the remaining 20% of public revenue available for allocation to the health system, and of this, nearly 54% comes from the Canada Health Transfer (which is provided to provincial governments on the condition that the principles of the *Canada Health Act, 1984* are adhered to), 21% from the Canada Social Transfer, and the rest through other mechanisms.(11)

The second important consideration relates to the remaining 32% of health expenditures in Ontario, which are financed from two major sources of private revenues. The first source of private financing is direct out-of-pocket payments for products and services not covered by the government, which accounted for 80% of private revenues in Ontario in 2013. The second source is insurance premiums paid to cover products and services not paid for by government, which accounted for the remaining 20% of private revenues in Ontario.(12)

While the majority of the money raised to pay for hospitals comes from public sources, hospitals typically have affiliated foundations that are registered charities, and in many cases, significant proportions of their total annual revenues are generated from donations and grants (see the bottom of Figure 3.1). For example, University Health Network, which is comprised of several hospital sites in downtown Toronto, received 14% ($279 million) of its total revenues from donations and grants in 2015.(13) The private charitable donations made by individual philanthropists and corporate foundations are particularly noteworthy because they are often used to pay for the construction of, or upgrades to, buildings (and related technology). For example, in 2014 the Rogers Foundation donated $130 million to University Health Network to establish the Ted Rogers Centre for Heart Research, while Michael G. DeGroote has donated more than $150 million since 2003 to the hospital-connected medical school that bears his name at McMaster University.(14; 15)

Expenditures

As previously mentioned, the substantial sums of money generated from the revenue sources outlined above are then spent on the health system, and the general trend over the last decade and a half has been towards increases in the amount spent. Total spending in 2002 dollars – both public and private – increased by 61% from $41 billion dollars in 2000 to nearly $66 billion dollars in 2013 (Table 3.1). Over this same time period, total per capita health spending in 2002 dollars increased from just over $3,500 per person to just under $4,900 per person, which is close to the Canadian average, although trends suggest the amounts spent per person in total are likely to remain constant, or decrease slightly (Figure 3.2).

Table 3.1: Total health expenditures, by public and private sources of finance[1]

Category of health expenditure ($ millions)	Ontario			Canada
	2000	2010	2013	2013
Total spending	41,008	63,113	65,977	205,981
Total public sector spending	27,267	43,060	44,669	145,685
Provincial government	25,148	40,171	41,914	135,300
Federal direct	1,170	1,802	1,821	6,749
Municipal government	590	604	408	799
Social security (Workplace Safety and Insurance Board)	357	483	526	2,837
Total private sector spending	13,742	20,053	21,308	60,297

Sources: 2; 4; 5; 8; 68-70

Note:
[1] Inflation adjusted to 2002, according to Statistics Canada's Consumer Price Index (healthcare), CANSIM 326-0020: value x (CPI 2002/CPIi) = value (2002) where i = year

The trends outlined above for total expenditures on the health system in the province (i.e., public and private combined) are broadly similar to those observed for public expenditures on the health system. Ninety-four percent of public spending is done by the provincial government (which includes money received from federal-provincial transfers) and 4% by the federal government (through federal direct spending on programs, services

Figure 3.2: Per capita health expenditures, both overall and by public and private sources of finance, 2000 to 2015[1,2]

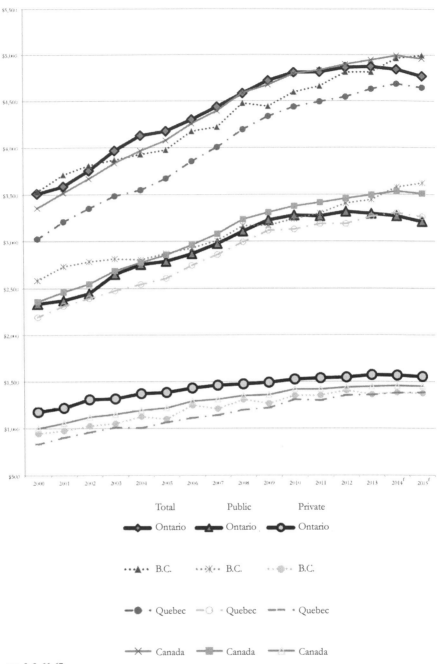

Sources: 3; 8; 66; 67

Notes:
[1] Inflation adjusted to 2002, according to Statistics Canada's Consumer Price Index (healthcare), CANSIM 326-0020: value x (CPI 2002/CPIi) = value (2002) where i = year
[2] Expenditures for 2014 and 2015 are forecasts. This is denoted by a superscript 'f' following the year indicated on the horizontal axis.

and drugs for First Nations communities, military personnel, etc.). The remainder comes from municipal governments and social security funds, the latter of which is made up of contributions to the Workplace Safety and Insurance Board (Table 3.1). The long-term trend has been an increase in total public expenditures in Ontario, with a 64% increase in total public spending in 2002 dollars – from just over $27 billion in 2000 to almost $45 billion in 2013 – and an increase in per capita public spending in 2002 dollars over the same time period from just over $2,300 per person to approximately $3,300 (Figure 3.2 and Table 3.1). However, over the shorter term (since 2011), the trend appears to be that per capita public expenditures are levelling off (Figure 3.2).

While total private spending is less than total public spending in absolute terms, private expenditures have increased in 2002 dollars by 55% between 2000 and 2013, from under $14 billion to over $21 billion (Table 3.1). Per capita private spending has increased in 2002 dollars from $1,176 in 2000 to $1,572 in 2013 in Ontario, which is higher than the Canadian average of $1,447 in 2013 (Figure 3.2). Private expenditures in part take the form of allocations from employers to private insurers, which then allocate funds to a wide variety of health organizations and health professionals in the province providing programs, services and drugs that are not covered publicly. In 2013, a total of $378 million in 2002 dollars was spent on health insurance premiums, of which approximately one quarter was used to pay (at least in part) for supplemental elements of hospital care, including private rooms (Table 3.2). Additionally, through out-of-pocket payments for programs, services and drugs (as well as other 'technologies'), individual Ontarians are directly responsible for 80% of private spending (see top of Figure 3.1). In 2013 over $1.5 billion in 2002 dollars in direct out-of-pocket payments were made by individuals (Table 3.2).

Finally, while not as easily measured or reported accurately with specific numbers, it is also important to consider tax revenues forgone because of the preferential tax treatment of select private health-related expenditures. Examples of these types of 'tax expenditures' include the exclusion of employer-provided health insurance from income, as well as the medical expense tax credit, the disability tax credit, and disability savings accounts.

Table 3.2: Private health expenditures, by type of product, service or insurance plan being paid for, 2010 and 2013[1]

Category of private health expenditures ($ millions)	Ontario		Canada
	2010	2013	2013
Private health expenditures[2]	1,579	1,919	2,479
Direct healthcare costs to household	1,297	1,541	1,733
Non-prescribed medicines, pharmaceutical products and healthcare supplies	349	523	484
Prescribed medicines and pharmaceutical products	338	273	452
Dental services	302	246	346
Eye-care goods and services	135	172	230
Healthcare services	174	166	221
Healthcare practitioners (excluding family physicians and specialists)	100	97	125
Hospital care, long-term care homes and other residential care facilities	39	32	39
Weight-control programs, smoking cessation programs and other medical services	23	21	30
Healthcare by family physicians and specialists	13	15	28
Health insurance premiums	281	378	746
Private health insurance plan premiums	217	285	528
Private healthcare plan premiums	122	177	355
Accident or disability insurance premiums	81	89	130
Dental plan premiums	14	20	43
Public hospital, medical and drug plan premiums	65	93	218

Sources: 8; 12

Notes:
[1] Inflation adjusted to 2002, according to Statistics Canada's Consumer Price Index (healthcare), CANSIM 326-0020: value x (CPI 2002/CPIi) = value (2002) where i = year
[2] Includes direct costs to household (out-of-pocket) net of the expenditures reimbursed, and health insurance premiums

Funding organizations

The second element in the process of financial flows through the health system in Ontario is the use of the revenues that are raised in order to fund organizations responsible for providing programs, services and drugs (represented by part of the right side of Figure 3.1). The most important aspect of how organizations are funded in Ontario's health system concerns the transfers from the Ministry of Health and Long-Term Care to the 14 Local Health Integration Networks (LHINs), which provide funding to independent organizations with (often high profile) boards of directors in their region (as opposed to the regional authorities in other provinces that fund programs and services directly rather than through organizations with separate boards of directors) (Figure 3.1). This process involves many home and community care organizations, all hospitals, and many long-term care homes (although some homes receive funding directly from the ministry). Hospitals, it is worth noting, receive 3.5 times the amount of public funding received by other organizations combined (Table 3.3). Importantly, while finances flow through LHINs, these administrative organizations generally have little discretion as to how funds are allocated because the recipients and the amounts they receive are largely determined by procedures (e.g., licensing of long-term care homes) and formulae (e.g., Health-Based Allocation Model for hospitals) set by government.

Table 3.3: Public and private health expenditures, by type of organization or program being funded, 2013

Category of public and private health expenditure ($ millions)	Ontario[1]	Canada	Ontario[1]	Canada
	2013		% distribution	
Public				
Total	53,915	148,143		
Hospitals	19,379	56,487	36%	38%
Physicians	12,790	31,288	24%	21%
Other institutions	5,481	15,537	10%	11%
Drugs	4,655	12,044	9%	8%
Prescribed	—	12,044	—	8%
Non-prescribed	—	0	—	0
Public health	4,550	11,368	8%	8%
Other health spending	3,229	9,435	6%	6%
Health research	—	2,053	—	1%
Other	—	7,381	—	5%
Capital	2,477	7,446	5%	5%
Administration	828	2,680	2%	2%
Other professionals	526	1,859	1%	1%
Dental services	—	791	—	0.5%
Vision care services	—	360	—	0.2%
Other	—	709	—	0.5%
Private				
Total	25,719	61,314		
Drugs	8,594	21,353	33%	35%
Prescribed	—	16,261	—	27%
Non-prescribed	—	5,092	—	8%
Other professionals	7,350	18,915	29%	31%
Dental services	—	12,087	—	20%

Continued on next page

Category of public and private health expenditure ($ millions)	Ontario[1]	Canada	Ontario[1]	Canada
	2013		% distribution	
Private – continued				
Vision care services	—	3,637	—	6%
Other	—	3,191	—	5%
Hospitals	3,306	5,894	13%	10%
Other institutions	2,566	6,402	10%	10%
Other health spending	1,626	3,311	6%	5%
Health research	—	1,529	—	3%
Other	—	1,782	—	3%
Administration	1,387	3,661	5%	6%
Capital	791	1,383	3%	2%
Physicians	98	395	0.4%	0.6%
Public health	0	0	0	0

Sources: 71-78

Note:
[1] Data not available for the specific reference period are denoted by —.

LHINs account for slighly more than half (51%) of all spending by the ministry (Table 3.4). Budget allocations from the Ministry of Health and Long-Term Care to each LHIN to pay these organizations varies across the regions, with the Toronto Central LHIN (in downtown Toronto) receiving the largest transfer. At close to $3,500 spent per person in 2002 dollars, per capita allocations (calculated by dividing the operating expenses of each region by the population served) are also highest in this LHIN, which is likely due to the large number of people who travel to Toronto from other regions to receive specialty care. The lowest per capita allocations (under $1,000 spent per person) are to the LHINs bordering Toronto Central (Central and Central West), where their populations are also served by Toronto Central. Allocations are generally similar across all other LHINs.

Table 3.4: Public health expenditures by the Ministry of Health and Long-Term Care, by type of program being paid for, 2011-12

Program	2011-12 operating expenses
Local Health Integration Networks (LHINs) and related health service providers[1] Transfer payments to 14 LHINs:	23,700,133,616
Toronto Central	4,429,833,600
Hamilton Niagara Haldimand Brant	2,648,185,300
Champlain (Ottawa)	2,398,969,800
South West (London)	2,116,960,100

Continued on next page

Program	2011-12 operating expenses
Transfer payments to 14 LHINs – continued	
Central East	2,095,556,2000
Central	1,795,391,200
North East (Timmins)	1,363,231,600
Mississauga Halton	1,302,317,300
South East (Kingston)	1,061,416,400
Erie St. Clair (Windsor)	1,056,645,300
Waterloo Wellington	959,137,200
Central West	805,145,400
North Simcoe Muskoka	761,496,000
North West (Thunder Bay)	595,657,400
Ontario Health Insurance Plan	16,888,990,910
Health Insurance Transfer payments for care provided by:	
physicians and other healthcare providers	12,753,267,700
midwifery services	125,488,200
colorectal cancer screening	75,457,100
Independent Health Facilities	69,427,300
Northern Travel Program	52,581,600
teletriage services	41,763,400
Health Quality Ontario	36,193,100
disease-prevention strategy	34,469,200
quality health initiatives	22,304,400
underserviced area plan	21,713,500
Quality Management Program - laboratory services	4,598,900
Drug programs Transfer payments to:	
Ontario Public Drug Programs	3,600,623,500
Assistive devices programs Transfer payments to:	
Assistive Devices Program	336,970,900
Home Oxygen Program	89,291,500
Provincial programs and stewardship Emergency health services Stewardship Provincial programs transfer payments to:	3,109,228,575
community and priority services	2,402,799,700
Cancer Care Ontario	652,173,000
Canadian Blood Services	497,758,700
chronic disease management	100,975,200
healthy homes renovation tax credit	85,775,700

Continued on next page

Program	2011-12 operating expenses
Provincial programs transfer payments – continued	
Ontario Breast Screening Program	72,542,400
HIV/AIDS and hepatitis C programs	54,802,200
operation and related facilities	40,375,900
Health policy and research program Transfer payments to:	774,426,268
clinical education	890,683,600
Health System Research Fund	42,688,700
Public health program Transfer payments to:	679,112,170
local public health agencies	367,856,100
outbreaks and diseases	168,678,400
Public Health Ontario	150,965,200
infection control	19,900,400
tuberculosis prevention	8,013,900
sexually transmitted diseases control	3,425,200
public health associations	332,300
eHealth and information management program Transfer payments to:	523,970,420
eHealth Ontario	367,186,600
information technology programs	52,492,000
health-system information management	25,608,600
Health promotion Transfer payments to:	342,751,973
official local health agencies	367,856,100
Smoke-Free Ontario	44,942,400
prevent disease, injury and addiction	14,540,000
healthy communities fund	7,675,000
nutrition/healthy eating	6,384,500
local capacity and coordination	1,096,800
Ministry administration program Ministry administration	
Ontario Review Board, which oversees individuals who have been found by a court to be either unfit to stand trial or not criminally responsible due to a mental disorder	93,029,971
Information systems	82,823,033
Information technology systems	
Health cluster	
Total operating expense[2]	46,194,466,936

Sources: 79; 80

Notes:
[1] LHIN funding covers Community Care Access Centres (includes home care services), community support services, community mental health and addiction agencies, assisted living services in supportive housing, Community Health Centres, Aboriginal Health Access Centres, hospitals, and long-term care homes.
[2] Covers the ministry's total operating expense and capital including consolidation and other adjustments (not including assets)

As with the mix of options available to finance the health system, a number of options can be used by LHINs (and by government) to fund the range of healthcare organizations involved in the provision of programs and services in the health system, including:

1) fee-for-service funding (organizations receive a fixed fee for each service performed in their facilities);

2) capitation (organizations receive a fixed fee for each patient under their care);

3) global budgets (organizations receive a fixed budget to cover all necessary care for a given period of time);

4) case-mix funding (organizations receive pre-determined payments for particular types of diagnoses or services that are meant to cover the costs associated with an entire episode of care, regardless of the programs, services and drugs provided; and

5) targeted payments and/or penalties (organizations receive additional payments for taking a measurable action or achieving a predetermined performance target, or penalties for failure to do so).

Organizations may also be given an indicative (or shadow) budget to guide their decisions about the amount of money available to care for their patients, and the optimal allocation of that budget, however, this is not used to determine the actual funding they receive.

While a diverse and complicated mix of these funding options have been used in Ontario (many of which are referred to using names unique to the province), LHINs have mostly relied on a mix of global budgets (option 3) complemented by case-mix funding (option 4) and targeted payments (option 5). The amounts that hospitals receive are established through agreements between hospitals and LHINs, and specified in Hospital Service Accountability Agreements. A similar process is followed to establish what are referred to as Multi-Sector Service Accountability Agreements for Community Care Access Centres (CCACs), Community Health Centres, community mental health and addictions organizations, other home and community care agencies, and long-term care homes. Table 3.5 details the main mechanisms used to fund organizations by sector in Ontario, and we discuss each briefly in turn below.

Table 3.5: Organizational funding mechanisms in use

Type of organization	Funding mechanism
Home and community care	
Community Care Access Centres (CCACs)	• (Currently transitioning to) global budgets (30%) and a combination of Health-Based Allocation Model and Quality-Based Procedures (70%) allocated by Local Health Integration Networks (LHINs) • Additional one-time funding available for targeted activities (e.g., achieving five-day wait-time targets)
Organizations providing home and community care	• Global budgets allocated by LHINs to provide a basket of services in a geographic area over a number of years as specified in Multi-Sector Service Accountability Agreements • One-time payments from CCACs to organizations that are prequalified by the Ontario Association of Community Care Access Centres to provide services to eligible citizens
Community mental health and addiction organizations	• Global budgets allocated by LHINs • One-time payments for amendments to service plans and targeted activities
Primary care	
Family Health Teams	• Global budgets approved annually and allocated by the Ministry of Health and Long-Term Care • Mixed physician-remuneration strategies (e.g., blended capitation, blended salary and/or complement-based remuneration), which we return to in Table 3.7 • Direct payments for clinical support staff
Aboriginal Health Access Centres	• Global budget allocated by LHINs • One-time payments for additional agreements (e.g., Business Intelligence Reporting Tool) or approved amendments to service plans
Nurse Practitioner-led Clinics	• Global budgets allocated by the Ministry of Health and Long-Term Care • Additional billings made by consulting physicians for each service they provide
Community Health Centres	• Global budgets allocated by LHINs • One-time payments for additional agreements (e.g., Project Funding agreements) or approved amendments to service plans
Specialty care (with a focus on hospital funding)	
Private not-for-profit hospitals	• Global budgets, Health-Based Allocation Model, and Quality-Based Procedures allocated by LHINs • (While not formally part of hospital budgets) standard physician fees based on the Schedule of Benefits for Physician Services
Independent Health Facilities	• Facility fees based on the Schedule of Facility Fees for Independent Health Facilities • Standard physician fees based on the Schedule of Benefits for Physician Services
Out of Hospital Premises	• For medically necessary (insured) services, standard physician fees based on the Schedule of Benefits for Physician Services • For non-insured services, individual fees or block payments from patients typically based on Ontario Medical Association recommendations for uninsured services

Continued on next page

Type of organization	Funding mechanism
Long-term care	
Long-term care homes	• Per diem payments (an average rate per resident per day) for all residents, either alone or alongside a global budget, which can be allocated by LHINs or directly by government • Resident payments of standardized accommodation charges (with a subsidy from government for those who cannot afford them) • (While not formally part of long-term care home budgets) standard physician fees based on the Schedule of Benefits for Physician Services
Public health	
Public health units	• Program-based grants for mandatory programs split 75% from the Ministry of Health and Long-Term Care and 25% from municipal funds • Ad hoc funding from other government sources for non-mandatory programs

Sources: 81-99

Home and community care funding

As mentioned above, publicly covered home and community care is funded by the LHINs (Table 3.5). Funding is approached in a number of ways, mostly through allocations to CCACs that then establish contracts with organizations providing nursing, personal support and homemaking services. Allocations to CCACs have historically been made through global budgets, but this has changed recently (and the changes are covered in greater detail in Chapter 10). Specifically, the health system funding reform that began in 2012 will eventually ensure that funding to CCACs is derived from a combination of global budgets (30%) and a mix of funds allocated through the Health-Based Allocation Model (a form of global budget) and Quality-Based Procedures (a form of case-mix funding), which together will account for the remaining 70% of CCAC funding annually (Table 3.5).

Details about how the Health-Based Allocation Model is calculated are not publicly available for CCACs (or for hospitals, which are discussed below), although it is known that payments are based on a number of inputs that can be used to predict how many services will be needed each year and the costs of those services (e.g., historical service volumes, expected population growth, and healthcare access patterns in a specific region). Quality-Based Procedures are calculated based on the costs of all of the services required as part of an optimal clinical pathway for an episode of care (or for a discrete part of the clinical pathway).(16; 17)

For the fiscal year ending March 31, 2015, a total of $2.5 billion in funding was received by CCACs (through LHINs) to provide home care services for 713,493 clients in the province, which means approximately $3,500 was spent on home care for each client receiving support.(18) This represents a 42% increase in funding (albeit with no correction for inflation), and a 22% increase in clients served, since 2009.(18) The government also announced plans to increase funding to the home and community care sector over three years (2015-16 to 2017-18) at 5% per year (approximately $750 million in additional funds).(18)

However, recent reform proposals first shared by the Ministry of Health and Long-Term Care in December 2015 and since described in the *Patients First Act, 2016* (also covered in greater detail in Chapter 10), involve the CCACs being eliminated and their current duties assumed by the LHINs. The scope of services that are funded, however, is unlikely to change.(19)

A number of other organizations fall within the home and community care sector, and these organizations are funded in different ways (Table 3.5). Organizations providing home and community care such as assisted living services in supportive housing, as well as community mental health and addictions organizations, are funded through global budgets, and all have access to additional targeted payments either for special projects or through amendments to their funding agreements.

Primary care funding

While the bulk of primary care is paid for through direct payments to physicians, which we cover in the next section on remunerating providers, recent changes in how primary care is organized in the province has resulted in the introduction of new organizational funding models (more details about these changes in primary care are covered in Chapter 6, which focuses on care in each sector). In particular, the establishment of physician-led Family Health Teams has created 184 primary-care organizations that are funded through a blend of annually approved global budgets, mixed physician-remuneration strategies (e.g., blended approaches that combine capitation payments for each enrolled patient, with set fees for each service provided), and direct payments for clinical support staff (Table 3.5). Nurse Practitioner-led Clinics, which are characterized by interprofessional team-based care with nurse practitioners as the 'most responsible' provider, are also a relatively recent addition to the primary-care sector. These clinics are funded by the Ministry of Health and Long-Term Care through global budgets, with additional billings made by consulting physicians for each service they provide.(20)

Aboriginal Health Access Centres and Community Health Centres are two additional types of publicly funded organizations in Ontario's primary-care sector. Aboriginal Health Access Centres are Indigenous community-led primary healthcare organizations that provide traditional healing in combination with primary-care services to First Nations, Inuit and Métis communities in Ontario. These organizations are funded by the Ministry of Health and Long-Term Care through global budgets as part of the Aboriginal Health and Wellness Strategy, and also receive additional one-time targeted payments from LHINs for activities such as cultural competency training (e.g., Indigenous Cultural Safety Training provided by the South West LHIN). Community Health Centres deliver services targeted to specific communities, and focus primarily on ensuring access to comprehensive primary-care services for low-income Ontarians, street youth, homeless persons, the isolated elderly, newcomers, and those living in rural and remote communities. These organizations receive annual budgets from LHINs, which are specified in a Multi-Sector Service Accountability Agreement.

Specialty care (hospital) funding

Because payments made to hospitals constitute the bulk of funding in specialty care, we focus here on the mechanisms used to fund hospitals. As pointed out earlier in this chapter, hospitals are the organizations that receive the greatest share of public funding. As of 2013, the total amount spent on hospitals amounted to nearly $20 billion, or 36% of all public spending on healthcare in the province (Table 3.3). Hospital funding covers nearly all of the costs associated with the programs, services and drugs provided in hospitals, with the notable exception of physician billings (which are covered by the Ontario Health Insurance Plan, or OHIP). These sums also cover the cost of hospital administration, including the salaries of senior executives, which are partly tied to achieving performance-improvement targets.(21) While the majority of hospital funding comes from public sources, more than $3 billion in private expenditures were channelled to hospitals in 2013 (Table 3.3).

Increasingly, in order to make the most of these budget allocations, hospitals within a single geographical region (e.g., Toronto Central LHIN) are entering into agreements with shared-service organizations to achieve supply-chain and operational efficiencies.(22) An expert panel on the development and implementation of a province-wide supply-chain management strategy for the healthcare sector has been established to provide recommendations about how to achieve further efficiencies.(23)

Hospitals receive their public funding from LHINs through a combination of three mechanisms: 1) global budgets; 2) the Health-Based Allocation Model (a form of global budget); and 3) Quality-Based Procedures (a form of case-mix funding). Global budgets (lump sum payments to cover operating costs for an entire year) are used to allocate approximately 30% of hospital budgets. The Health-Based Allocation Model accounts for the allocation of approximately 40% of hospital budgets in the province (Table 3.5). As with CCACs, specific details of how this model is calculated for each hospital are not publicly available. As noted above, the approach tries to predict the volume and cost of services in the coming year by looking at historical service volumes, expected population growth, and healthcare access patterns in a specific region, as well as the size and teaching status of a hospital. The remainder of hospital budgets (30%) is funded through Quality-Based Procedures, which are described in relation to CCAC funding above, and apply to all or part of an episode of care, rather than a single service, again without including physician billings. Ten types of patient services are currently paid as Quality-Based Procedures in hospitals: hip replacement, knee replacement, treatment for chronic kidney disease, treatment for cataract, gastrointestinal endoscopy, chemotherapy/systemic treatment, non-cardiac vascular repairs, treatment for congestive heart failure, treatment for chronic obstructive pulmonary disease, and treatment for stroke.(24) Hospitals also supplement these public revenues with donations and grants, as well as revenue from parking, space rental (e.g., for coffee shops in hospital lobbies), and other sources.

Alternative approaches that link hospital care to other sectors such as home and community care by funding an entire episode of care – including all services provided across all settings within each episode – are also being piloted. For example, since 2012 St. Joseph's Health Care Hamilton has been experimenting with 'bundled care,' another form of case-mix funding, in which hospital and home-care dollars are combined and 'tied' to individual patients (particularly those undergoing lung-cancer surgery or hip/knee replacements, and those with chronic obstructive pulmonary disease). In this model, staff working in hospitals are linked with their counterparts in the community, many of whom are responsible for home visits and follow-up care. Healthcare providers are paid from the same patient-allocated bundle to provide care that is coordinated within the team. The rationale behind this funding approach is that it motivates providers to consider the budget for each patient episode in a coordinated way, ensuring each patient receives the most appropriate care at the right time from the right provider (and in the right setting). By providing patients with more coordinated care, and ways to keep in touch with a member of the care team (e.g., a toll-free number to contact a member of the care team with access to health records 24/7), the approach also makes patients feel more comfortable outside of hospital settings.

Unique among organizations that are considered part of the specialty sector, but that are based within community settings, are two types of what can broadly be considered to be community-based specialty clinics. The first type includes Independent Health Facilities that provide a high volume of low-risk procedures that were traditionally provided in hospitals – both diagnostic (e.g., computed tomography or CT, magnetic resonance imaging or MRI, positron emission tomography or PET scans, sleep-study tests) and therapeutic (e.g., abortion, dialysis and many types of surgery). One example of such a facility is the Kensington Eye Institute in Toronto. The second type includes what are called Out of Hospital Premises, providing cosmetic surgery (which typically is not publicly funded), endoscopy and interventional pain management (see Chapter 6 for a more detailed description of the types of care provided in community-based specialty clinics). In both cases, these organizations are funded on a fee-for-service basis, however, Independent Health Facilities also receive facility fees for medically necessary services (Tables 3.5 and 4.6). In 2010-11, Independent Health Facilities received nearly $408 million in facility fees from the Ministry of Health and Long-Term Care, of which the majority (92%) were used to pay for diagnostic procedures and the remainder used for therapeutic procedures (Table 4.6).

Long-term care funding

The funding of long-term care homes in Ontario is characterized by a combination of transfers from various sources. Public sources that help fund long-term care homes include:

1) the provincial health budget, either directly or through LHINs, which accounted for more than half (57%) of all long-term care homes' revenues in 2012;

2) the provincial social assistance budget and other government departments, which accounted for nearly 8% of revenues in 2012; and

3) direct transfers from municipalities and other agencies, which collectively accounted for nearly 6% of long-term care home budgets in 2012.(25)

These public sources of organizational funding are used to cover the professional (e.g., nursing) services, personal support services (e.g., bathing), and homemaking services (e.g., meals) provided in long-term care homes (Table 3.5). Payments are made through 'per diem' charges (which is a type of capitation budget calculated based on an average rate per resident per day), either alone or alongside a global budget, and can come from LHINs or directly from government.

Additional standardized charges for accommodation are paid for by residents (with a subsidy from the government for those who cannot afford it), with the charges set by the Ministry of Health and Long-Term Care. In 2012, these charges amounted to approximately 25% of total revenues.(25) Also, while not formally part of long-term care home budgets, standard physician fees based on the Ontario Health Insurance Plan (OHIP) Schedule of Benefits cover the medical care provided on a fee-for-service basis in long-term care homes.

Public health funding

Finally, local public health agencies are funded through a mix of program-based grants that function similarly to global budgets, with 75% coming from the Ministry of Health and Long-Term Care, and the remainder from municipalities. In 2011-12, nearly $680 million was spent on public health (approximately 1.5% of total public expenditures on the health system), with more than half ($368 million) allocated to local public health agencies, and the remainder spent on specific programs or on Public Health Ontario to support the delivery of programs (Table 3.4).

Remunerating providers

The third element in the process of financial flows through the Ontario health system concerns how the revenues raised are used to pay the health professionals responsible for providing programs and services to citizens (represented by part of the right side of Figure 3.1). The most costly and perhaps complex aspect of this process relates to what amounts to the second-largest source of public expenditures in the province after payments to LHINs: allocations made to OHIP to pay physicians, and to a much lesser extent, other healthcare providers. Transfers to OHIP accounted for approximately 37% of all public financial flows from the Ministry of Health and Long-Term Care in 2011-12, and close to $13 billion – or 76% of OHIP allocations – was spent on remunerating physicians in the same year (represented in Figure 3.1, with detailed expenditure breakdowns provided in Table 3.4).

Six options are generally considered when using public revenues to pay health professionals – also commonly referred to as remuneration:
1) fee-for-service (providers receive a fixed fee for each healthcare service performed);
2) capitation (providers receive a fixed fee for each patient under their care);
3) salary (providers receive a fixed income on a regular basis, which may vary depending on the hours worked);
4) episode-based payment (providers receive a pre-determined amount for particular types of diagnoses for an entire episode of care, regardless of the services performed);
5) fundholding (providers receive a fixed budget to cover all necessary care provided in their practice, often including prescription drugs, and to purchase the necessary secondary care for patients registered to their practice for a given period of time); and
6) targeted payments and/or penalties (providers receive additional payments/penalties for taking a measurable action or achieving a pre-determined performance target).

Professionals may also be given an indicative (or shadow) budget to guide their decisions about the amount of money available to care for their patients, and the optimal allocation of that budget, however, as was the case for organizational funding, this is not used to determine the actual remuneration they receive.

Historically, fee-for-service has been the main option used to remunerate physicians, while nurses both in home and community care settings and in hospitals, for example, have received salaries (paid for out of organizational budgets). However, provider remuneration has shifted a great deal in the last decade and a half, particularly for physicians, many of whom are now paid using a complex array of mixed remuneration models.

Physician remuneration

The specifics of physician remuneration are typically negotiated between the Ontario Medical Association and the Ministry of Health and Long-Term Care under the terms of a Physician Services Agreement, the last one having been negotiated for the period of October 2012 through March 2014 inclusive.(26) Since the conclusion of the last Physician Services Agreement, and during the period in which the two parties have been unable to reach a new agreement, the government has made several unilateral cuts to physician fees, but also clarified that the *Patients First Act, 2016* will not delegate to LHINs the authority to negotiate physician contracts on behalf of the Ministry of Health and Long-Term Care.

While nearly two thirds of all physician remuneration continues to be paid through fee-for-service, whereby physicians bill OHIP for each service they provide to patients based on the rates outlined in the Schedule of Benefits for Physician Services (see the OHIP box in Figure 3.1), the other one third is now covered through a range of alternative payments (Table 3.6). This is a dramatic shift from the roughly 92% of physician remuneration paid through fee-for-service and 8% of remuneration paid through alternative payments in 2000-01 (Table 3.6). This general breakdown is similar for family physicians and specialists, although the ways in which different remuneration models are mixed with fee-for-service differs between these two groups.

In parallel with dramatic shifts in how primary care is organized in Ontario (see Chapter 6 for more detail), family physicians are increasingly paid through a number of blended mechanisms depending on the primary-care model in which they practice (Table 3.7). For example, physicians working in a Family Health Team are paid through one of blended capitation, blended salary or blended complement-based (full-time equivalent) payments. Some other models rely on blended capitation payments (for physicians working

Table 3.6: Public health expenditures on physicians, by type of physician-remuneration mechanism[1]

Category of payments ($ thousands)	Ontario			Canada
	2000-01[2]	2010-11	2013-14	2013-14
Total clinical payments to physicians	4,535,118	7,320,013	8,191,649	23,681,424
Fee-for-service clinical payments to physicians	4,161,511	4,800,351	5,176,714	16,859,685
Alternative clinical payments to physicians	373,607	2,519,661	3,014,935	6,821,739
Average gross clinical payment per physician	—	297,864	304,658	330,317

Sources: 8; 100-103

Notes:
[1] Inflation adjusted to 2002, according to Statistics Canada's Consumer Price Index (healthcare), CANSIM 326-0020: value x (CPI 2002/CPIi) = value (2002) where i = year
[2] Data not available for the specific reference period are denoted by —.

in Family Health Networks and Family Health Organizations) or salary (for physicians working in Community Health Centres). The Schedule of Benefits also includes a number of pay-for-performance billing codes that are unique to family physicians, such as premiums for services billed outside of regular work hours, and annual bonus payments for meeting particular targets (e.g., number of house calls for complex and continuing care patients).(27) We return to financial incentives below.

Specialists are compensated either through fee-for-service entirely (with billings working in a similar way to primary care), or a range of other blended 'alternative funding plans' or 'alternative payment plans', which are contracts between groups of specialist physicians and the Ministry of Health and Long-Term Care.(28) However, the fee billed for these services is dependent on a referral from a family physician: if a patient is not referred, the specialist receives a lower fee for the same service.(29) Specialists engaged in 'alternative funding plans' or 'alternative payment plans' usually work in university teaching hospitals and have a mix of clinical, teaching and research commitments. These specialists are remunerated through a number of blended models that often utilize base rates with additional incentive payments, and which sometimes incorporate a fee-for-service component. Other remuneration models used in 'alternative funding plans' and 'alternative payment plans' include: 1) global/block funding for specific services or locations; 2) blended models that include a base rate for clinical services, teaching, research and administration plus premium payments; 3) payments made based on bed utilization rates; and

Table 3.7: Primary-care organization-funding mechanisms and physician-remuneration mechanisms in use

Model	Primary-care payment methods					
	Fee-for-service[1]	Fee-for-service with programmatic capitation[2]	Blended capitation[3]	Blended salary[4]	Blended complement[5]	Salaried
No model	✓					
Comprehensive Care Model		✓				
Family Health Groups		✓	✓			
Family Health Neworks			✓			
Family Health Organizations			✓	✓	✓	
Family Health Teams[6]						
Community-Sponsored Family Health Teams				✓		
Rural and Northern Physician Group Agreement					✓	
Community Health Centres						✓

Sources: 104-107

Notes:
[1] Fee-for-service is billed through the Ontario Health Insurance Plan and is based on the Schedule of Benefits for Physician Services.
[2] Programmatic capitation provides monthly comprehensive-care capitation payments for patients enrolled in programs (e.g., chronic-disease management programs).
[3] Blended capitation provides a fixed payment per patient, adjusted for age and sex for a predetermined set of primary-care services, while fee-for-service payments are given for other services that fall outside of the capitation model.
[4] Blended salary provides a base salary determined by the number of enrolled patients (e.g., a roster of fewer than 1,300 patients is considered part-time), as well as incentives, premiums and special payments for the provision of specific primary healthcare services.
[5] Blended complement provides a base payment determined by the number of physicians in the group, as well as incentives, premiums and special payments for the provision of specific primary healthcare services. The compensation model is available to identified communities with an underserviced designation for the provision of primary healthcare services and emergency services.
[6] Family Health Teams have the option of one of three compensation models: blended capitation, blended salary or blended complement.

4) sessional payments plus fee-for-service billings.(30) In the 2012-13 fiscal year, 18% of the $7.1 billion the Ministry of Health and Long-Term Care paid to specialist physicians was under an alternative funding arrangement, with an estimated 50% of all specialists, and 90% of emergency department physicians paid at least in part through this mechanism.(31)

While some physicians – both family physicians and specialists – receive private payments for services not covered publicly, this accounts for less than 1% of all private expenditures in Ontario (Table 3.3).

In addition to the unique mix of mechanisms used to remunerate physicians in Ontario, there are a number of noteworthy aspects related to: 1) what their earnings are meant to cover; 2) how their 'retained' earnings are taxed; 3) how their retirement is planned for and their benefits are paid; and 4) how their gross or net income is not publicly reported as it is for other high-earners in the health system.

First, most physician earnings are typically meant to cover the overhead costs involved in operating their private practice, such as office space, equipment, malpractice insurance premiums, and staff. These staff can include those to whom physicians can delegate tasks (e.g., physician assistants) while billing OHIP for a medical service.(32) Taking overhead into account has been found to substantially affect estimates of what physicians actually 'take home' as pay, with the significant variations in how much overhead is paid translating into significant variations in net income across specialties.(33) For example, based on one study's analysis of billing information and public payments only, ophthalmologists appear to be one of the highest-paid specialties (ranked second to diagnostic radiologists), although their income is eighth on the list once overhead is taken into account.(33) Furthermore, the same study also found that nearly 90% of ophthalmologists report that more than 30% of their income goes towards keeping their practice running, which is much higher than those reporting similar overhead costs as a proportion of income in family medicine (68%), cardiology (48%), diagnostic radiology (31%) and anaesthesia (10%).(33) It should be noted that these figures do not take into account certain specialists' opportunities to generate non-OHIP revenue (e.g., ophthalmologists frequently rent out space to opticians). Like many other health professionals, physicians are also required to cover some of the costs of paying malpractice insurance premiums out of their income, which also contributes to their overhead costs. In 2017 the average fee paid by Ontario physicians to the Canadian Medical Protective Association will be $9,991, although the fee can vary significantly by specialty (e.g., in 2017 an Ontario dermatologist will pay $7,092 whereas an Ontario obstetrician will pay $99,072).(34) The provincial government reimburses physicians for at least a portion of these fees (with some estimates suggesting this number is as high as 83%), and in 2008 the government paid approximately $112 million to physicians for this reason.(35)

Second, most physicians earn income through a corporation, whether as a medicine professional corporation (e.g., many family physicians and specialists in private practice) or as a partnership or corporation (e.g., many specialists in teaching hospitals), so their retained earnings (i.e., their earnings after expenses like overhead costs have been deducted from their earned income) are taxed at a corporate rate (15% for the first $500,000), rather than at a personal rate (53.53% for income above $220,000). They can also benefit from the federal government's small business deduction (although this may be changed under the terms of proposed legislation). While physicians will need to pay personal income tax on the income they draw from their corporation, the assets left within the corporation are able to accrue from a more generous starting position. Additionally, tax rates will be different if physicians withdraw this income as dividends (rather than as personal income), and by naming spouses and children as co-owners of the corporation they may also benefit from splitting income in ways that effectively lower tax rates on withdrawn income.

Third, most physicians – as business owners – must plan for their own retirements and pay for other benefits that are typically earned by salaried employees. Physicians typically are not able to participate in the pension plans administered by, say, the hospitals where they work (although there may be some exceptions among the minority of physicians who are paid by salary). However, as a benefit of their membership in the Canadian Medical Association (CMA), they can invest their personal and corporate assets in MD Management, a wholly owned subsidiary of CMA that can provide preferred rates to CMA members and their families. Additionally, most physicians are also required to cover the costs of paying for their own benefits packages (e.g., private insurance premiums to cover prescription drugs, dental services and vision care).

Fourth, neither physicians' gross income nor their net income (i.e., their earnings less their overhead costs and personal or corporate tax payments) is publicly reported on the province's 'sunshine list' as is the gross income for other high-earners in the health system and broader public sector (i.e., those earning more than $100,000 per year), and as it is for physicians in the health systems of provinces like B.C. and Manitoba.(36)

Other providers' remuneration

The remuneration of nurses and many other regulated health professionals and many unregulated health workers is negotiated very differently, typically through collective bargaining between unions (e.g., Ontario Nurses' Association and Ontario Public Service Employees Union) and the organizations that employ and pay these individuals (e.g., hospitals), not with government. The Ontario Nurses' Association represents approximately 62,000 registered nurses, registered practical nurses, and nurse practitioners (although the vast majority are registered nurses) and it negotiates wages, benefits, employment conditions and other issues through a mix of master contracts, such as the Hospital Central Agreement with the Ontario Hospital Association,(37) and local contracts (via local bargaining units). The Ontario Public Service Employees Union represents a broader array of professionals and workers, including 12,000 staff in more than 250 occupations (e.g., laboratory and radiation technologists, laboratory assistants, physiotherapists, occupational therapists, social workers and pharmacy technicians) in hospitals alone.(38) Other unions also engage in collective bargaining in the health system. Occasionally payment rates are explicitly set by government, as has been done for publicly paid personal support workers, whose hourly base wage was increased over three years by $4.00 to $16.50 per hour.(39) Many factors, only one of which is the bargaining strength of unions, explain the significant differences in wages, benefits and employment conditions across sectors that complicate efforts to, for example, transition care from hospitals to the community.

Unlike physicians, many health professionals receive private payments for services not paid for publicly (e.g., dental services), whether directly from patients through out-of-pocket payments or indirectly through fee-for-service payments from private insurers. As of 2013, these payments accounted for almost 29% of all private expenditures, which was almost as much as drugs (which accounted for 33%), and more than double what is paid privately to hospitals (Table 3.3).

Financial incentives

In addition to the options outlined above, Ontario has also utilized targeted payments and/or penalties (option 6) over the last decade and a half in order to incentivize specific provider behaviors. While all of the system financing, organizational funding and professional remuneration mechanisms discussed thus far create incentives, in this section we focus on targeted payments or penalties that seek to achieve particular health-system goals, and that are layered on top of, or operate alongside, existing financing, funding and remuneration mechanisms. In Ontario, these have mostly been characterized by individual bonuses paid directly to health professionals and managers, and included incentives for:

- encouraging community pharmacists to support smoking cessation among Ontario Drug Benefit (ODB) Program recipients;(40)
- supporting family physicians to provide flu shots for seniors, toddler immunizations, Pap smears, mammograms, and colorectal cancer screening;(41; 42)
- encouraging family physicians to engage in diabetes assessment and diabetes management;(43-45)
- encouraging surgeons to use laparoscopic techniques for colon surgery;(46)
- improving the recruitment (47) and retention (48) of physicians in rural and northern Ontario;
- encouraging allied health professionals to practise in northern Ontario;(49) and
- supporting senior hospital executives to achieve performance-improvement targets.(50)

Ontario has experienced variable results in introducing financial incentives targeted to individual health professionals, with evaluations indicating that they can help improve diabetes care, and increase the use of specific surgical methods for performing colon and rectal cancer surgery.(43; 44; 51) Additional details about Ontario's experience with financial incentives can be found in the McMaster Health Forum's evidence brief on the same topic.(52)

Purchasing products and services

The fourth element in the process of financial flows through the health system involves purchasing the products and services that are used by citizens (represented by the double line at the top of Figure 3.1). While the language 'providing programs, services and drugs' works well in terms of what healthcare providers do, we use the term 'purchasing products and services' when discussing this element of financial flows. The process of financial flows through the health system determines the nature of coverage for products and services, and the extent to which universal (public) coverage for products and services has been established in the province.

The World Health Organization has proposed three dimensions that can assist with describing the extent of universal coverage in a particular health system, including defining who is covered in the population, what is covered, and the proportion of the direct costs covered.(53; 54) Figure 3.3 provides an illustrated representation of these dimensions. As an orienting framework, it shows that, in making decisions about the nature of coverage in a particular health system, policymakers generally grapple with three types of decisions:

1) whether to extend coverage to populations not currently covered (represented in Figure 3.3 by the line on the horizontal axis at the front of the cube);

2) whether to include other products and services not currently covered (represented by the line on the axis from the front to the back of the cube); and

3) whether to reduce or remove cost-sharing and fees for certain products and services (represented by the line along the vertical axis of the cube).

Figure 3.3: Three dimensions to consider when moving towards universal coverage

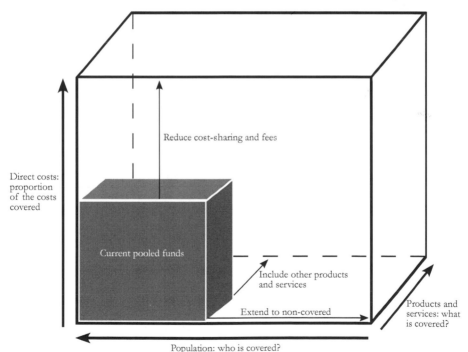

Furthermore, the details within each of these dimensions of coverage can be established through a number of different options:

1) making changes to the scope and nature of insurance plans;
2) establishing and iteratively revising lists of covered/reimbursed organizations, providers, and products and services;
3) placing or removing restrictions in coverage/reimbursement rates for organizations, providers, and products and services;
4) placing caps on coverage/reimbursement for organizations, providers, and products and services;
5) establishing prior approval requirements for organizations, providers, and products and services (e.g., requiring organizations or providers to obtain authorization from third-party payers/healthcare administrators before delivering a product or service); and
6) adjusting the lists of substitutable products and services (e.g., establishing which products and services are not currently covered or may be substituted for similar covered products and services).

In Ontario, the first three have been used most frequently in determining the nature of coverage in the health system, whereas the others – while used to some extent in specific instances – are not used as visibly or in as many circumstances. As already noted in the introductory chapter of this book, the core bargain stipulates that all citizens in Ontario (i.e., who is covered) receive hospital-based and physician-provided services deemed 'medically necessary' (i.e., what services are covered) for free at the point of use (i.e., the proportion of direct costs covered). In fact, under the *Commitment to the Future of Medicare Act, 2004* (and like some other provinces), physicians cannot accept payments from private insurers or from patients for medically necessary services that are publicly insured. Coverage even extends to medically necessary hospital-based and physician-provided care received in other parts of Canada. Ontarians receiving such care in another province or territory are covered up to the equivalent amount of the Ontario rate for the same service, either through the hospital or physician billing the Ministry of Health and Long-Term Care directly (all provinces except Quebec), or by paying the charges themselves and then being reimbursed by the Ministry of Health and Long-Term Care (all provinces).(55) Formal reciprocal billing agreements exist between Ontario and all provinces and territories except Quebec, although it operates in a similar way despite the lack of a formal agreement. No similar arrangement exists for home care.

While medically necessary hospital-based and physician-provided care is free at the point of use for all Ontarians, one organization has estimated that roughly 200,000 people living in the province may not be covered by OHIP at any given time.(56) As such, these people may have to pay out-of-pocket for healthcare services or forgo them if they cannot afford to pay (although they will not be turned away if they are extremely sick). This number includes individuals who are subject to a three-month waiting period established by the government for OHIP eligibility, such as: new immigrants, temporary foreign workers, returning Canadian citizens who have been out of the country for more than 212 days in the previous year (57) and who have not met continuous OHIP eligibility requirements,(58) international students who have not purchased the private health insurance usually mandated by colleges and universities, and non-status people (i.e., those who lack citizenship/immigration status). Some Community Health Centres provide healthcare services (free or for a small fee) to people who do not have a valid health card.(59)

Certain groups may be exempt from the three-month waiting period, with the most recent example being Syrian refugees. Most refugees (including those arriving from Syria) are also eligible for the Interim Federal Health Program, which is provided by the federal government to provide them with access to healthcare services immediately upon arrival and until registration with a provincial health-insurance plan is completed. After the Conservative Government limited benefits under this program in 2012 to those posing a public-health threat, an expanded version was re-introduced by the Liberal Government in 2016.(60) The program now also covers supplementary benefits (e.g., prescription drugs, dental services, and vision care) for refugees who have registered with a provincial plan, as well as services provided before resettlement in Canada (e.g., the immigration medical examination, pre-departure vaccinations, services to manage disease outbreaks in refugee camps, and medical support during travel for those who need it).(61)

The broad coverage trends outlined above become considerably more complicated when considering the nature of coverage for products and services across each sector. In Table 3.8, we provide an overview of the nature of coverage across each sector. Below, we discuss each sector briefly, focusing on who is covered, what is covered, and which costs are covered. When considering what is covered, it is important to note that coverage can and does change as new products (e.g., prescription drugs) and services (e.g., physician services) are added to the list of those that are covered (e.g., by ODB and OHIP, respectively), and as other services (some of which may no longer be the most cost-effective option) are 'delisted' – a process that is often referred to as 'disinvestment.' The government publicizes additions and delistings through the ODB Program (www.formulary.health.gov.on.ca/formulary/) and OHIP (www.health.gov.on.ca/en/pro/programs/ohip/bulletins/). When appropriate, we also refer to tables introduced earlier in this chapter to illustrate the nature and extent of costs covered.

Because the aim in this chapter is to focus on the big picture of how products and services are purchased publicly in the province (and thus the nature and extent of public coverage), we do not provide an overview of all the products and services that fall within each sector, or that are provided for select conditions, as part of select treatments or for the select population of Indigenous peoples (which are covered in Chapters 6-9, respectively), nor do we provide a list of those that are not covered. However, we do flag when an important coverage gap exists, such as for prescription drugs, which we turn to first.

Table 3.8: Public coverage of programs and services, by sector[1]

Population covered	Services covered[2]	Costs covered[3]
Prescription drugs		
All seniors and Ontarians with high prescription drug costs relative to their household income holding a valid health card	• Prescription drugs • Select over-the-counter drugs	Partial (patients pay a means-tested deductible and co-payments on each prescription)
Other technologies		
All Ontarians with a valid health card who meet eligibility requirements	• Medical devices • Assistive devices • Laboratory tests	Full coverage when ordered by a physician for necessary medical devices and laboratory tests, partial coverage (75%) for most necessary assistive devices, although Ontarians in financial need may be eligible for additional financial support
Home and community care		
All Ontarians with a valid health card	• All services approved by a Community Care Access Centre (CCAC) (professional, personal support and homemaking services)	All when approved by a CCAC (no public funding otherwise)

Continued on next page

Population covered	Services covered[2]	Costs covered[3]
Primary care		
All Ontarians with a valid health card (or recent immigrants with a temporary card)	• Medically necessary family physician services (or services provided by health professionals working in physician-led interprofessional teams) • Primary-care services in community-governed primary-care organizations (e.g., Community Health Centres, Aboriginal Health Access Centres) • After-hours care and walk-in clinics • Midwifery and diabetes services • Travel to/from necessary health services that are more than 100 km away from place of residence (through the Northern Health Travel Program) • Dental and optometry services not covered	All with some exceptions (Northern Health Travel Program only covers partial travel and accommodation costs for those who have to travel more than 100 km one way to access health services)
Specialty care		
All Ontarians with a valid health card	• Urgent care • Emergency health services • Hospital services • Specialty programs • Complex continuing care	All with some exceptions (co-payment of $45 dollars for ambulance if medically necessary and $240 if not, and emergency air ambulance only covered if physician ordered; additional costs for private hospital rooms, private duty nurses and ambulatory aids such as canes and walkers)
Rehabilitation care		
All Ontarians with a valid health card	• Rehabilitation services provided at home (when deemed eligible by a CCAC), in community settings (when deemed eligible for care in a Community Physiotherapy Centre), and in both hospitals and long-term care homes (when needed)	All when these conditions are met (no public funding otherwise)
Long-term care		
All Ontarians with a valid health card	• Assistance with admission to a long-term care home (provided by staff at CCACs) • Professional, personal support and home-making services in long-term care homes • Standardized accommodation charges are not covered unless the resident is eligible for a subsidy	All approved professional, personal support and homemaking services Partial for residents needing financial assistance with accommodation charges
Public health		
All Ontarians in public health unit area (and those with a valid health card for individually targeted vaccination programs)	• Population-based strategies (e.g., health promotion, infectious and chronic disease prevention and control, environmental health) • Individual-level services (e.g., influenza immunization program)	All

Continued on next page

Population covered	Services covered[2]	Costs covered[3]
Other: Information services		
All Ontarians	• Assistance with finding local healthcare services (Health Care Options program) • Assistance with finding a primary-care provider (Health Care Connect) • Advice from a registered nurse over the telephone (Telehealth Ontario)	All
Cross-sectoral: Health Links		
All Ontarians with a valid health card	• A range of programs and services designed to support patients with complex needs (ideally without admission to a hospital)	All

Sources: 89; 108-112

Notes:
[1] For a more comprehensive description of each sector including the policies, programs, places and people involved in it, see Chapter 6.
[2] For a more comprehensive description of each service, see Chapter 6.
[3] Full=100% publicly financed; partial=services not entirely financed publicly, patient co-payment and/or specific eligibility criteria may apply

Coverage of prescription drugs and other 'technologies'

As the introductory chapter in this book highlighted, there are many products and services that are not currently covered by the core bargain and are therefore often financed and paid for privately. The most visible omission from the basket of covered products and services in Ontario is prescription drugs. At present, 65% of prescription drug costs are paid for privately (Figure 1.2), either through direct out-of-pocket spending or through premium contributions to private-insurance plans, which are often linked to employment. As of 2013, 18% of all direct out-of-pocket healthcare spending by households was for prescribed medicines and pharmaceutical products (Table 3.2), which we refer to as prescription drugs in Chapter 8.

However, while prescription drugs are not covered for the majority of the population in Ontario, there are additional programs that aim to provide some coverage for specific segments of the population. The ODB Program provides prescription drug coverage to all seniors in the province. It also covers the cost of select over-the-counter drugs that meet one or more of the following criteria:

- there are no alternatives, and lack of access could lead to a serious medical crisis;
- there are only toxic and/or more costly alternatives;
- they are needed for use with another ODB-covered drug product; and

- they are used to treat a serious disease that can be passed on to others, such as tuberculosis.(62)

The program does not cover all costs, however, and includes an annual means-tested deductible, as well as a $2 co-payment for each prescription (Table 3.8). The Trillium Drug Benefit is targeted to lower-income Ontarians who have high prescription drug costs relative to their household income. Similar to the ODB Program, those eligible for the Trillium Drug Benefit pay an annual means-tested deductible and a co-payment per prescription. Chapter 8 provides a more detailed description of these programs.

Three types of other 'technologies' are covered publicly, in full or in part, in Ontario: 1) assistive devices; 2) medical devices; and 3) laboratory tests. For assistive devices, the Ministry of Health and Long-Term Care oversees the Assistive Device Program, which helps Ontarians who have lived with a disability for six months or longer pay for assistive devices such as wheelchairs, positioning and ambulation aids, communication aids, enteral feeding aids, diabetic supplies, ostomy supplies, hearing and vision aids, orthotics and prosthesis aids, respiratory aids and pressure modification aids.(63) For most devices, 75% of the costs are covered, as long as a physician has provided a diagnosis and prescription, with the remaining cost covered privately (either through out-of-pocket spending or a private insurance plan).

As a complement to this program, the Ontario Disability Support Program, which is administered by the Ministry of Community and Social Services, helps Ontarians in financial need pay for costs not covered by the Assistive Devices Program. Support is also provided for some devices not covered by the Assistive Devices Program (e.g., bathroom aids, computer and access technologies, and life alert systems). Additionally, CCACs provide support with respect to assistive devices by enabling Ontarians who are deemed by an occupational therapist to be at risk for falls and mobility issues to use mobility aids and safety devices for a 28-day trial while they apply for coverage through the Assistive Devices Program.

Both medical devices (e.g., heart monitors) and laboratory tests (e.g., bloodwork) that are deemed necessary and ordered by a physician are fully covered. However, certain devices (e.g., medication pumps) and tests (e.g., vitamin D deficiency testing) are not covered by the government and must be paid for privately, again either through out-of-pocket spending or a private insurance plan.

Coverage by sector

Home and community care

The many for-profit, not-for-profit and public organizations that provide home and community care to Ontarians are funded in whole or in part by CCACs. Any Ontarian can directly approach a CCAC and receive services at no charge from staff, who are able to: 1) provide information about home and community care (and long-term care) options, regardless of whether they are funded by the government; 2) determine eligibility for government-funded services and settings; 3) arrange for and coordinate the delivery of government-funded professional, personal support and homemaking services for people living in their own homes, and for school children with special needs (i.e., home care); and 4) make arrangements for admission to (or for getting on the waiting list for) many day programs and supportive housing programs (i.e., community care), as well as to some chronic care and rehabilitation beds, and all long-term care homes (which we turn to later in this chapter).

Ontarians who are deemed eligible by the CCAC get full or partial coverage for the following government-funded services: 1) professional services, which include assessing a client's needs, providing care or helping the client to care for herself (and the client's family to cope); 2) personal support services, which include helping clients with daily care or helping clients to safely manage these activities on their own, and can range from help with getting in and out of bed or a chair to bathing, dressing (and undressing), eating, personal hygiene (e.g., mouth and hair care), and toilet hygiene; 3) homemaking services, which include housework (e.g., cleaning, doing laundry), planning and preparing meals, shopping for food or clothing, managing money, and caring for children; and 4) end-of-life care at home.

Primary care

As already mentioned a number of times in this chapter and throughout this book, in the primary-care sector, all Ontarians have full coverage for medically necessary physician-provided services and for services provided by health professionals working in physician- or nurse practitioner-led interprofessional teams. Midwifery services and some targeted diabetes support services are also covered. The Northern Health Travel Program provides financial assistance for Ontarians who have to travel long distances to access needed healthcare services, although coverage only includes some transportation and accommodation costs, calculated based on the number of kilometres travelled (see Table 3.8).

There are also some important omissions in primary-care coverage in Ontario – particularly for dental services and vision care (specifically optometry services). Ninety-three percent of spending on other health professionals (including care provided by dentists and optometry professionals) is paid for privately in the province (Figure 1.2). Twenty-seven percent of all direct out-of-pocket household spending is on dental services and vision care (16% and 11%, respectively), while 5% of all health insurance premiums are for dental services (Table 3.2).

Specialty care

Most types of medically necessary specialty services are fully covered for all Ontarians. These include:
- care provided in urgent-care centres (e.g., hospital-based services addressing non-emergencies requiring immediate attention);
- emergency healthcare services (e.g., dispatch centres, ambulance services, base hospitals and emergency rooms);
- medically necessary hospital services (e.g., emergency and acute care, specialist services and mental health and addictions services provided in hospitals);
- specialty programs (e.g., internal medicine, surgical specialties, anesthesia, obstetrics and gynecology, pediatrics, psychiatry, radiology and laboratory medicine); and
- complex continuing care (e.g., long-term medically complex care that cannot be provided in long-term care homes or in the patient's home).

There is no formal limit on the number of second opinions that patients can obtain from specialists, as long as they get a referral from a family physician or a specialist they have visited within the last 12 months.

While most costs are fully covered for all of the above types of specialty care (if deemed medically necessary), there are some costs that individual Ontarians have to cover privately. First, Ontarians pay a $45 co-payment for land ambulance services if medically necessary, and $240 if a land ambulance is used for something that is not considered medically necessary. For air ambulance services, Ontarians are fully covered as long as the services are ordered by a physician (a type of prior approval requirement referred to in option 5 above). Second, hospital parking, particularly for patients and caregivers who need to visit the hospital often, has been found to place a significant financial burden on frequent visitors, and in some instances they create a financial barrier to accessing needed care or providing support to someone who does. These costs are still covered out-of-pocket by Ontarians, although as of October 2016, hospitals that charge more than $10 per day were mandated to reduce their fees by 50% on five-, 10- and 30-day passes, and ensure such passes are transferrable (across people and vehicles), provide in/out privileges, can be used for consecutive or non-consecutive days, and are valid for up to a year after purchase.(64)

Rehabilitation care

Rehabilitation services are unique in that they are a key element of many sectors (i.e., home and community, primary, specialty and long-term care), and they have been more extensively 'privatized' than services in other sectors, given shifts towards more private payment and more private for-profit delivery (additional details for which are provided in Chapter 6). However, there are a number of rehabilitation services that are covered by government funds. Specifically, Ontarians are covered for professional rehabilitation services provided at home (when deemed eligible by a CCAC), in community settings (when deemed eligible for care in a Community Physiotherapy Centre), and in both hospitals and long-term care homes (when needed).

Ontarians may also be eligible for other 'third-party' funding for rehabilitation services if they have a work-related injury or disease (through the Workplace Safety and Insurance Board if eligible) or have been injured in an automobile accident (through their automobile insurance). Outside of these scenarios, most patients pay for rehabilitation services provided in privately owned and operated clinics/practices using their own money, or by drawing on private insurance coverage.

Long-term care

As noted above, long-term care homes provide a mix of professional, personal support and homemaking services, all of which are publicly covered, whereas residents pay a standardized accommodation charge (although this may be subsidized depending on a resident's ability to pay). Some Ontarians may be covered for these additional costs if they hold long-term care insurance through their private insurer.

Public health

All Ontarians can benefit from population-based strategies (e.g., health promotion, chronic-disease prevention, infectious disease control and environmental health programs) and obtain many individual-level services (e.g., influenza immunizations) without paying directly out-of-pocket or through insurance premiums. However, only some Ontarians are eligible to receive services such as dental services (which we discuss in Chapter 6).

Cross-sectoral and other programs

A range of information services are also available to all Ontarians free at the point of use, such as Health Care Options (providing assistance with finding local healthcare services), Health Care Connect (providing assistance finding a primary-care provider), and Telehealth Ontario (advice provided by a registered nurse over the telephone). Health Links, a cross-sectoral initiative that includes a range of programs to support patients with complex needs, ideally without being admitted to hospital emergency departments, is also fully covered.

Incentivizing consumers

The fifth and final element in the process of financial flows through the health system is not an element in the process per se, but a consequence of the other financial arrangements in the province (represented at the top of Figure 3.1). As with all other financial arrangements considered in this chapter, there are a number of options available to governments and other third-party payers to incentivize the behaviour of individual 'consumers' of healthcare. For citizens, incentives may be used to encourage engagement in healthy behaviours, effective self-management or appropriate care seeking. Options for achieving these behaviours include:

1) setting the level and features of premiums (establishing the amount paid out-of-pocket by individuals to be enrolled in, and receive healthcare

coverage from, an insurance scheme);

2) cost-sharing (requiring patients to pay a portion of the costs of products and services);

3) health savings accounts (allocating funds to individual savings accounts earmarked for purchasing products and services, thereby shifting the responsibility for purchasing them to the patient); and

4) targeted payments and/or penalties (giving money to households on the condition that they comply with behavioural requirements).

While there are several examples of financial incentives targeted at health professionals and organizations in Ontario (see above), there are few (if any) intentionally targeting citizens, and the aforementioned options for incentivizing consumers have not been widely used in the province. Premiums paid to private insurers to cover products and services not covered publicly, cost-sharing for prescription drugs (including the co-payments required by both government drug benefit programs as well as private insurance plans), and cost-sharing for prescription lenses and dental services in private insurance plans (which also require patient co-payments or deductibles) can all be viewed as financial (dis)incentives – particularly for prescription drug use, given that reductions in use are typically seen with drug co-payments. However, the payment of premiums and existence of cost-sharing may be viewed more accurately as a consequence of past decisions about what is covered and what is not, rather than the result of intentional policies that align with broader health-system goals introduced by government.

Conclusion

The financial arrangements that characterize Ontario's health system consist of a unique mix of options that define how revenue (i.e., money) flows through the system. This process is represented in Figure 3.1, starting at the top left corner and moving counter-clockwise through the figure. Throughout this chapter we have covered many of the specific details related to how the system is financed (i.e., element one in the process concerning how revenue is raised), how organizations are funded (i.e., element two in the process concerning how revenues are allocated to organizations), how health professionals are remunerated (i.e., element three in the process concerning how revenues are used to pay providers), how products and services are purchased publicly (i.e., element four in the process whereby revenues become the programs, services and drugs used by citizens) and how consumers are incentivized (which are typically the consequences of other financial arrangements in the system).

Despite the importance of the many specific details covered throughout this chapter, there are five defining aspects of financial arrangements in Ontario's health system that readers interested in the 'big picture' can take away. First, Ontario's health system is mainly financed through taxes that pay for publicly covered programs, services and drugs, although a significant amount is financed privately – either through direct out-of-pocket payments, or through premiums to private insurance plans – to pay for products and services that are not publicly covered (e.g., most prescription drugs, dental services). Second, LHINs receive the greatest proportion of public revenues in order to fund a number of organizations in the health system, such as hospitals and CCACs that are in turn responsible for purchasing services from home and community care organizations. Generally, such funding is approached through a mix of global budgets and other approaches. Third, physician remuneration through OHIP constitutes the largest proportion of public money earmarked for a specific category of health professionals, and while fee-for-service has traditionally been the dominant form of payment, this has changed to include a wider range of blended approaches to remuneration (particularly in the primary-care sector). Most other health professionals, including nurses, are paid salaries. Fourth, medically necessary hospital-based and physician-provided services are fully covered for all Ontarians, and a range of other services across sectors are also covered. Notable exemptions in coverage include prescription drugs, dental services, and optometry, all of which are paid for privately by citizens, either through out-of-pocket payments or through premiums paid to private insurance plans. Fifth, while these omissions were not designed to affect how Ontarians use healthcare services, they may create disincentives for accessing non-covered products and services.

References

1. CIHI. National health expenditure trends, 1975 to 2015. Series B, table B.3.3, public sector health expenditure as a proportion of total health expenditure, by province/territory and Canada, 1975 to 2015 - Current dollars ($' 000,000). Ottawa: Canadian Institute for Health Information; 2015.

2. CIHI. National health expenditure trends, 1975 to 2015. Series B, table B.1.1, total health expenditure, by province/territory and Canada, 1975 to 2015 - Current dollars ($' 000,000). Ottawa: Canadian Institute for Health Information; 2015.

3. CIHI. National health expenditure trends, 1975 to 2015. Series B, table B.3.2, public sector health expenditure, by province/territory and Canada, 1975 to 2015 - Current dollars ($' per capita). Ottawa: Canadian Institute for Health Information; 2015.

4. CIHI. National health expenditure trends, 1975 to 2015. Series B, table B.2.1, private sector health expenditure, by province/territory and Canada, 1975 to 2015 - Current dollars ($' 000,000). Ottawa: Canadian Institute for Health Information; 2015.

5. CIHI. National health expenditure trends, 1975 to 2015. Series B, table B.3.1, public sector health expenditure, by province/territory and Canada, 1975 to 2015 - Current dollars ($' 000,000). Ottawa: Canadian Institute for Health Information; 2015.

6. Statistics Canada. Table 384-00384 - Gross domestic product, expenditure-based, provincial and territorial, annual, CANSIM (database). Ottawa: Statistics Canada; 2014. http://www.statcan.gc.ca/tables-tableaux/sum-som/l01/cst01/econ15-eng.htm (accessed 24 August 2016).

7. Statistics Canada. Table 151-0001 - Estimates of population by age group and sex for July 1, Canada, provinces and territories. Ottawa: Statistics Canada; 2015. http://www5.statcan.gc.ca/cansim/a26?lang=eng&retrLang=eng&id=0510001&pattern=Estimates+of+population+by+age+group+and+sex+for+July+1%2C+Canada%2C+provinces+and+territories&tabMode=dataTable&srchLan=-1&p1=1&p2=-1 (accessed 25 August 2016).

8. Statistics Canada. Table 326-0020 - Consumer Price Index, monthly (2002=100 unless otherwise noted), CANSIM (database). Ottawa: Statistics Canada; 2016. http://www5.statcan.gc.ca/cansim/a26?id=3260020 (accessed 24 August 2016).

9. CIHI. National health expenditure trends, 1975 to 2015. Series A1, table A.1, total health expenditure, Canada, 1975 to 2015 - Summary. Ottawa: Canadian Institute for Health Information; 2015.

10. Muir Gray JA. How to practice population medicine. Oxford: Offox Press; 2014.

11. Ministry of Finance. Public accounts of Ontario 2013-2014. Annual report and consolidated financial statements. Toronto: Queen's Printer for Ontario; 2014.

12. Statistics Canada. Table 203-0021 - Survey of household spending (SHS), household spending, Canada, regions and provinces, annual dollars, CANSIM (database). Ottawa: Statistics Canada; 2015. http://www5.statcan.gc.ca/cansim/a05?lang=eng&id=2030021 (accessed 26 August 2016).

13. Ernst and Young. Financial statements University Health Network, March 31, 2015. Toronto: University Health Network; 2015. http://www.uhn.ca/corporate/AboutUHN/Fiscal_Accountability/Documents/AR_Financial_2015.pdf (accessed 24 August 2016).

14. Nolan D. DeGroote surprise is $50M gift. Hamilton Spectator. 24 May 2014.

15. University Health Network. Rogers Foundation $130-million donation builds on history of UHN support. Toronto: University Health Network; 2014. http://www.uhn.ca/corporate/News/Pages/Rogers_Foundation_announces_landmark_gift.aspx (accessed 23 October 2016).

16. Kralj B, Barber J. Physician payment reform - Part II: Implementation of episode bundling/quality based procedures. Ontario Medical Review. 2013;March: 4.

17. Lavis JN, Neves JB, Pi L, Gauvin FP. Evidence brief: Creating community-based specialty clinics in Ontario. Hamilton: McMaster Health Forum; 2013.

18. Office of the Auditor General of Ontario. 2015 annual report of the Office of the Auditor General of Ontario. Chapter 3, section 3.01: CCACs - Community Care Access Centres - Home care program. Toronto: Office of the Auditor General of Ontario; 2015.

19. Ministry of Health and Long-Term Care. Patients first: A roadmap to strengthen home and community care. Toronto: Queen's Printer for Ontario; 2015.

20. DiCenso A, Bourgeault I, Abelson J, et al. Utilization of nurse practitioners to increase patient access to primary healthcare in Canada – Thinking outside the box. Nursing Leadership 2010;23(Special Issue): 20.

21. Ontario Hospital Association. Report of the independent expert panel on executive compensation in the hospital sector. Toronto: Ontario Hospital Association; 2011.

22. Ministry of Government and Consumer Services. Collaborative procurement in Ontario. Toronto: Queen's Printer for Ontario; 2016. https://www.doingbusiness.mgs.gov.on.ca/mbs/psb/psb.nsf/EN/map-collaborative-procurement (accessed 23 October 2016).

23. Ministry of Health and Long-Term Care. Healthcare sector supply chain strategy. Toronto: Queen's Printer for Ontario; 2016. http://www.health.gov.on.ca/en/pro/ministry/supplychain/ (accessed 23 October 2016).

24. Ontario Hospital Association. Toolkit to support the implementation of Quality-Based Procedures. Toronto: Ontario Hospital Association; 2013. http://www.oha.com/CurrentIssues/Issues/HSFR/Pages/QBPResources.aspx (accessed 23 October 2016).

25. CIHI. Residential long-term care financial data tables. Table 4.1: Revenue ($000) by source reported by selected residential long-term care facilities, by province and territories, 2012. Ottawa: Canadian Institute for Health Information; 2014.

26. Ministry of Health and Long-Term Care. 2012 Physician Services Agreement. Toronto: Queen's Printer for Ontario; 2012. http://www.health.gov.on.ca/en/pro/programs/phys_services/docs/phys_services_agreemnt_en.pdf (accessed 25 August 2016).

27. Ministry of Health and Long-Term Care. Billing and payment guide for Family Health Organization (FHO) physicians – Opting for solo payment. Toronto: Queen's Printer for Ontario; 2014. http://www.health.gov.on.ca/en/pro/programs/ohip/publications/docs/fho_billing_payment_guide_nov2014_en.pdf (accessed 23 October 2016).

28. Legislative Assembly of Ontario. Health Insurance Act (R.S.O. 1990, c. H.6). Last amendment: 2009, c. 33, Sched. 18, ss. 11, 17 (2). Toronto: Queen's Printer for Ontario; 2009. http://www.e-laws.gov.on.ca/html/statutes/english/elaws_statutes_90h06_e.htm (accessed 25 August 2016).

29. Ministry of Health and Long-term Care. Resource manual for physicians. Toronto: Queen's Printer for Ontario; 2014.

30. HealthForceOntario. Specialist practice models. Toronto: Queen's Printer for Ontario; 2014. http://www.healthforceontario.ca/en/Home/Physicians/Training_%7C_Practising_in_Ontario/Physician_Roles/Specialist_Practice_Models (accessed 24 August 2016).

31. Office of the Auditor General of Ontario. 2013 annual report of the Office of the Auditor General of Ontario. Chapter 3, section 3.02: Health human resources. Toronto: Office of the Auditor General of Ontario; 2013.

32. Ontario Medical Association. OHIP payments for delegated services: Quick reference guide. Toronto: Ontario Medical Association; 2015.

33. Petch J, Dhalla IA, Henry DA, et al. Public payments to physicians in Ontario adjusted for overhead costs. Healthcare Policy 2012;8(2): 30–36.

34. Canadian Medical Association Journal. Larger claims push CMPA fees up. Ottawa: Canadian Medical Association Journal; 2016. http://www.cmaj.ca/content/early/2016/09/12/cmaj.109-5323.full.pdf+html (accessed 23 October 2016).

35. Law Library of Congress. Medical malpractice liability: Canada. Washington: Law Library of Congress; 2009. http://www.loc.gov/law/help/medical-malpractice-liability/canada.php (accessed 1 November 2016).

36. Picard A. Doctors' billings: Transparency is the best medicine. The Globe and Mail. 7 June 2016.

37. Ontario Nurses' Association. Hospital Central Agreement. Toronto: Ontario Nurses' Association; 2016. http://www.ona.org/documents/File/pdf/cas/hospitals/ONA_HospCentralAgreementDraft_20180331.pdf (accessed 23 October 2016).

38. The Canadian Press. Staff at 53 Ontario hospitals ratify new collective agreement: Union. CBC News. 1 July 2016.

39. Ministry of Health and Long-Term Care. Ontario increasing wages for personal support workers. Toronto: Queen's Printer for Ontario; 2015. http://www.health.gov.on.ca/en/news/bulletin/2015/hb_20150622.aspx (accessed 23 October 2016).

40. Ministry of Health and Long-Term Care. Pharmacy smoking cessation program: The pharmacist's role in a smoking cessation system. Toronto: Queen's Printer for Ontario; 2014. http://health.gov.on.ca/en/pro/programs/drugs/smoking/ (accessed 26 August 2016).

41. Cancer Care Ontario. Ontario's new colorectal cancer screening program. Toronto: Cancer Care Ontario; 2007.

42. Ministry of Health and Long-Term Care. Information and procedures for claiming the cumulative preventative care bonus. Toronto: Queen's Printer for Ontario; 2012.

43. Glazier R, Kopp A, Schultz SE, Kiran T, Henry DA. All the right intentions but few of the desired results: Lessons on access to primary care from Ontario's patient enrolment models. Healthcare Quarterly 2012;15(3): 17.

44. Kantarevic J, Kralj B. Link between pay for performance incentives and physician payment mechanisms: Evidence from the diabetes management incentive in Ontario. Health Economics 2012;22(12): 1417-1439

45. Ministry of Health and Long-Term Care. Diabetics billed for assessment or management incentive. Toronto: Queen's Printer for Ontario; 2013.

46. Ministry of Health and Long-Term Care. Update to implementation of 2004 Physician Services Agreement. Toronto: Queen's Printer for Ontario; 2005.

47. Ministry of Health and Long-Term Care. HealthForceOntario northern and rural recruitment and retention initiative guidelines. Toronto: Queen's Printer for Ontario; 2013. http://www.health.gov.on.ca/en/pro/programs/northernhealth/nrrr.aspx (accessed 25 August 2016).

48. Ministry of Health and Long-Term Care. Northern Physician Retention Initiative (NPRI). Toronto: Queen's Printer for Ontario; 2015. http://www.health.gov.on.ca/en/pro/programs/northernhealth/npri.aspx (accessed 25 August 2016).

49. Ministry of Health and Long-Term Care. Rehabilitation Professional Incentive Grant program guidelines. Toronto: Queen's Printer for Ontario; 2015. http://www.health.gov.on.ca/en/pro/programs/northernhealth/rehabilitation.aspx (accessed 25 August 2016).

50. Ministry of Health and Long-Term Care. Excellent Care for All Act updates: Performance-based compensation. Toronto: Queen's Printer for Ontario; 2015. http://www.health.gov.on.ca/en/pro/programs/ecfa/legislation/performancecomp/update.aspx (accessed 25 August 2016).

51. Simunovic M, Baxter NN, Sutradhar R, Liu N, Cadeddu M, Urbach D. Uptake and patient outcomes of laparoscopic colon and rectal cancer surgery in a publicly funded system and following financial incentives. Annals of Surgical Oncology 2013;20(12): 3740-46.

52. Lavis JN, Wilson MG, Grimshaw JM, Hurley J. Evidence brief: Using financial incentives to achieve health-system goals in Ontario. Hamilton: McMaster Health Forum; 2015.

53. World Health Organization. Universal coverage - Three dimensions. Geneva: World Health Organization; 2016. http://www.who.int/health_financing/strategy/dimensions/en/ (accessed 24 August 2016).

54. World Health Organization. Health systems financing: The path to universal coverage. Geneva: World Health Organization; 2010.

55. Healthy Debate. Travelling to another province? Why you may need private health insurance. Toronto: Healthy Debate; 2015. http://healthydebate.ca/personal-health-navigator/canadian-travel-health-insurance (accessed 23 October 2016).

56. OHIP For ALL. A universal healthcare system. Toronto: OHIP For ALL; 2016. http://ohipforall.ca/why-ohip-for-all/ (accessed 25 October 2016).

57. Ministry of Health and Long-Term Care. OHIP coverage waiting period. Toronto: Queen's Printer for Ontario; 2016. http://www.health.gov.on.ca/en/public/publications/ohip/ohip_waiting_pd.aspx (accessed 25 October 2016).

58. Ministry of Health and Long-Term Care. Longer absences from Ontario. Toronto: Queen's Printer for Ontario; 2016. http://www.health.gov.on.ca/en/public/publications/ohip/longer_absences.aspx (accessed 25 October 2016).

59. Settlement.Org. How can I pay for health care in my first 3 months in Ontario, or if I don't have OHIP? Toronto: Ontario Council of Agencies Serving Immigrants; 2015. http://settlement.org/ontario/health/ohip-and-health-insurance/private-insurance/how-can-i-pay-for-health-care-in-my-first-3-months-in-ontario-or-if-i-don-t-have-ohip/ (accessed 25 October 2016).

60. Zilio M. Liberals restore refugee health benefits cut by previous government. The Globe and Mail. 18 February 2016.

61. Keresteci M. Syrian refugee resettlement: update for physicians, health service contact information. Ontario Medical Review 2016: 22 – 23.

62. Ministry of Health and Long-Term Care. Ontario Drug Benefit Program: Over-the-counter drug products. Toronto: Queen's Printer for Ontario; 2016. http://www.health.gov.on.ca/en/public/programs/drugs/programs/odb/opdp_over_counter.aspx (accessed 25 August 2016).

63. Ministry of Health and Long-Term Care. Assistive Devices Program. Toronto: Queen's Printer for Ontario; 2016. http://www.health.gov.on.ca/en/public/programs/adp/ (accessed 25 August 2016).

64. Government of Ontario. News release. Ontario making hospital parking more affordable. Toronto: Queen's Printer for Ontario; 2016. https://news.ontario.ca/opo/en/2016/10/ontario-making-hospital-parking-more-affordable.html (accessed 23 October 2016).

65. National Forum on Health. The public and private financing of Canada's health system. Ottawa: National Forum on Health; 1995.

66. CIHI. National health expenditure trends, 1975 to 2015. Series B, table B.1.2, total health expenditure, by province/territory and Canada, 1975 to 2015 - Current dollars ($' per capita). Ottawa: Canadian Institute for Health Information; 2015.

67. CIHI. National health expenditure trends, 1975 to 2015. Series B, table B.2.2, private sector health expenditure, by province/territory and Canada, 1975 to 2015 - Current dollars ($' per capita). Ottawa: Canadian Institute for Health Information; 2015.

68. CIHI. National health expenditure trends, 1975 to 2015. Series B, table B.6.1, federal direct health expenditure, by province/territory and Canada, 1975 to 2015 - Current dollars ($' 000,000). Ottawa: Canadian Institute for Health Information; 2015.

69. CIHI. National health expenditure trends, 1975 to 2015. Series B, table B.7.1, municipal government health expenditure, by province/territory and Canada, 1975 to 2015 - Current dollars ($' 000,000). Ottawa: Canadian Institute for Health Information; 2015.

70. CIHI. National health expenditure trends, 1975 to 2015. Series B, table B.8.1, social security funds health expenditure, by province/territory and Canada, 1975 to 2015 - Current dollars ($' 000,000). Ottawa: Canadian Institute for Health Information; 2015.

71. CIHI. National health expenditure trends, 1975 to 2015. Series A, table A.3.2.1, private sector health expenditure by use of funds, Canada, 1975 to 2015 - Current dollars. Ottawa: Canadian Institute for Health Information; 2015.

72. CIHI. National health expenditure trends, 1975 to 2015. Series A, table A.3.2.2, private sector health expenditure by use of funds, Canada, 1975 to 2015 - Current dollars. Ottawa: Canadian Institute for Health Information; 2015.

73. CIHI. National health expenditure trends, 1975 to 2015. Series A, table A.3.3.2, public sector health expenditure by use of funds, Canada, 1975 to 2015 - Current dollars. Ottawa: Canadian Institute for Health Information; 2015.

74. CIHI. National health expenditure trends, 1975 to 2015. Series A, table A.3.3.1, public sector health expenditure by use of funds, Canada, 1975 to 2015 - Current dollars. Ottawa: Canadian Institute for Health Information; 2015.

75. CIHI. National health expenditure trends, 1975 to 2015. Series D table D.2.6.1, private sector health expenditure, by use of funds, Ontario, 1975 to 2015 - Current dollars ($' 000,000). Ottawa: Canadian Institute for Health Information; 2015.

76. CIHI. National health expenditure trends, 1975 to 2015. Series D table D.2.6.2, private sector health expenditure, by use of funds, Ontario, 1975 to 2015 - Current dollars (percentage distribution). Ottawa: Canadian Institute for Health Information; 2015.

77. CIHI. National health expenditure trends, 1975 to 2015. Series D table D.3.6.2, public sector health expenditure, by use of funds, Ontario, 1975 to 2015 - Current dollars (percentage distribution). Ottawa: Canadian Institute for Health Information; 2015.

78. CIHI. National health expenditure trends, 1975 to 2015. Series D table D.3.6.1, public sector health expenditure, by use of funds, Ontario, 1975 to 2015 - Current dollars ($' 000,000). Ottawa: Canadian Institute for Health Information; 2015.

79. Ministry of Finance. Ministry of Health and Long-Term Care. The estimates 2013-2014. Ministry program summary. Toronto: Queen's Printer for Ontario; 2014.

80. Ontario Review Board. About us. Toronto: Queen's Printer for Ontario; 2011. http://www.orb.on.ca/scripts/en/about.asp (accessed 24 August 2016).

81. Association of Municipalities of Ontario. Health funding report and allocation announcement. Toronto: Association of Municipalities of Ontario; 2015. https://www.amo.on.ca/AMO-Content/Policy-Updates/2015/Health-Funding-Review-Report-and-Allocation-Announ.aspx (accessed 24 August 2016).

82. Central East Local Health Integration Network. 2015/16 health system funding reform and other allocations. Ajax: Queen's Printer for Ontario; 2015.

83. Central East Local Health Integration Network. Community support services sector: Funding allocation. Toronto: Queen's Printer for Ontario; 2015. http://www.centraleatlhin.on.ca/accountability/funding/Community Support Services.aspx (accessed 25 August 2016).

84. Central Local Health Integration Network. Service accountability agreement with Access Independent Living Services. Toronto: Queen's Printer for Ontario; 2014.

85. Hamilton Niagara Haldimand Brant Local Health Integration Network. Funding allocation by sector. Grimsby: Queen's Printer for Ontario; 2015. http://www.hnhblhin.on.ca/accountability/funding.aspx (accessed 24 August 2016).

86. Ministry of Health and Long-Term Care. Assisted living services for high risk seniors policy: An updated supporting housing program for frail or cognitively impaired seniors. Toronto: Queen's Printer for Ontario; 2011.

87. Ministry of Health and Long-Term Care. A policy guide for creating community-based specialty clinics. Toronto: Queen's Printer for Ontario; 2013.

88. Ministry of Health and Long-Term Care. Health system funding reform (HSFR). Toronto: Queen's Printer for Ontario; 2014. http://www.health.gov.on.ca/en/pro/programs/ecfa/funding/hs_funding.aspx (accessed 25 August 2016).

89. Ministry of Health and Long-Term Care. Independent Health Facilities fact sheet. Toronto: Queen's Printer for Ontario; 2014. http://www.health.gov.on.ca/en/public/programs/ihf/docs/ihf_fact.pdf (accessed 25 August 2016).

90. Central Local Health Integration Network. Multi-sector service accountability agreements (M-SAAs). Toronto: Queen's Printer for Ontario; 2014. http://www.centrallhin.on.ca/forhsps/capsandmsaa/msaas.aspx (accessed 25 August 2016).

91. Hamilton Niagara Haldimand Brant Local Health Integration Network. Service accountability agreement with Community Support Services of the Niagara Region. Grimsby: Queen's Printer for Ontario; 2011.

92. Hamilton Niagara Haldimand Brant Local Health Integration Network. Minutes of the meeting of the audit committee December 3, 2014. Grimsby: Queen's Printer for Ontario; 2014.

93. Local Health Integration Network. Provincial Aboriginal LHIN report 2014/2015. Toronto: Queen's Printer for Ontario; 2014.

94. North East Local Health Integration Network. Service accountability agreement with Shkagamik Kwe Aboriginal Health Access Centre. North Bay: Queen's Printer for Ontario; 2014.

95. South East Local Health Integration Network. Service Acountability Agreement with Country Roads Community Health Centre. Bellville: Queen's Printer for Ontario; 2014.

96. South East Local Health Integration Network. Service Accountability Agreement with Belleville & Quinte West Community Health Centre. Bellville: Queen's Printer for Ontario; 2014.

97. South West Local Health Integrated Network. Community health service providers. London: Queen's Printer for Ontario; 2015. http://www.southwestlhin.on.ca/forhsps/Community.aspx (accessed 24 August 2016).

98. Centre for Health Services and Policy Research. Evidence and perspectives on funding healthcare in Canada: Long-term care. Vancouver: University of British Columbia; 2016. http://healthcarefunding.ca/long-term-care/ (accessed 26 August 2016).

99. Steele Gray C, Berta W, Raisa B, Lum J. Home and community care sector accountability. Healthcare Policy 2014;10(Special issue): 56-66.

100. CIHI. National physician database - Payments data, 2013–2014. Table A.1.1: Total clinical payments to physicians by province/territory, 1999–2000 to 2013–2014. Ottawa: Canadian Institute for Health Information; 2015.

101. CIHI. National physician database - Payments data, 2013–2014.Table A.1.2: Fee-for-service clinical payments to physicians by province/territory, 1999–2000 to 2013–2014. Ottawa: Canadian Institute for Health Information; 2015.

102. CIHI. National physician database - Payments data, 2013–2014. Table A.1.3: Alternative clinical payments to physicians by province/territory, 1999–2000 to 2013–2014. Ottawa: Canadian Institute for Health Information; 2015.

103. CIHI. National physician database - Payments data, 2013–2014. Table A.1.4: Average gross clinical payment per physician by province, 2009–2010 to 2013–2014. Ottawa: Canadian Institute for Health Information; 2015.

104. HealthForceOntario. Family practice compensation models. Toronto: Queen's Printer for Ontario; 2014. http://www.healthforceontario.ca/en/Home/Physicians/Training_%7C_Practising_in_Ontario/Physician_Roles/Family_Practice_Models/Family_Practice_Compensation_Models (accessed 24 August 2016).

105. Ontario Medical Association. Primary care comparison. Fee for service, comprehensive care model, family health groups, family health networks, and family health organizations. Toronto: Ontario Medical Association; 2013.

106. Ministry of Health and Long-Term Care. Schedule of benefits for physician services under the Health Insurance Act. Toronto: Queen's Printer for Ontario; 2014. http://www.health.gov.on.ca/english/providers/program/ohip/sob/physserv/physserv_mn.html (accessed 25 August 2016).

107. Government of Ontario. Family health teams. Advancing family health care. Guide to physician compensation. Toronto: Queen's Printer for Ontario; 2009. https://www.rtso.ca/wp-content/uploads/2015/06/MOHLTC-fht_inter_provider-Oct-2013.pdf (accessed 25 August 2016).

108. Ministry of Finance. Ontario Health Insurance Program - Vote 1405. Toronto: Queen's Printer for Ontario; 2103. http://www.fin.gov.on.ca/en/budget/estimates/2013-14/volume1/MOHLTC_750.html (accessed 25 August 2016).

109. Ministry of Health and Long-Term Care. Ontario Health Insurance Plan (OHIP). Toronto: Queen's Printer for Ontario; 2015. http://www.health.gov.on.ca/en/public/programs/ohip/ (accessed 25 August 2016).

110. Ministry of Health and Long-Term Care. Programs and services. Toronto: Queen's Printer for Ontario; 2015. http://www.health.gov.on.ca/en/public/programs/default.aspx (accessed 25 August 2016).

111. Ministry of Health and Long-Term Care. Ontario's drug plans. Toronto: Queen's Printer for Ontario; 2015. http://www.health.gov.on.ca/en/public/programs/drugs/programs/odb/opdp_pay.aspx (accessed 25 August 2016).

112. Ministry of Health and Long-Term Care. Publicly-funded physiotherapy: Clinic locations. Toronto: Queen's Printer for Ontario; 2015. http://www.health.gov.on.ca/en/public/programs/physio/pub_clinics.aspx (accessed 25 August 2016).

4. Delivery arrangements 1: Infrastructure

Michael G. Wilson, Cristina A. Mattison and John N. Lavis

Key messages for citizens

- The health system's infrastructure includes both the places where care is delivered (e.g., hospitals) and the supports for that care (e.g., electronic health records and platforms for data analysis, evidence synthesis, and guideline development).

- Some of this infrastructure is planned for and financially supported by government (e.g., Community Care Access Centres, private not-for-profit hospitals, and local public health agencies) whereas other parts are not, or are indirectly supported with government funds (e.g., community support service agencies, most primary-care practices, and Independent Health Facilities).

- Technology is used to support the delivery of care through a teletriage system called Telehealth Ontario (to assess a health problem and provide advice, but not diagnose or prescribe treatment) and through telemedicine (videoconferencing to provide clinical care at a distance through the Ontario Telemedicine Network), as well as through an increasing number of patient portals that provide patients with access to their personal health information.

- Charitable donations support some infrastructure (e.g., hospitals or technology), but often not its ongoing operating costs.

Key messages for health professionals

- Most health professionals work in one of three types of settings outside a citizen's home – 1) offices, clinics, pharmacies and laboratories in the community; 2) hospitals; and 3) long-term care homes – most of which are located in independently owned or leased space.

- Facilities such as hospitals and long-term care homes, and the professionals who provide care within them, are typically operating with very little reserve capacity.

- Ontario has the third highest percentage of physicians who are using electronic medical records in Canada (83% compared to 87% in Alberta and 85% in British Columbia), but 72% of the physicians in Ontario who are not yet using electronic medical records report that they do not intend to do so in the next two years.

Key messages for policymakers

- Many services traditionally provided in capital-intensive hospitals are now being provided in community-based speciality clinics (e.g., low-risk diagnostic and therapeutic procedures in Independent Health Facilities).

- Ontario is among a relatively small number of jurisdictions globally that hosts a high number of centres and initiatives that can support improvements to the care provided to Ontarians based on the best available data, evidence and guidelines.

- The Ministry of Health and Long-Term Care, Local Health Integration Networks and Cancer Care Ontario carry out capacity planning for select types of infrastructure (e.g., hospitals and regional cancer centres), but there is no formal approach used in many parts of the health system.

- Approximately 80% of capital spending is publicly financed, and the amount allocated to health-system infrastructure in Ontario's 2016-17 provincial budget is $1.45 billion, much of which (87%) goes to hospitals.

. . .

In this third of four chapters focused on the building blocks of the health system, we focus on three areas: 1) infrastructure, which includes the places where care is delivered and the supports for that care; 2) capacity planning (i.e., determining what infrastructure is needed in future); and 3) capital spending (i.e., making investments to develop needed infrastructure). For the places where care is delivered, we focus primarily on the infrastructure used in the six sectors that we describe in more detail in Chapter 6, namely home and community care, primary care, specialty care, rehabilitation care, long-term care, and public health. For the supports for care, we focus on:

1) information and communication technology that support those who receive care (e.g., a teletriage system called Telehealth Ontario for providing advice, telemedicine for providing clinical services remotely, and patient portals for giving access to personal health information and supports for self-management) and those who provide care (e.g., electronic medical records or EMRs); and

2) platforms for data analysis, evidence synthesis and guideline develop-

ment to support improvements to the care provided to Ontarians.

Most of the chapter is dedicated to highlighting the key features of, and observations about, the health system's infrastructure, with less detail provided about capacity planning and capital spending given the limited amount of information available about these activities. In describing the available infrastructure, we include both data about the amount of infrastructure (e.g., number of hospitals) and data about how much the infrastructure is used (e.g., number of emergency department visits). Details about the governance and financial arrangements within which infrastructure is used, and about the health workforce that uses it (i.e., the other three building blocks of the health system) are covered in Chapters 2, 3 and 5. Additional details about infrastructure use are also addressed for each sector (Chapter 6), for select conditions (Chapter 7) and treatments (Chapter 8), and for Indigenous peoples (Chapter 9).

Infrastructure – Places where care is provided

In Table 4.1 we give an overview of where care is provided in Ontario by sector, and a brief description of each sector below. We focus on care included in the 'basket of services' that receives full or partial public (i.e., government) funding. We provide information about other types of care that typically do not receive public funding (e.g., dentistry and complementary and alternative therapy) in Chapter 8.

Table 4.1: Infrastructure as of 2014, by sector

Type of infrastructure	Number
Home and community care	
Community Care Access Centres	14
Community support service agencies	>800
Mental health and addiction organizations	>300
Diabetes education centres	245
Primary care	
Clinic models	
Family Health Organizations	475
Comprehensive Care Model practices	379
Family Health Groups	237
Family Health Teams	184
Community Health Centres[1]	105
Nursing stations[2]	72
Nurse Practitioner-led Clinics	26
Family Health Networks	21

Continued on next page

Type of infrastructure	Number
Primary care – continued	
Targeted models	
Pharmacies	4,012
Midwifery clinics	103
Aboriginal Health Access Centres[1]	10
Birthing centres	3
Specialty care	
Hospitals	
Private not-for-profit hospitals[3]	151
Private for-profit hospitals	6
Condition-specific care facilities	
Regional cancer centres	14
Specialty psychiatric hospitals	4
Other sources of specialty care	934
Independent Health Facilities	325
Private laboratories	273
Out of Hospital Premises	
Rehabilitation care	
Community Physiotherapy Centres[4]	>300
Hospitals for which rehabilitation is a significant focus	173
Children's Treatment Centres	21
Long-term care	
Long-term care homes	636
Hospital-based continuing care facilities	117
Public health	
Local public health agency satellite offices	105
Local public health agencies	36
Public health laboratories	11
Cross-sectoral	
Health Links[5]	82

Sources: 4; 103-115

Notes:
[1] New capital projects announced in April of 2014 include 12 Community Health Centres and four Aboriginal Health Access Centres.
[2] The 72 nursing stations include 43 nursing stations in small and rural communities funded by Local Health Integration Networks (LHINs), with funds from the Ministry of Health and Long-Term Care, as well as 29 federal government-funded nursing stations in First Nations communities (four community operated and 25 run by Health Canada nurses).
[3] The legislation officially refers to these as public hospitals, however they are private not-for-profit hospitals.
[4] Community Physiotherapy Centres provide publicly covered services for seniors and other eligible patients. We were not able to identify the total number of physiotherapy clinics in Ontario, which would include those that receive public payment (e.g., Community Physiotherapy Centres), as well as those that exclusively provide services paid for privately.
[5] Health Links are in the process of being implemented and the total number is anticipated to be 100.

Home and community care

The 14 Community Care Access Centres (CCACs) – one for each Local Health Integration Network (LHIN) – currently have responsibility for determining need for home and community care, and then funding that care up to the limit set for that level of need. As we outline in Table 4.2, the number of Ontarians accessing home and community care through

CCACs has increased 18% from 2010-11 to 2014-15, with the majority of clients being 65 years of age or older.(1) Moreover, Table 4.2 points to the wide range of services provided, including nursing, rehabilitation and personal support and homemaking services, all of which have seen total service provision increase over the same time frame. The increases in rehabilitation services are exclusively driven by large increases in physiotherapy visits. However, as we describe in Chapter 10, the *Patients First Act, 2016* amended 20 existing acts. Key changes will include an expansion of the role of the LHINs for planning and integrating home and community care and primary care, with CCAC functions being absorbed into the

Table 4.2: Profile of Community Care Access Centre clients, employees and services, 2010-11 to 2014-15

Indicators	Numbers (and % of total)			Four-year percentage change[2]
	2010-11	2013-14	2014-15[1]	
Profile of clients served				
Clients served	616,952	699,020	713,493	18%
Age 65+	345,493 (56%)	405,432 (58%)	—	24%
Age 19-64	172,747 (28%)	223,686 (32%)	—	24%
Age 0-18	98,712 (16%)	69,902 (10%)	—	-28%
Clients placed to a funded long-term care home	25,761	26,374	~27,000	<1%
Full-time employees (approximately)	5,701	6,627	6,684	19%
Profile of services provided				
Service units	29,821,293	37,991,053	38,687,656	32%
Personal support/homemaking hours	20,965,448	27,719,897	28,529,882	40%
Nursing	7,606,320	7,980,381	8,344,089	8%
Nursing visits	5,799,127	5,713,359	5,932,298	-0.5%
Shift nursing hours	1,807,193	2,267,022	2,411,791	39%
Rehabilitation	1,249,525	1,623,478	1,782,933	31%
Occupational therapy visits	482,051	553,209	414,416	-18%
Physiotherapy visits	426,690	705,052	778,482	61%
Speech-language therapy visits	242,998	263,571	59,247	-76%
Dietitian service visits	45,384	49,014	48,067	-9%
Social work visits	52,402	52,542	54,519	-22%

Source: Adapted from: 1

Notes:
1 Data not available for the specific reference period are denoted by —.
2 Percentage changes were calculated based on the number of clients served, not the change in the proportion of the total.

LHINs.(2) As a result, this component of infrastructure will likely change significantly in the near future.

While the CCACs coordinate access to and fund home and community care, services are delivered through many points of contact. The largest source of home and community care is through the more than 800 private not-for-profit and private for-profit community support service agencies that provide professional, personal support and homemaking services to more than 800,000 community-dwelling Ontarians (including older adults and people with physical disabilities).(3)

Other targeted services complement those provided through community support service agencies and are focused on providing services to specific populations. For example, more than 300 community mental health and addiction organizations provide community mental health services (e.g., intensive case management, assertive community treatment, crisis intervention, and early psychosis intervention), drug and alcohol addiction support and treatment, as well as supports for problem gambling.(4) Also, 245 diabetes education centres provide education and support for adults and their families, individual and group counselling for patients and family members, and life plans to minimize diabetes-related symptoms.(5)

Primary care

Primary care can be accessed by Ontarians through clinic-based models and targeted models (i.e., for specific populations, locations or products and services). Most clinic-based primary care is provided by family physicians working in fee-for-service models (what the Ministry of Health and Long-Term Care calls Comprehensive Care Model practices and Family Health Groups) or in blended capitation models for groups of physicians (who may not necessarily be located in the same office) that the Ministry of Health and Long-Term Care calls Family Health Networks and Family Health Organizations (see Chapter 6 for details about these models).(6)

Team-based care currently reaches 25% of the population through both clinic-based and targeted models of primary care.(7) Team-based care delivered through clinic-based models include:
- 184 Family Health Teams that include a team consisting of family physicians, nurses (including nurse practitioners) and other health

professionals (e.g., social workers and dietitians), with some working in the same location (e.g., for smaller teams) and others working across multiple locations (e.g., for larger teams that serve a city or region);

- 105 Community Health Centres, which consist of interprofessional teams that serve hard-to-service communities and populations that may otherwise have trouble accessing health services; and
- 26 Nurse Practitioner-led Clinics that provide primary-care services that can be delivered within the scope of practice for nurse practitioners.

For targeted team-based primary-care models, 10 Aboriginal Health Access Centres provide community-led primary healthcare, including many services related to chronic-disease prevention and management, as well as a combination of traditional healing, primary care, cultural programs, health-promotion programs, community-development initiatives, and social-support services to First Nations, Métis and Inuit communities.(8)

Access to primary-care providers working within this infrastructure varies within the province with, at the low end, 87% of those living in the North West LHIN and 88% of those living in the North East LHIN reporting having a primary-care provider that they see regularly, as compared to 97% in the South East LHIN.(9) Those in need of primary care but who lack access to a primary-care provider who they see regularly, typically turn to less-than-optimal settings for primary care, such as walk-in clinics, urgent care centres or emergency departments (or forgo seeking care altogether).

Other targeted models of primary care in the province include:
- 4,012 pharmacies, which are increasingly providers of drug-related primary-care services (e.g., by filling prescriptions, providing medication counselling, providing additional services such as counselling to support smoking cessation and diabetes management, and providing flu shots);(10)
- 103 midwifery clinics, which provide primary care to low-risk pregnant women throughout pregnancy, labour and up to six-weeks postpartum; and
- three midwifery-led birthing centres, which provide out-of-hospital births for midwifery clients in Ottawa, Six Nations of the Grand River (near Hamilton), and Toronto.

Also, Rural and Northern Physician Group Agreements support one to seven physicians per location to serve rural and northern communities with a nurse-staffed, after-hours Telephone Health Advisory Service for enrolled patients seeking care for a range of issues, including chronic diseases.(6)

In terms of pharmacies specifically, there is a fair degree of consolidation, with half of locations being run by: 1) franchises such as Shoppers Drug Mart or banner retailers like Guardian (1,051, 26%); 2) large chains (872, 22%) that have more than 15 stores (e.g., Rexall); and 3) small chains (122, 3%) that have three to 15 stores.(11) However, the number of locations is not an ideal indicator of market share given some franchises and chains likely have higher volumes of sales than independent locations. Unfortunately, Ontario-level market-share data are not publicly available, but Canadian data indicate that nearly two thirds of national market share is held by three companies: 1) Shoppers Drug Mart (35%); 2) Katz Group Pharmacies Inc. (18%), which includes retailers such as Rexall that itself recently purchased Pharmaplus; and 3) Jean Coutu Group PJC Inc. (8%), although the latter's national data are of limited value given that in Ontario it serves only a small area in the east of the province (8.3%).(12)

Specialty care

Speciality care in the province is provided in hospitals, using emergency-service infrastructure, in condition-specific (e.g., cancer or mental health and addictions) facilities, and in a mix of other facilities (e.g., Independent Health Facilities, Out of Hospital Premises, and private laboratories), and with a variety of types of technology (e.g., diagnostic technology). Also, as highlighted in Chapter 3, hospitals are increasingly supported by shared-service organizations that seek to achieve supply chain and operational efficiencies.(13)

Hospitals

There are 151 private not-for-profit hospital corporations with 224 hospital sites in Ontario. The Ministry of Health and Long-Term Care classifies these hospitals as general hospitals, hospitals providing cancer care, convalescent hospitals, hospitals for chronic patients, active treatment teaching psychiatric hospitals, active treatment hospitals for alcoholism and drug addiction, and regional rehabilitation hospitals.(14) The most visible hospitals in many communities are general/teaching hospitals (what the Ministry of Health and Long-Term Care calls 'group A' hospitals), general hospitals with more than 100 beds (group B), and hospitals providing cancer care (group D, which are a subset of group A) (Table 4.3). A list of general hospitals with fewer than 100 beds (group C) is available through the Ministry of Health Long-Term Care website.(14) Another measure of

Table 4.3: List of general/teaching hospitals, hospitals providing cancer care, and general hospitals with more than 100 beds

City (corporation name where different from name of main hospital site)[1]	Number of sites[1]	Name of sites[2]	Hospital group[1]		
			General/ teaching (group A)	Cancer care (group D)	General >100 beds (group B)
Barrie	1	Royal Victoria Regional Health Centre			✓
Belleville (Quinte Healthcare Corporation)	4	Bancroft North Hastings Hospital; Belleville General Hospital; Prince Edward County Memorial Hospital; Trenton Memorial Hospital			✓
Brampton (William Osler Health System)	2	Brampton Civic Hospital; Etobicoke General Hospital			✓
Brantford (Brant Community Healthcare)	2	Brantford General Hospital; The Willet Hospital			✓
Brockville	2	Brockville General Hospital; Brockville General Hospital – Garden Street (formerly St Vincent de Paul Hospital)			✓
Burlington	1	Joseph Brant Hospital			✓
Cambridge	1	Cambridge Memorial Hospital			✓
Chatham (Chatham-Kent Health Alliance)	2	Chatham Public General Hospital; St. Joseph's Hospital			✓
Cobourg	2	Northumberland Hills Hospital; Cobourg District General			✓
Cornwall	1	Cornwall Community Hospital			✓
Guelph	1	Guelph General Hospital			✓

Continued on next page

City (corporation name where different from name of main hospital site)[1]	Number of sites[1]	Name of sites[2]	General/ teaching (group A)	Cancer care (group D)	General >100 beds (group B)
Hamilton (Hamilton Health Sciences)	6	Chedoke Hospital; Hamilton General Hospital; Juravinski Hospital Cancer Centre; McMaster University Medical Centre; St. Peter's Hospital; West Lincoln Memorial Hospital	✓	✓	
Hamilton (St. Joseph's Hospital Site)	2	St. Joseph's Hospital; St. Joseph's Hospital – West 5th	✓	✓	
Kingston	1	Kingston General Hospital	✓	✓	
Kingston	1	Hotel Dieu Hospital	✓		
Kitchener	1	St. Mary's General Hospital			✓
Kitchener	2	Grand River Hospital; Kitchener Freeport Hospital			✓
Lindsay	1	Ross Memorial Hospital			✓
London (London Health Sciences Centre)	2	University Hospital; Victoria Hospital	✓	✓	
London (St. Joseph's Health Care)	3	Parkwood Institute; St. Joseph's Hospital; South West Centre for Forensic Mental Health Care	✓		
Markham	2	Markham-Stouffville Hospital; Uxbridge Cottage Hospital			✓
Mississauga (Trillium Health Partners)	2	Credit Valley Hospital; Mississauga Hospital			✓
Newmarket	1	Southlake Regional Health Centre			✓
North Bay	1	North Bay Regional Health Centre			✓
Oakville (Halton Healthcare Services Corporation)	1	Oakville Trafalgar Memorial Hospital			✓

Continued on next page

City (corporation name where different from name of main hospital site)[1]	Number of sites[1]	Name of sites[2]	Hospital group[1]		
			General/ teaching (group A)	Cancer care (group D)	General >100 beds (group B)
Orangeville	3	Headwater Health Care Centre; Orangeville Dufferin Area Hospital; Shelburne District Hospital			✓
Orillia	1	Orillia Soldiers' Memorial Hospital			✓
Oshawa (Lakeridge Health)	3	Lakeridge Health Oshawa; Lakeridge Health Port Perry; Lakeridge Health Whitby			✓
Ottawa	1	Children's Hospital of Eastern Ontario	✓		
Ottawa	1	Hôpital Montfort	✓		
Ottawa (The Ottawa Hospital)	4	Ottawa Civic Hospital; Ottawa General Hospital; Ottawa Riverside Hospital; The Ottawa Hospital Rehabilitation Centre	✓	✓	
Ottawa	1	Queensway-Carleton Hospital			✓
Owen Sound (Grey Bruce Health Services)	5	Lion's Head Hospital; Markdale Hospital; Owen Sound Hospital; Southamptom Hospital; Wiarton Hospital			✓
Pembroke	1	Pembroke Regional Hospital			✓
Peterborough	1	Peterborough Regional Health Centre			✓
Richmond Hill (Mackenzie Health)	1	Mackenzie Richmond Hill Hospital			✓
Sarnia (Bluewater Health)	2	Bluewater Health Hospital; Petrolia Charlotte Eleanor Englehart Hospital			✓
Sault Ste. Marie (Sault Area Hospital)	3	Sault Area General Hospital; Sault Area Hospital - Richards Landing; Sault Area Hospital - Thessalon			✓

Continued on next page

City (corporation name where different from name of main hospital site)[1]	Number of sites[1]	Name of sites[2]	Hospital group[1] General/teaching (group A)	Cancer care (group D)	General >100 beds (group B)
Simcoe	1	Norfolk General Hospital			✓
St Catharines (Niagara Health System)	6	Fort Erie-Douglas Memorial Hospital; Greater Niagara General Hospital; Niagara-on-the-Lake Hospital; Port Colborne General Hospital; St. Catharines Hospital; Welland County General Hospital			✓
Stratford	1	Stratford General Hospital			✓
Sudbury	1	Health Sciences North	✓	✓	
Thunder Bay	1	Thunder Bay Regional Health Sciences Centre	✓	✓	
Timmins	1	Timmins and District General Hospital			✓
Toronto	1	The Hospital for Sick Children (SickKids)	✓		
Toronto	2	Humber River Hospital - Finch; Humber River Hospital - Wilson			✓
Toronto	2	North York General Hospital; Branson Ambulatory Care Centre			✓
Toronto	2	Rouge Valley Ajax and Pickering; Rouge Valley Centenary			✓
Toronto	2	The Scarborough General Hospital; The Scarborough Hospital - Birchmount			✓
Toronto (Sinai Health System)	1	Mount Sinai Hospital	✓		
Toronto	1	St. Joseph's Health Centre			✓
Toronto	1	St. Michael's Hospital	✓		
Toronto	2	Sunnybrook Health Sciences; Sunnybook Health Sciences - Orthopaedic and Arthritic	✓	✓	

Continued on next page

City (corporation name where different from name of main hospital site)[1]	Number of sites[1]	Name of sites[2]	Hospital group[1]		
			General/ teaching (group A)	Cancer care (group D)	General >100 beds (group B)
Toronto (Toronto East Health Network	1	Michael Garron Hospital			✓
Toronto (University Hospital Network)	3	Princess Margaret Hospital/ Ontario Cancer Institute; Toronto General Hospital; Toronto Western Hospital	✓	✓	
Toronto	1	Women's College Hospital	✓		
Windsor	4	Windsor Regional Hospital; Windsor Metropolitan General Hospital; Windsor Regional Hospital – Ouellete; Windsor Regional Cancer Centre		✓	✓
Windsor	1	Hotel Dieu Grace General Hospital			✓
Woodstock	1	Woodstock General Hospital			✓

Source: 14

Note:
[1] Data is based on 2009 publicly available lists from the Ministry of Health and Long-Term Care.
[2] Where possible, an effort has been made to update site names using publicly available information from hospital websites.

scale is the number of acute-care beds per 1,000 people, and as of 2012, Ontario has fewer than either Canada as a whole or countries that are members of the Organisation of Economic Cooperation and Development (OECD), with 1.4 acute-care beds per 1,000 people in Ontario compared to 1.7 in Canada and 3.3 in OECD countries.(15)

A sense of the scale of the hospital infrastructure can also be captured through the volume of care they provide. Volume of care includes ambulatory-care visits (e.g., hospital visits for diagnosis, observation, consultation, outpatient treatment, and rehabilitation services), day/night care visits (e.g., hospital visits for surgical procedures that do not require inpatient care), emergency room visits, and inpatient care (Table 4.4). Ontario has a low average length-of-stay in hospital (6.6 days compared to 7.6 in Canada and across OECD countries), which means that more patients can be admitted and discharged for the same scale of infrastructure.(15)

Table 4.4: Number (in thousands) of ambulatory care visits, day/night care visits, emergency visits, inpatient admissions and inpatient days, 2000-01, 2010-11 and 2013-14

Indicators	Ontario[1]				Canada
	2000-01	2010-11	2013-14	13-year percentage change	2013-14
Ambulatory care service visits	14,889	18,126	18,944	27%	35,686
General	14,141	16,607	17,519	24%	31,690
Specialty - psychiatric	90	770	787	780%	907
Specialty - pediatric	381	439	460	21%	983
Specialty - other	170	—	—	—	766
Rehabilitation	105	10	8	-92%	126
Extended care/chronic	155	299	170	9%	1,214
Day/night care visits	1,859	3,479	3,472	87%	6,493
General	1,786	3,324	3,344	87%	5,627
Specialty - psychiatric	8	74	55	618%	96
Specialty - pediatric	22	39	45	110%	135
Specialty - other	4	—	—	—	379
Rehabilitation	8	—	—	—	37
Extended care/chronic	32	42	28	-14%	219
Emergency visits	5,245	5,689	6,002	14%	13,423
General	5,135	5,448	5,755	12%	12,339
Specialty - psychiatric	7	99	90	1190%	94
Specialty - pediatric	103	118	136	32%	268
Specialty - other	—	—	—	—	64
Rehabilitation	—	—	—	—	10
Extended care/chronic	—	24	22	—	649
Inpatient admissions	1,148	1,168	1,217	6%	2,466
General	1,095	1,100	1,165	6%	2,286
Specialty - psychiatric	15	25	15	-1%	22
Specialty - pediatric	19	21	22	15%	46
Specialty - other	11	7	6	-45%	35
Rehabilitation	3	3	0.2	-93%	3
Extended care/chronic	6	12	9	69%	74
Inpatient days	8,454	10,204	9,254	9%	20,278
General	7,343	7,912	7,875	7%	17,312
Specialty - psychiatric	561	1,121	794	74%	1,274
Specialty - pediatric	130	145	148	14%	282
Specialty - other	50	29	27	-45%	176
Rehabilitation	162	66	14	-92%	173
Extended care/chronic	209	931	397	90%	1,063

Source: 116

Note:
[1] Data not available for the specific reference period are denoted by —.

While all types of visits have increased between 2000-01 and 2013-14, day/night care visits (e.g., for surgeries that now only require a day visit instead of inpatient admission) have increased the most overall (87%) (Table 4.4). The most striking increases are for psychiatric care, whether that care was provided through ambulatory-care service visits (780%), day/night care visits (618%) or emergency visits (1,190%).

Acute inpatient hospitalizations over the last decade and a half (from 1995-96 to 2011-12), on the other hand, have decreased by 33% (slightly more than the Canadian average of 31% over the same time period) (Table 4.5). As well, the average length of acute inpatient hospital stay has decreased by 7% (almost double the average decrease in Canada of 4%).

Table 4.5: Age- and sex-standardized inpatient hospital utilization, 1995-96 and 2011-12

	Ontario		Canada	Ontario	Canada
	1995-96	2011-12	2011-12	16-year percentage change[1]	16-year percentage change[1]
Acute inpatient hospitalization rate per 100,000[1]	10,466	7,038	7,672	-33%	-31%
Average length of acute inpatient hospital stay (in days)[2]	6.9	6.4	7.2	-7%	-4%

Source: 117

Notes:
[1] Percentage change is from 1995-96 to 2011-12.
[2] Age- and sex-standardized based on the 2001-02 post-censal Canadian population

In addition to these private not-for-profit hospitals, there are also six private for-profit hospitals (Beachwood Private Hospital, Bellwood Health Services, Don Mills Surgical Unit, Shouldice Hospital, St. Joseph's Infirmary and Private Hospital, and Woodstock Private Hospital), which were grandfathered under the *Ontario Private Hospitals Act, 1990* when hospital insurance was introduced in Ontario.(16) All of these are small facilities, although Shouldice (89 beds) is larger than the other hospitals, which have 12 to 35 beds. Three of the hospitals provide care to chronically ill patients with a focus on complex continuing long-term care (St. Joseph's and Woodstock) and palliative care (Beachwood). The other hospitals provide alcohol-addiction treatment (Bellwood Health Services), general surgical procedures (Don Mills Surgical Unit), and abdominal wall and hernia surgery (Shouldice).

Emergency services infrastructure

Emergency services, which consist of land and air ambulance services and care in emergency departments, are often the entry point into hospital-based care. Land and air emergency medical services provide emergency pre-hospital care. Land ambulance services are coordinated and provided through 53 certified land ambulance operators (which are a mix of private not-for-profit hospitals, private for-profit companies, municipal governments, First Nations bands, and volunteer providers), 19 Central Ambulance Communication Centres, three Ambulance Communications Services, and seven regional land ambulance base hospitals.(17) Air ambulance services across Ontario are provided by Ornge (a not-for-profit corporation) to approximately 18,000 patients per year through its fleet that consists of 10 helicopters and 10 airplanes, with its services coordinated by the Operations Control Centre.(18; 19) In addition, Ornge provides land paramedic services for critically ill patients in the greater Toronto area, Ottawa and Peterborough regions.(20)

For in-hospital emergency care, hospitals managed 5.8 million emergency department visits in 2014, which accounted for 57% of all emergency department visits across Canada that year.(21) The majority of visits are handled in large (40%) and medium (23%) community hospitals with the remaining patients coming to teaching hospitals (21%) and small community hospitals (16%). As displayed in Figure 4.1, the median time (in hours) spent in emergency departments in Ontario is 2.5, which is approximately the same as the Canadian median of 2.4 hours. However, the time spent by Ontarians whose emergency department wait times are among the longest (the 90th percentile) is 6.5 hours, which is less than the Canadian average of 7.4 hours (Figure 4.1). Also, the time spent by patients who are admitted to hospital and whose emergency department wait times are among the longest (again the 90th percentile) is substantially longer (29.9 hours) than those who are discharged.

Figure 4.1: Age-standardized[1] total time spent (in hours) in an emergency department, 2014-15

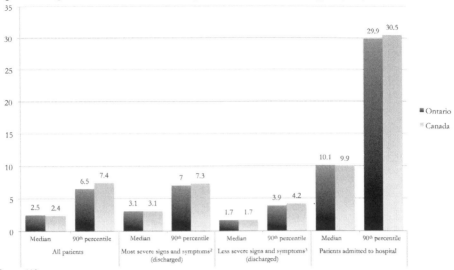

Source: 118

Notes:
[1] Standardized based on the 2014-15 National Ambulatory Care Reporting System emergency department population. Also, the Canadian Institute for Health Information report, from which these data are drawn, indicates that the data are representative of only the facilities that submitted to the National Ambulatory Care Reporting System in 2014-2015, as not all facilities in these jurisdictions are captured in the National Ambulatory Care Reporting System database. Given this, the Canadian Institute for Health Information report notes that comparisons involving these jurisdictions should be made with caution.
[2] Those with the most severe signs and symptoms include categories I (resuscitation), II (emergent) and III (urgent) on the Canadian Triage and Acuity Scale.
[3] Those with less severe signs and symptoms include categories IV (less urgent – semi-urgent) and V (non urgent).

Condition-specific facilities

Ontario also has facilities designed specifically for people with cancer and mental illness or addiction (see Chapter 7 for more details). For cancer, there are 14 regional cancer centres (hosted within a hospital in each of the 14 LHINs), which are overseen and funded by Cancer Care Ontario.(22) The centres are responsible for responding to local cancer issues, as well as coordinating cancer care across local and regional healthcare providers.(23) For people living with mental illness or addiction, in addition to the hospitals in the province that are equipped to provide varying levels of care for such challenges, there are also four 'psychiatric hospitals' with eight sites in the province that provide specialty mental health and addictions care.(24)

Other facilities providing specialty care

There are 934 Independent Health Facilities, and they are independently owned and operated, with almost all (98%) of them being for-profit corporations. These facilities can take several forms including being part of an existing health facility (a hospital, Community Health Centre or a physician's office), being located within a multi-office complex, being free-standing facilities, or being provided on a mobile basis when specific approval has been provided.(25) These facilities receive a facility fee for the publicly insured diagnostic and therapeutic procedures they provide (Table 4.6). For the facilities providing diagnostic procedures/services, most of the services provided include ultrasound and radiology (e.g., X-rays), but services such as nuclear medicine and medical resonance imaging/computed tomography (MRI/CT) scans, as well as those used as part of sleep and pulmonary function studies, are also provided. Among the facilities providing therapeutic procedures, the most commonly provided procedures (in terms of total facility fees paid) are dialysis, abortion and ophthalmologic procedures, with other services provided including plastic and vascular surgeries, and laser therapy.(25-29)

Table 4.6: Facility fees paid and number of services performed by 934 Independent Health Facilities

Types of services provided	Facility fees paid ($ millions)		Number of services performed[1]
	2006-07	2010-11	2010-11
Diagnostic procedures/services			
Ultrasound	129.9	173.0	4,267,000
Radiology (includes X-rays)	116.1	111.0	3,878,000
Nuclear medicine	39.5	40.8	432,000
Sleep studies	29.3	39.6	106,000
Computed tomography/ magnetic resonance imaging	5.7	10.0	—
Pulmonary function studies	2.1	2.4	152,000
Subtotal	322.6	376.8	8,835,000
Therapeutic procedures			
Dialysis	9.9	15.2	—
Abortion	6.4	7.1	—
Ophthalmology	6.4	6.4	—
Plastic surgery	1.0	1.1	—
Vascular surgery	0.9	0.8	—
Laser therapy	0.4	0.4	—
Subtotal	25.0	31.0	—
Total	347.6	407.8	—

Sources: 25-29

Notes:
[1] Data not available for the specific reference period are denoted by —.

In addition, there are 273 Out of Hospital Premises that provide services that would once have been provided in hospitals (cosmetic surgery, endoscopy and interventional pain management under the administration of a variety of types of anesthesia).(29) While the Out of Hospital Premises receive professional fees for these services, unlike Independent Health Facilities they do not receive a facility fee from the government for these services (but they are accountable to the College of Physicians and Surgeons of Ontario for the safety and quality of care they provide).(30; 31)

More generally, the Government of Ontario has signalled its intention to move more care from hospitals to community-based specialty clinics that can provide high volumes of low-risk diagnostic and surgical procedures that do not require overnight stays (e.g., colonoscopies and cataract procedures). Just as would have been the case had the procedures been performed in hospital, the medically necessary procedures provided in community-based specialty clinics are free at the point of use. These clinics can take many forms, including a private not-for-profit hospital (e.g., Hotel Dieu Hospital in Kingston), a satellite site or ambulatory-care centre operated by a not-for-profit hospital (e.g., the Queensway Health Centre's Surgicentre, which is the largest free-standing ambulatory centre in North America and provides peri-operative services to 13,000 patients each year in eight operating rooms), and an Independent Health Facility (e.g., Kensington Eye Institute for cataract procedures).

Lastly, most laboratory tests (60%) ordered by clinicians (e.g., including routine laboratory tests, as well as more specialized tests such as for detecting cancer) are analyzed by the 325 private laboratories in the province, with the rest being analyzed by hospitals or public health laboratories.(32) There is a significant degree of consolidation in private laboratories, with 90% run by Lifelabs (which provides approximately two thirds of laboratory testing) and Gamma-Dynacare.(33)

While hospitals and some of the other infrastructure for speciality care have had dedicated quality monitoring and improvement mechanisms in place for some time, other parts of the specialty-care infrastructure have only recently been given attention. For example, the Quality Management Partnership is a collaboration between the College of Physicians and Surgeons of Ontario and Cancer Care Ontario that is focused on implementing provincial quality-management programs in three key areas.(34) These include: 1) colonoscopy (through ColonCancer Check, Gastrointestinal Endoscopy Quality-Based Procedure, and the Out of Hospital Premises Inspection Program); 2) mammography (through the Ontario Breast Cancer Screening Program, Independent Health Facilities program, diagnostic imaging peer review program, and other safety and quality processes); and 3) pathology (through the Pathology and Laboratory Medicine Program, Path2Quality, Peer Assessment Program and the Institute for Quality Management in Healthcare).(35)

Technology used in specialty care

A wide array of technologies (other than information and communication technology, which we cover later as part of the section about supports for care) are used in the provision of specialty care. These can range from commonly used technologies such as ultrasound, X-ray and laboratory-based technology to more specialized (and often very expensive) technologies for diagnosis (e.g., imaging devices and equipment for auditory deficit testing) and treatment (e.g., radiation treatment for cancer and eye surgeries). However, data about the technology available is focused on imaging devices – computed tomography (CT), magnetic resonance imaging (MRI), positron emission tomography (PET), and nuclear medicine cameras – the first three of which we present data about in Table 4.7.

Table 4.7: Number of devices, number of devices per million people and number of exams per 1,000 people, 2015

Imaging device	Number available		Number available per million people		Number of exams per 1,000 people
	Ontario	Percentage of total in Canada	Ontario	Canada	Ontario
Computed tomography (CT)	186	35%	13	15	136
Magnetic resonance imaging (MRI)	125	37%	9	9	71
Single-photon emission CT (SPECT)	99	38%	7	7	12
Single-photon emission CT – CT (SPECT – CT)	38	18%	3	6	6
Positron emission tomography (PET) – CT (PET – CT)	15	32%	1	1	0.7

Source: 119

Data regarding the use of these devices is limited to CT and MRI scans, and show a significant increase (165%) in the number of MRI exams from 2003-04 to 2014-15, as well as an increase in CT exams (83%) over the same time period (Table 4.8).(36; 37) For technology related to treatment, the most recent capital-investment strategy report from Cancer Care Ontario (April 2012) indicates that there were 103 approved and funded radiation treatment machines. However, the same report indicated that the treatment-utilization rate of these machines (i.e., the proportion of people with cancer who receive at least one course of radiation therapy in their lifetime) is 38%,(38) which was below the international average of 50-55% and Cancer Care Ontario's target of 48%.(39)

Table 4.8: Number of computed tomography and magnetic resonance imaging exams in Ontario and Canada, 2003-04, 2010-11 and 2014-15

Types of exams	2003-04 (thousands)		2010-11 (thousands)		2014-15 (thousands)		11-year percentage change	
	Ontario	Canada	Ontario	Canada	Ontario	Canada	Ontario	Canada
Computed tomography (CT) exams	1,017	2,767	1,538	4,326	1,871	5,278	83%	91%
Magnetic resonance imaging (MRI) exams	367	768	728	1,594	974	1,952	165%	154%

Source: 120, 121

Turning to wait times for CT and MRI scans, data from April to September 2015 indicate that as compared to the other five provinces for which data are available, Ontario has:

- the lowest median wait time for CT scans (n=7 days with the others ranging from 17 to 30 days);
- the second-lowest CT scan wait time for those whose waits are among the longest (i.e., those in the 90th percentile of wait times) for CT scans (n=37 days with the lowest being 28 days and the rest ranging from 50 to 74 days);
- the second-lowest median wait time for MRIs (n=36 days with the lowest being 30 days and the rest ranging from 55 to 99 days); and
- the lowest MRI wait time for those in the 90th percentile (n=91 days with the others ranging from 149 to 202 days).(40)

Rehabilitation care

As outlined in more detail in Chapter 6 (care by sector), rehabilitation care is different from other sectors in how it is more an element of other sectors than a sector in its own right, it does not have a single key player involved as the central point of contact (e.g., CCACs, primary-care teams or family physicians, hospitals, and long-term care homes), much of the focus is outside of what is sometimes considered to be the health system (e.g., children and youth with physical, communication or developmental disabilities), and it has been extensively 'privatized' as compared to other sectors. In this case privatization has meant both shifting from public payment to private payment (i.e., paid for out-of-pocket or with private insurance) and shifting from private not-for-profit delivery to more private for-profit delivery.

As such, the infrastructure in the province for providing rehabilitation care is comprised of multiple points of access that depend on the nature of care needed, among other factors. This includes rehabilitation care (physiotherapy, occupational therapy and speech-language therapy) delivered in:
- a patient's own home or a long-term care home;
- more than 300 Community Physiotherapy Centres, which provide a mix of government-funded rehabilitation care (i.e., Ontario Health Insurance Plan-funded) and privately funded rehabilitation care (i.e., paid for through out-of-pocket payments or through private insurance);
- 21 Children's Treatment Centres for children and youth with physical, communication and/or development challenges;(41) and
- hospitals, including:
  - 55 general rehabilitation hospitals (labelled 'group E' hospitals under the *Public Hospitals Act, 1990*) that provide general rehabilitation services (e.g., dedicated 'rehabilitation beds' in acute-care hospitals where physiatrists focus specifically on physical medicine and rehabilitation, as well as inpatient or outpatient rehabilitation care from health professionals such as occupational therapists);(42)
  - 10 special rehabilitation hospitals (group J) that provide specialty rehabilitation services;(43)
  - three 'continuing care centres' (group R) that provide 'low intensity, long duration' rehabilitation; and
  - 108 chronic-care hospitals (groups F and G) that provide rehabilitation care for some of their 'complex continuing care' patients.

These numbers do not add to the 173 hospitals listed in Table 4.1 because some hospitals can appear in more than one group. With no defined 'basket' of rehabilitation services, each hospital (sometimes in collaboration with its LHIN) decides on the inpatient and outpatient rehabilitation care that will be provided (if any).(44)

Long-term care

While not considered part of the long-term care sector, it is important to distinguish licensed retirement homes (of which there are 716) from the long-term care homes with which they are sometimes confused. Most retirement homes are private for-profit facilities, which can accommodate between six and 250 residents who require little to no support, and which do not provide access to 24-hour nursing care.(45; 46) More than 55,000 older adults in Ontario live in retirement homes, eligibility for them is determined by one's ability to pay, and there is no requirement to provide proof of one's health status or the amount of support needed (although retirement homes may assess an individual's needs to determine whether it can provide the supports they require).(45; 46)

Turning to long-term care homes, as of 2013 more than half of them are private for-profit (51%), almost one quarter are private not-for-profit (22%) and the rest are owned by municipal governments or others (27%) (Table 4.9). The picture changes slightly based on data from 2015,

Table 4.9: Characteristics of select long-term care homes, 2013

Characteristics of select homes[1]	Ontario	Canada
Homes[2]	598	1,334
Size		
4–99 beds	239	720
>100 beds	359	614
Type of care[3]		
Type II	344	650
Type III or higher	254	669
Type of ownership[4]		
Private for-profit	306	499
Private not-for-profit	129	410
Public	163	425
Occupancy rate[5]	97%	97%
Beds staffed and in operation	78,427	147,926

Continued on next page

Characteristics of select homes[1]	Ontario	Canada
Age and sex of residents		
Females		
<45	0.3%	0.4%
45–64	4%	4%
65–74	10%	9%
75–84	28%	28%
>85	58%	58%
Males		
<45	1%	1%
45–64	9%	9%
65–74	15%	15%
75–84	34%	34%
>85	41%	41%

Sources: 52; 122; 123

Notes:
[1] The Long-Term Care Facilities Survey includes only long-term care homes that provide residents with a minimum of professional nursing care and/or medical supervision. For the purpose of the survey, long-term care homes were defined as non-hospital facilities that have more than four beds and are approved and licensed by the Ministry of Health and Long-Term Care. Cells were sometimes combined to prevent disclosure of long-term care homes when few homes had a specific characteristic.
[2] The most recent data indicate that the total number of long-term care homes is 636, but the data do not include the additional variables that we summarize in this table. Given this, we present the earlier data in this table, but in Table 4.1 we provide the most up-to-date number of long-term care homes.
[3] The available data from the Canadian Institute for Health Information only consider those providing type II care or higher. Type II care includes people with chronic disease or functional disability, who are relatively stabilized. Personal care is required for a total of 1.5-2.5 hours per day and medical supervision is provided to meet psychosocial needs. Type III care includes people who are chronically ill and/or have a functional disability and may not be in stable condition. A range of therapeutic services, medical management and nursing care are provided (a minimum of 2.5 hours per day of therapeutic or medical care is required in a day). A higher type of care includes people who need a significant amount of nursing and/or medical care. Care above type III is most commonly provided in hospital settings.
[4] Ownership is aggregated into the following groups: private for-profit, private not-for-profit, and public (e.g., municipal).
[5] The occupancy rate is calculated by dividing resident days by the multiplied result of beds staffed and in operation × 365.

which indicate that 57% are private for-profit and 24% are private not-for-profit.(47) Also, this profile differs from the rest of Canada where 37% (499) are operating under private for-profit ownership and 31% (410) under private not-for-profit ownership.(52) Based on our own calculations using publicly available data, there has been some consolidation among licensed operators, with five operators owning the licenses for 20,633 (28%) of the 76,569 long-term beds in the province.(48) Relatively few operators outsource the management of their long-term care homes, but when they do it has been primarily to three companies. The occupancy rate of long-term care homes is consistently very high, and was 97% in 2013.

The availability of long-term care beds varies by region within the province, and detailed data about the number of beds available in each long-term care home, the number of people on the wait lists for those facilities, and the average number of beds that come available each month are provided for each CCAC through the Ontario Association of Community Care Access Centres' website.(49) However, 2014 data from the Ontario

Long Term Care Association indicate that more than 23,000 older adults were on waiting lists for admission to a long-term care home, and that the median wait time is 108 days (with more specialized facilities having wait times of several years). Moreover, it has also been found that 52% of these long-term care homes are not compliant with most of the 2009 provincial design standards.(50; 51)

Using the more detailed data available from 2013, when there were fewer (598) long-term care homes than counted in the most recent 2015 data (636), Ontario had 45% of all such facilities in Canada that are available to adults aged 18 and older (but as shown in Table 4.9, residents are almost exclusively 65 years or older).(52) Based on these more detailed data, long-term care homes also vary in size, type of ownership and type of care provided. In terms of size, there are more large (>100 beds) long-term care homes (359, 60%) than small (4-99 beds) homes (239, 40%), which differs from the total numbers across Canada where there are more small long-term care homes (720, 54%) than large ones (614, 46%).(52) Lastly, 344 (58%) of the long-term care homes in Ontario provide type II care, which typically includes people with chronic disease or functional disability who are relatively stabilized, and who require approximately 1.5-2.5 hours of care per day along with medical supervision for psychosocial needs.(52) The remaining 254 (42%) provide type III care or higher, with the former including people who are chronically ill and/or with a functional disability, who may not be in stable condition and who require a minimum of 2.5 hours per day of a broader range of therapeutic services, medical management and nursing care.(52) The available data only cover those receiving type II care or higher.

Those requiring higher levels of care are typically accommodated in the 117 hospital-based continuing care facilities. These facilities provide care to Ontarians (regardless of age) who are in need of complex and specialized services that are not available through home care or long-term care homes (e.g., for those who have long-term illness or disabilities which need skilled and/or technology-based care).(53)

Public health

The 36 local public health agencies' geographic boundaries (which define the public health 'units' that they serve) are not aligned with the boundaries of the LHINs and instead are typically linked to municipal governments. However, the *Patients First Act, 2016* seeks to strengthen relationships between the LHINs and local boards of health even though their boundaries do not fully align.(54) Local public health agencies provide a range of health-promotion and disease-prevention programs, including those that inform the public about healthy lifestyles, provide communicable disease control (e.g., education about sexually transmitted diseases and HIV/AIDS, immunizations, and food inspection), and support healthy growth and development (e.g., parenting education, health education for all age groups, and selected screening services).(55) In addition, 105 local public health agency satellite offices provide targeted services within the areas covered by the local public health agencies (e.g., when front-line services need to be delivered across a large geographical boundary served by the local public health agency). The services delivered are also supported by 11 public health laboratories, which provide clinical (e.g., HIV testing) and environmental testing (e.g., water and food-borne illness testing) related to public health services provided by the province.

Cross-sectoral models

To provide patient-centred care for those with complex health needs (the approximately 5% of the population that accounts for two thirds of healthcare costs), Ontario developed and is currently implementing Health Links. At present 82 Health Links (of approximately 100 planned Health Links) have been implemented, and the model continues to evolve.(56) In general, Health Links aim to support coordinated team-based approaches to care across the sectors outlined above. This includes providing patients with an individualized care plan; having care providers who are responsible for ensuring the plan is followed; providing support to ensure correct medications are taken; and ensuring access to a care provider who knows the patient and their situation to enable them to provide help when needed.(56) Recent data indicate that Health Links have led to a total of 18,926 complex patients having been provided with coordinated care plans, and 29,946 patients having been connected to regular and timely access to primary care.(57)

Infrastructure – Supports for care

Information and communication technology that support those who receive and provide care

The main information and communication technology used to support those who receive care (as distinct from the technology, like EMRs, used primarily by those who provide care, which we turn to below) are Telehealth Ontario (i.e., a teletriage system that assesses a health problem and provides advice, but that does not diagnose or prescribe treatment) and telemedicine (i.e., providing remote clinical services, including diagnosis and prescribing treatment), as well as a small number of newly developed patient portals. Telehealth Ontario provides 24/7 access to a registered nurse who can assess the caller's health problem (but not diagnose it) and provide advice about whether and where the caller should seek care. This advice could include helping a caller decide if they can manage their health problem on their own or should seek medical attention (e.g., by visiting a family physician, going to a primary-care team's clinic, contacting a CCAC or going to a hospital or emergency room).(58)

Telemedicine refers to the use of technology (e.g., videoconferencing) to provide clinical care at a distance in order to improve access to some types of care that are typically not available in rural, northern and remote regions.(59) The Ontario Telemedicine Network was originally designed for such regions, but now is available to meet the needs of all Ontarians and is one of the largest telemedicine networks in the world.(59) The network uses two-way videoconferencing to help address the difficulties faced by hard-to-serve residents from across large rural and northern geographical areas, and to prevent patients from having to travel long distances to be seen by a specialist (which can reduce costs for patients and reduce the carbon footprint associated with providing care in the north).(60) At present, 49% of care provided through the network is for northern Ontario. The network also supports the delivery of several specialized programs in this large geographic area, including the Northern Ontario Francophone Psychiatry Program and Telemedicine Critical Care pilots in Kenora and Thunder Bay, which allow those in critical condition to access life-saving care.(60)

Data from 2013-14 indicate that the network includes sites based in 516 health facilities, 327 community/shared facilities, and 877 clinical centres, as well as 434 virtual (i.e., personal videoconferencing) sites.(61) In that fiscal year these sites delivered:

- 305,269 real-time clinical sessions, which is 74% of the 411,778 total sessions in Canada and a substantial increase (150%) from the 122,029 real-time clinical sessions in 2010;
- 22,371 education sessions (104 education sessions involving patients/ families and 22,267 for healthcare providers), which was a 113% increase from 10,492 education sessions provided in 2010;
- 28,215 administrative meetings (a 125% increase from the 12,518 meetings supported in 2010); and
- 2,176 other sessions, such as legal assessments (a category that was not reported in earlier data).(61; 62)

The government agency eHealth Ontario also reports that more than 38,000 consultations for neurotrauma are made remotely each year as a result of stroke patients having 24/7 access to a neurological specialist.(63)

Complementing the Ontario Telemedicine Network, 10 of the 14 LHINs provide telehomecare services (i.e., remote patient monitoring) as part of efforts to reduce emergency room visits and hospital stays.(64) As of 2015, 5,800 patients had enrolled in telehomecare services over a two-year period. The Ontario Telemedicine Network conducted a survey of patient experience with telehomecare services and found positive findings, including 98% being generally satisfied with their care, 99% being satisfied with the quality of the healthcare, teaching and coaching they received, 86% indicating less need to visit an emergency department, and 79% indicating less need to visit a primary-care provider.(64)

While these are established resources in the province, the 2014 National Physician Survey revealed that only 24% of physicians in Ontario indicated that they have used telemedicine in their practice (e.g., to identify when patients have sought advice and then to follow up with them).(65) For those who have used these resources, 32% indicated using them 'live' to follow up with patients, and 22% indicated using them 'live' for patient treatment.(65)

There are now also some examples of patient health records and patient portals that allow patients to access and manage their health information. As an example of the former, MyOSCAR provides an online version of a patient's health record that is 'owned' by them and can only be accessed by the patient and those to whom they grant permission (as opposed to a patient portal that allows patients to view the portions of their health information that are made available to them by others).(66) MyOSCAR allows patients to control the addition or modification of data and to change who can view or change their record. Also, the system provides users with access to health-management tools to help with tracking information, identifying trends in health indicators (e.g., blood sugar), and monitoring potential side-effects of medications.

As an example of a patient portal, Sunnybrook Health Sciences Centre in Toronto has implemented MyChart, which allows patients to use a secure website (www.mychart.ca, which employs the same type of encryption as the major banks in Canada) to view the portions of their health information that are made available to them.(67) Access to MyChart is provided to patients at participating hospitals, and access can also be granted to caregivers, clinicians in other hospitals, primary-care providers, CCACs, pharmacists, and other providers. The key features of MyChart include:

- access to clinical information from Sunnybrook's electronic patient record system (e.g., medical imaging, laboratory results and progress notes);
- ability to self-enter or upload personal health information;
- access to appointment information, ability to make appointment requests, and opportunity to receive appointment reminders;
- access to Psychiatry Release of Information module;
- access to communications (e.g., announcements, patient information and surveys); and
- access to customizable tools and resources (e.g., mood tracker, weight tracker, and blood pressure measurement).(67)

While MyChart is likely the most widely used patient portal in the province currently, some primary-care teams such as Group Health Centre in Sault Ste. Marie – using myCare (68) – and Wise Elephant Family Health Team – using miDash (69) – also give their patients online access to their personal health information as well as the opportunity to manage their appointments online. In addition, LifeLabs provides a patient portal called *my results*, which allows patients in Ontario (as well as in B.C.) to access their laboratory results online.(70) However, patient portals such as these and MyChart typically do not provide patients with access to the best available research evidence about how to manage their disease or condition.

Instead, patients (and their families and informal caregivers) can seek out this type of information from resources such as the McMaster Optimal Aging Portal (www.mcmasteroptimalaging.org).

The availability of these types of consumer-oriented digital health technologies that aim to improve the patient experience is likely to grow given strong demand from patients and their families. For example, consultations conducted by Canada Health Infoway about how such technology could be harnessed going forward included several consumer-focused technologies in the top-five priorities, including mobile patient monitoring, online access to personal health information, e-visits, and e-scheduling.(71)

While many of these resources also help those who provide care, the main information and technology support for providers is electronic medical record (EMR) systems, for which eHealth Ontario is responsible for supporting implementation (and reporting on implementation progress). An EMR refers to a computer-based medical record that is specific to and maintained by clinicians or the practice or organization in which they work (as opposed to interoperable electronic health record systems that integrate all medical information about a patient from all clinicians, practices and organizations in a system).(72) EMRs also typically include order sets (i.e., checklists or decision support for what tests to order or services to provide to specific patients based on information in their EMR), but there is no statutory requirement that they be based on the best available research evidence.(73)

The most recent (2014) National Physician Survey found that Ontario has the third highest percentage of EMR adoption by physicians in Canada (83%) as compared to Alberta (87%) and B.C. (85%).(74) The percentage of family physicians (86%) who either use a mix of paper charts and EMRs or exclusively use EMRs is slightly higher than specialists (81%) (Table 4.10).(65) These levels of EMR adoption in Ontario are substantially higher than those reported in the 2010 National Physician Survey, which found that 58% of family physicians and 55% of specialists were using EMRs (either exclusively or in combination with paper charts).(75) Moreover, eHealth Ontario reports that 75% of Ontarians receive care from physicians who use an EMR, 3,000 types of laboratory results can be accessed through physicians' EMRs, the medication history of all seniors in Ontario is accessible to providers in all hospitals and

Table 4.10: Electronic medical record use as reported in the 2010 and 2014 National Physician Surveys

Indicators	All physicians		Family physicians		Specialists	
	2010	2014	2010	2014	2010	2014
Mechanism used to capture patient-related information[1]						
Paper chart only	32%	17%	33%	14%	31%	19%
Paper chart and electronic medical record (EMR)	37%	48%	29%	34%	44%	62%
EMR only	20%	35%	29%	52%	11%	19%
Duration of EMR use in practice						
<1 year	—	8%	—	7%	—	8%
1-2 years	—	14%	—	14%	—	13%
3-4 years	—	22%	—	23%	—	21%
5-6 years	—	14%	—	16%	—	13%
> 6 years	—	42%	—	39%	—	44%
Not reported	—	<1%	—	1%	—	1%
Plans to use EMRs in next two years among those currently using paper records[2]						
Yes	11%	27%	12%	32%	10%	22%
No	—	72%	—	67%	—	76%
Not reported	—	1%	—	1%	—	2%
Perceived access to EMRs						
Excellent	—	13%	—	16%	—	10%
Satisfactory	—	44%	—	42%	—	46%
Unsatisfactory	—	20%	—	18%	—	22%
Not available in jurisdiction	—	21%	—	22%	—	20%
Not reported	—	2%	—	2%	—	2%
Access points for EMRs						
Office/community clinic/Community Health Centre	54%	64%	72%	84%	38%	44%
Hospital	60%	59%	46%	38%	73%	80%
University/research unit	10%	6.3%	5%	3%	14%	9%
Long-term care home	4%	4.6%	8%	8%	1%	1%
Outside of a healthcare setting	—	41%	—	51%	—	32%
Other	14%	1%	20%	0.4%	9%	1%
Connection of records used across different settings of practice						
Yes	28%	79%	26%	81%	30%	76%
Some	24%	14%	23%	11%	24%	18%
None	19%	7%	23%	7%	15%	6%
Not reported	30%	<1%	28%	1%	31%	<1%
Use of EMRs to manage chronic conditions[3]	37%	81%	—	87%	—	68%

Sources: 65; 75

Notes:

[1] The results from the 2010 survey for this question provided the percentage of respondents who selected 'not applicable – I do not provide patient care' (2.6% of family physicians and 4.9% of specialists) and for whom data were not reported (6.6% of family physicians and 9% of specialists), but these categories were not provided in the 2014 survey.

[2] The question about plans to use EMRs was different in the 2010 survey from that in 2014, with the former not phrasing it as a discrete 'yes' or 'no' question as in 2014, but as one option that could be selected among a much longer list of electronic resources respondents planned to use.

[3] Data for this question on the 2010 survey are only available for all physicians and are not separated by family physicians and specialists.

emergency rooms, and all hospital sites in the province can digitally share diagnostic images and reports within their region.(63)

Key additional findings for Ontario from the most recent National Physician Survey (Table 4.10) include:
- two-thirds (67%) of family physicians and three quarters (76%) of specialists who indicated not using EMRs in 2014 also indicated that they do not intend to use EMRs in the next two years;
- more than half of physicians rated their perceived access to EMRs as excellent (16% of family physicians and 10% of specialists) or satisfactory (42% of family physicians and 46% of specialists);
- the percentage of physicians accessing EMRs in different settings (e.g., in offices, clinics, Community Health Centres, hospitals, university/research units, and long-term care homes) has been relatively constant since 2010 (but 41% of physicians now indicate that they access EMRs outside of a healthcare setting, which was not included in the 2010 data);
- substantially higher numbers of physicians reported that EMRs are connected across the different settings in which they work; and
- many more physicians reported using EMRs to manage patients' chronic conditions (81% of all physicians in 2014 as compared to 37% in 2010).(65; 75)

However, when compared internationally, Ontario's performance in EMR use is mixed. Specifically, results from the Commonwealth Fund 2015 International Health Policy Survey of Primary Care Physicians indicate that EMR use in Ontario has tripled in the past decade, however:
- the adoption of EMRs is below the 88% average among the countries that were included in the survey (Australia, Germany, Netherlands, New Zealand, Norway, Sweden, Switzerland, U.K., and U.S.);
- the use of EMR functionality is in some cases above average (e.g., for using at least functions related to population-health management), in others average (e.g., using at least two decision-support functions), and in still others below average (e.g., using at least two patient-management functions); and
- the use of EMRs for patient communication is low, with 12% of practices using EMRs for appointment or referral requests (compared to 11% nationally), 10% of practices using them for prescription-refill requests (compared to 7% nationally), and 13% allowing for test re-

sults to be viewed securely online (compared to 18% nationally).(76)

Among the 78% of physicians in Ontario reporting barriers to accessing EMRs in the 2014 National Physician Survey, the identified barriers included:
- technical difficulty/reliability (52%);
- compatibility with other electronic systems (46%);
- firewalls or security issues (25%);
- hardware availability (16%);
- lack of training (16%); and
- privacy (14%).(65)

Other examples of EMR expansion in Ontario include:
- the implementation of more than 5,100 ambulatory EMR seats (i.e., access points in hospital ambulatory settings that may be used by multiple health professionals) in 36 hospitals;
- enhanced connectedness of EMRs between sites with more than 5,000 community-based clinicians having access to hospital reports (e.g., discharge summaries) through their EMRs (which are sent through the Hospital Report Manager); and
- ongoing implementation of the Ontario Laboratory Information System, which currently houses 86% of laboratory results in the province, and is accessible to more than 9,000 community-based health professionals and more than 26,000 hospital-based health professionals.(64; 73)

Turning now to electronic health records (EHRs), meaning health record systems that integrate all medical information about a patient from all clinicians, practices and organizations, eHealth Ontario reports that more than 77,000 health professionals can now access EHRs, and that more than 1,970 health organizations are connected to the provincial EHR.(63) At the national level, Canada Health Infoway reports that approximately 139,000 health professionals (as of 2015) are active users of EHR systems, which they defined as regular consultation of two or more electronic systems (e.g., laboratory or drug information systems and diagnostic imaging repositories).(64) This suggests that Ontario is home to more than half of the health professional users of EHRs in Canada.

In addition to EMRs and EHRs, the Panorama public health surveillance system is being implemented in Canada to digitally track immunizations, to manage vaccine inventories, and, in some cases, to monitor communicable disease outbreaks.(64) At present, all of Ontario's 36 local public health agencies are using Panorama to track immunizations, and the agencies that need to track vaccine supply are using the inventory module.(64)

Research infrastructure that supports clinical practice and health-system policymaking

As described in a recent evidence brief published by the McMaster Health Forum, Ontario shares with other provinces and countries the challenge of consistently improving care based on data, evidence and guidelines.(77) However, Ontario is among a relatively small number of jurisdictions globally that hosts a high number of centres of expertise and small-to-medium-scale initiatives that can support rigorously informed improvements to care. To illustrate this richness, we identified examples of centres and initiatives that are active in Ontario (Table 4.11, which is adapted from the evidence brief), many of which are widely seen as global leaders. While we have assigned each centre or initiative a single area of focus, several of them are active across multiple areas of focus (as we note in parentheses in the table, where applicable). In addition to these examples, efforts to support high-quality and safe clinical practice are supplemented by the efforts of a national accreditation agency (Accreditation Canada), more focused accreditation initiatives (e.g., through the Canadian Association of Radiologists), and a national safety agency (Canadian Patient Safety Institute). Such resources are important given the many challenges that professionals and policymakers face when trying to find and use unbiased, understandable and current knowledge about health and healthcare.(78)

Many of the initiatives and some of the centres that are highlighted as examples in Table 4.11 are particularly noteworthy for how they are:
1) organized as research projects (not as institutionalized programs within the health system);
2) funded on a one-off, time-limited basis by research-funding agencies or government (not as sustainable enterprises); and
3) geographically restricted (not system-wide endeavours and not positioned with a view to exporting the approach to other health systems, as the National Institute for Health and Care Excellence (NICE) has so successfully done with NICE International).

Table 4.11: Examples of centres and initiatives that support improvements to the care provided to Ontarians using data, evidence and guidelines

Ontario and Canadian centres and initiatives that support Ontario (and their principal contributions)

Data analytics

- Institute for Clinical Evaluative Sciences (performance, capacity and other types of data, which are available through atlases/reports and customizable data and analytical service requests)
- Canadian Institute for Health Information (performance, capacity and other types of data, which are available through reports, interactive online databases like Your Health System, and customizable data and analytical service requests)
- Statistics Canada (statistics about the health of the population, lifestyle and environmental factors affecting health, access to and use of healthcare services, and analyses about health-related topics)

Evidence synthesis (best evidence on specific topics)

- Cochrane Canada (production of, and capacity building for, systematic reviews of effects, with five of six review groups, including the one focused on optimizing practice, and all four of the methods groups, based in Ontario)

Evidence 'refineries' (best evidence across a broad range of topics)

- McMaster Optimal Aging Portal (database and customizable evidence service with evidence, website reviews and blogs targeted primarily to citizens, but also to clinicians, public health practitioners and policymakers)
- ACCESSSS (database and customizable evidence service for pre-appraised studies and reviews about clinical care)
- Tools for Practice (bi-weekly summary of evidence that can change primary-care practice)
- Health Evidence (database and customizable evidence service for pre-appraised reviews of effects about public health)
- Health Systems Evidence (database and customizable evidence service for pre-appraised reviews, as well as overviews of reviews, economic evaluations, and other types of evidence, about health-system arrangements and implementation strategies)

Guideline methods development

- AGREE II (tool to assess the quality and reporting of practice guidelines, the development of which was led by Ontario-based researchers)
- GRADE (tool to assess the quality of evidence and the strength of recommendations, the development of which was led in part by Ontario-based researchers and a co-chair who is an Ontario-based researcher)
- Guideline Implementability for Decision Excellence Model – GUIDE-M (tool to create optimally implementable guidelines and to support the better use of guidelines)

Guideline production

- MacGRADE Centre (methodological support for the use of GRADE to assess the quality of evidence and strength of recommendations in guidelines, as well as for the preparation of many World Health Organization and professional association guidelines)
- Registered Nurses' Association of Ontario's Best Practice Guidelines (clinical and healthy work place environment guidelines, as well as related order sets, quality indicators (through its NQuIRE program), implementation resources, and Best Practice Spotlight Organization designations)
- Cancer Care Ontario's Program in Evidence-Based Care (production of clinical practice guidelines on the full spectrum of cancer care)
- Canadian Agency for Drugs and Technologies in Health (evidence and guidelines about drugs and technologies)
- Canadian Task Force on Preventive Health Care (clinical practice guidelines that support primary-care providers in delivering preventive healthcare)

Continued on next page

Evidence and guideline implementation

- Centre for Effective Practice (guideline quality ratings, tool development, continuing professional development, and guideline implementation supports)
- Centre for Practice-Changing Research at the Ottawa Hospital Research Institute (evidence and guideline implementation supports, as well as patient decision aids and rapid reviews)
- National Collaborating Centre for Methods and Tools (supports for optimizing practice in public health)
- Initiatives such as Knowledge Translation Canada's consultation service (evidence and guideline implementation supports)

Quality improvement

- Health Quality Ontario (supporting continuous quality improvement, as well as public reporting about clinical practice, among other topics, and making – with the support of the Ontario Health Technology Advisory Committee – evidence-based recommendations about standards of care and funding of technologies)
- Initiatives such as:
  - Adopting Research to Improve Care - ARTIC (evidence and guideline implementation supports through projects in Ontario academic hospitals)
  - Building Bridges to Integrate Care – BRIDGE (supports for the evaluation of care-integration models in the greater Toronto area)
  - Improving and Driving Excellence Across Sectors - IDEAS (capacity building for quality improvement, leadership and change management)

Continuing professional development

- Ontario's faculties of health sciences and health professions offer a broad range of continuing professional development opportunities that can support practice optimization (although these opportunities can vary dramatically in the extent to which they are based on data, evidence and guidelines)
- McMaster Health Forum's Health Systems Learning, which is an educational program designed to provide online and in-person training about how to reform, renew or strengthen health systems, and how to get cost-effective programs, services and drugs to those who need them.

Source: Adapted from: 77

In addition to these initiatives, there are 16 provincial and five national hosts of publicly reported performance indicators for the health system (Table 4.12). Performance indicators can be used to support patient choice about where to obtain care (e.g., based on the shortest wait time or the highest quality), to provide the basis for establishing 'external accountability' for the performance of providers and the system as a whole, to inform internal quality-improvement processes, and to conduct research. The second of these four purposes appears to dominate in Ontario. Indeed, a patient (or their family or informal caregiver) would be exceptionally hard pressed to find and make sense of this crowded landscape.

Table 4.12: Sources for public reporting about the health system

Host	Statement of purpose	Type of indicator(s) provided
Government		
Ontario Ministry of Health Long-Term Care	"To help improve your access to care, this site provides the best available data on wait times for hospitals all across Ontario" (124) "The reports on LTC [long-term care] homes will help you find LTC homes within a desired area and see general information about the home…. You can also view ministry inspection reports and see if any orders have been issued to a particular home"	• Home care wait times • Emergency room wait times • Surgery, magnetic resonance imaging and computed tomography wait times • Long-term care home incident reports
Government agency[1]		
Cancer Care Ontario	"The Cancer System Quality Index tracks Ontario's progress against cancer and points out where cancer service providers can make quality and performance improvements" (125) "As the provincial agency that steers and coordinates cancer services and prevention efforts in Ontario, one of Cancer Care Ontario's priorities is to improve access and wait times for cancer care" (126)	• Quality and performance improvement (Cancer System Quality Index) • Wait times
Health Quality Ontario	"Transparent data drives accountability and improvement. That's why Health Quality Ontario has been monitoring and reporting on the province's health system performance since 2006" (127)	• Home care sector performance • Primary care sector performance • Hospital care sector performance • Long-term care sector performance
Local Health Integration Networks (LHINs)	"Provides an update on the milestones, achievements and progress of… LHIN initiatives" (128)	• Access to healthcare services • Integration and coordination of care • Quality and improved health outcomes
Ontario Renal Network (a division of Cancer Care Ontario)	"Responsible for establishing consistent standards and guidelines to support quality kidney care, and putting in place information systems to measure performance" (129)	• Ontario Renal Reporting System collects data on all re-dialysis, acute dialysis and chronic dialysis patients in Ontario
Public Health Ontario (PHO)	"Our Annual Reports reflect PHO's core activities and progress on key commitments including: our performance scorecard and targets, laboratory performance standards, financial statements and Board of Directors appointees" (130)	• Progress on priority initiatives by strategic direction

Continued on next page

Host	Statement of purpose	Type of indicator(s) provided
Government-funded organization		
BORN Ontario: Better Outcomes Registry & Network	"Collect, interpret, share and rigorously protect critical data about pregnancy, birth and childhood" (131)	• Pregnancy, maternal and child health outcomes
Cancer Quality Council of Ontario	"Provide an overall assessment for each dimension of quality in an effort to track Ontario's progress towards better outcomes in cancer care and highlight where cancer service providers can advance the quality and performance of care" (132)	• Cancer System Quality Index • Wait times
Cardiac Care Network of Ontario	"Using data and consensus-driven methods, we offer planning advice for the future of cardiac services and the provision of exemplary care in collaboration with the Ministry and others" (133)	• Cardiac procedure volumes by hospital • Patient characteristics • Cardiac wait times • Treatment of ST elevation of myocardial infarction by hospital • Market share analysis by LHIN
Institute for Clinical Evaluative Sciences (ICES)	"ICES researchers access a vast and secure array of Ontario's health-related data, including population-based health surveys, anonymous patient records, as well as clinical and administrative databases" (134)	• Health system performance • Drug safety and effectiveness • Primary care • Surgery and transplantation • Population health • Mental health and addictions • Chronic diseases
Provincial Council for Maternal and Child Health	"The 2015 Report represents the key initial step of an extensive redesign process motivated by our commitment to on-going quality improvement in providing relevant information to the maternal and child healthcare community" (135)	• Hospital profiles • Hospital level indicators • LHIN-level indicators
Association initiative		
Association of Family Health Teams of Ontario	"Supporting, measuring, and promoting the value of well-integrated interprofessional primary care, and advocating for its expansion so that more Ontarians can access this high-quality comprehensive care" (136)	• Family Health Team performance

Continued on next page

Host	Statement of purpose	Type of indicator(s) provided
Association initiative – continued		
Children's Mental Health Ontario	"The Report Card highlights the government's progress toward key policy commitments and identifies critical areas where we must work together to make important improvements" (137)	• Mental healthcare for children and youth (e.g., wait times, coordination of treatment, emergency department visits, and hospitalizations)
Ontario Association of Community Care Access Centres	"To promote continuous improvement and share learning, CCACs [Community Care Access Centres] measure key metrics and issue annual quality reports" (138)	• Home and community care (e.g., expenditures) • Wait times (e.g., long-term care home placement) • Complex health needs
Ontario Hospital Association (OHA)	"The OHA is committed to providing members with current Human Resources (HR) metrics to support and inform leaders and managers in Ontario hospitals" (139) "To promote transparency and the advancement of integration through eHealth, the OHA makes available a searchable online registry of the clinical and administrative applications in use by Ontario's hospitals" (140)	• Health human resources • eHealth Applications Registry • Green Hospital Scorecard
Ontario Long Term Care Association	"We strive to lead the sector in innovation, quality care and services, building excellence in long-term care through leadership, analysis, advocacy and member services" (141)	• Long-term care (e.g., number of homes, wait times, staffing, and health conditions of residents)
Federal or national body[1]		
Statistics Canada (federal government)	"Information on the health of the population, lifestyle and environmental factors affecting health, access to and use of health care services, and research into health topics" (142)	• Population health • Disability • Disease and health conditions • Life expectancy and death • Lifestyle and environmental factors affecting health • Mental health and well-being • Pregnancy and births • Healthcare services • Prevention and detection of disease
Canada Health Infoway (federal government)	"Infoway, the provinces and territories, and our other partners have worked together to deploy core systems such as registries of patients and providers; drug, lab and diagnostic imaging systems; and clinical reports and immunizations" (143)	• Use of digital health resources (electronic health records and electronic medical records)

Continued on next page

Host	Statement of purpose	Type of indicator(s) provided
Canadian Institute for Health Information (CIHI) (federal and provincial goverment-funded organization)	CIHI site: "Deliver comparable and actionable information to accelerate improvements in health care, health system performance and population health across the continuum of care" (144) 'Your Health System' site: "Explore indicators to better understand your health system and the health of Canadians. Search by hospital, long-term care organization, city, health region, province or territory" (144)	• Health statistics (e.g., health system perfor- mance, population health and health services)
Canadian Partnership Against Can- cer (federal government organization)	"The Partnership engages in collaborative efforts with pro- vincial and national partners to identify aspects of the cancer control system that need to be measured, define performance indicators, collect valid and comparable data and report findings" (145)	• CAREX Canada – a multi-institution research project – provides nation- al surveillance on occupa- tional and environment carcinogen exposure • Cancer system perfor- mance (prevention, screen- ing, diagnosis, treatment, patient experience and end-of-life care, research and long-term outcomes)
Canadian Medical Association (CMA) (association initiative)	"The CMA's Physician Data Centre conducts research that promotes the appropriate supply, mix and distribution of physicians to meet Canada's needs" (146)	• Canadian physician data (e.g., demographics and supply, migration, train- ing, physician-to-popula- tion ratios, workload, and remuneration)

Note:
[1] Other sources that could be considered as being engaged in public reporting include eHealth Ontario (a government agency that sup- ports the implementation of and reporting about the use of electronic medical records) and the Canadian Mental Health Association (a national organization that provides information about mental health services and the mental health workforce).

Two other mechanisms for public reporting are the Quality Improvement Plan that must be submitted annually to Health Quality Ontario (HQO) by four types of health organizations (CCACs, interprofessional team-based primary-care organizations, hospitals, and long-term care homes), (79) and the long-term care home inspection reports that must be completed annu- ally and that are posted on the Ministry of Health and Long-Term Care website.(80) Regarding the former, each plan describes how an organiza- tion will address quality issues and meet quality-improvement goals. Based on analyses of these plans, HQO creates and makes publicly available sec- tor-specific reports.(81) On a related point, eight partners (Ministry of Health and Long-Term Care, LHINs, Cancer Care Ontario, HQO, Public Health Ontario, Cardiac Care Network, Canadian Institute for Health Information, and Institute for Clinical Evaluative Sciences) are engaging in an effort to advance timely practice-level reporting and to explore new models to incentivize quality and timely care.(82)

There are also 21 universities, 17 hospitals, seven non-governmental organizations, two professional associations and five government agencies in Ontario that are eligible to conduct health-related research with funding from the Canadian Institutes of Health Research. Also, nine of the 26 Statistics Canada's Research Data Centres are hosted in Ontario. These are funded by the Canadian Research Data Centre Network, the Social Sciences and Humanities Research Council, Canadian Institutes of Health Research, the Canadian Foundation for Innovation, and Statistics Canada. Other sources for data and analyses that are often called upon include: 1) consulting firms hired to conduct analyses to support planning and/or policy or organizational decisions; 2) expert advisory groups that are periodically convened to address priorities, with recent examples of such groups focusing on home care and primary-care reform;(3; 83) and 3) hospital-based research institutes (although these often focus on investigator-driven research that advance scientific knowledge, and they may or may not directly inform organizational or policy priorities).

In addition to funding from the Canadian Institutes of Health Research, the Ministry of Health and Long-Term Care provides stable long-term funding to two specialized research centres (Institute for Clinical Evaluative Sciences, and Women's College Hospital: Women's Xchange), and has historically provided funding to support health-related research in Ontario. Most recently, the Ministry of Health and Long-Term Care provided program awards to 11 research groups from 2012-15, as well as 11 shorter and focused capacity awards to another 11 research groups through its Health System Research Fund. However, the funding through this program has been temporarily paused.

Capacity planning

Capacity planning generally refers to processes that are used for determining what infrastructure is needed in the future.(84) Central to this is examining the extent to which existing health-system infrastructure (and the resources invested in using it) is able to meet policy or organizational objectives, as well as determining whether the existing levels of capacity are sustainable given available resources.(85) This could include assessing the impacts of changes in policies, demographics and budgeted resources on available health-system capacity.(85) Also, the focus of capacity planning varies depending on who and for what purpose it is being conducted. For example, capacity planning for hospitals would focus on planning for investments needed in facilities, technology (e.g., MRI scanners), and service delivery, as well as for human and financial resources. In contrast, capacity planning in the home and community care sector would focus on what is needed across a range of different access points (e.g., home care, community service agencies).

At present, capacity planning for select types of infrastructure is carried out by the Ministry of Health and Long-Term Care (e.g., for health workforce planning),(86) LHINs (e.g., for hospitals and long-term care homes), and Cancer Care Ontario (for regional cancer centres).(84) However, with the LHINs not having responsibility for planning across all sectors, they are not able to support an integrated planning approach across the health system.(87) This leaves many parts of the system with no formal approach to capacity planning, and various (often uncoordinated) capacity-planning activities carried out by a range of stakeholders in the system. For example, system-wide capacity planning has been conducted for ophthalmology services, with one of the resulting recommendations being that ophthalmology-service providers should engage in central purchasing to reduce costs.(88) Moreover, agencies (e.g., eHealth Ontario) (89) and associations of organizations (e.g., Home Care Ontario),(90) as well as intergovernmental agencies (e.g., Canadian Agency for Drugs and Technologies in Health and Canada Health Infoway) are often involved in sector-based capacity-planning activities.(91) These efforts are also supported by groups that provide data analytics such as the Institute of Clinical Evaluative Sciences and the Canadian Institute for Health Information.

Capital spending

Capital spending generally refers to processes used to make investments to develop needed infrastructure. Expenditures on capital can range in size (from thousands of dollars to hundreds of millions of dollars), as well as in the complexity of instruments used to support capital investments (e.g., from debt-based investments for a single facility to investments in multiple institutions that involve public and private partners over long periods of time and across locations and financing structures).(92) In contrast to the funds that are used to operate health-system infrastructure such as hospitals, which draw almost exclusively on government resources, capital spending can come from a mix of government sources (e.g., budget allocations specifically for infrastructure funds), as well as from donations from individuals (e.g., through donations from a philanthropist or community fundraising initiatives), foundations (e.g., hospital foundations and government-sponsored foundations such as the Canadian Foundation for Innovation) or corporations.(92)

While capital spending comes from a range of sources, public finances accounted for 76% of capital spending in 2013, with the rest accounted for by private sources.(92-99) However, there has been a substantial decrease in capital spending in recent years in Ontario (Table 4.13), with a 22% decrease in total spending from 2010 to 2013, which was mostly accounted for by a 27% decrease in public financing. These decreases are much larger than the 13% decrease in capital spending across Canada, which were accounted for by a 7% decrease in public financing and 33% decrease in private sources.

Table 4.13: Total public and private health-system capital expenditures in Ontario and Canada, 2010 and 2013

Capital expenditures	Ontario			Canada		
	2010 ($ millions)	2013 ($ millions)	% change	2010 ($ millions)	2013 ($ millions)	% change
Total capital expenditure	$4,195	$3,269	-22%	$10,101	$8,828	-13%
Public capital expenditure (% of total capital expenditure)	$3,407 (81%)	$2,477 (76%)	-27%	$8,044 (80%)	$7,446 (84%)	-7%
Private capital expenditure (% of total capital expenditure)	$788 (19%)	$791 (24%)	<1%	$2,057 (20%)	$1,383 (16%)	-33%

Source: 93-99

Capital spending appears to be continuing to decline in Ontario. The total estimated publicly-financed capital expenses for health-system infrastructure in Ontario in the 2016-17 fiscal year is $1.45 billion (Table 4.14), the majority (87%) of which is allocated to hospitals through major hospital projects ($1.1 billion, 75%) and the Health Infrastructure Renewal Fund ($175 million, 12%).(100) The Health Infrastructure Renewal Fund is a source of capital for hospitals that supplements existing capital funds to address additional priorities. Under the Health Infrastructure Renewal Fund, each LHIN is allocated a portion of the fund using an activity-based distribution formula that has a minimum allocation per hospital site. There is also $20 million allocated to a Small and Rural Hospital Transformation Fund.(101) The third largest health-system capital expense is for community-health infrastructure ($81 million, 6%). These funds are designed to support the ongoing shift of care from hospitals to community settings, which include Community Health Centres, Aboriginal Health Access Centres, and community-based mental health and addictions agencies.(102) The province has also indicated that an additional Community Infrastructure Renewal Fund will be created, which would be directed to other community organizations such as Family Health Teams, Nurse Practitioner-led Clinics, and local public health agencies.(102)

Table 4.14: Estimated public capital expenses in the health system, 2016-17

Item	Amount	Percent of all capital expenses
Major hospital projects	$1,084,805,000	75%
Health Infrastructure Renewal Fund	$175,000,000	12%
Community health programs	$80,865,500	6%
Small hospital projects	$40,000,000	3%
Medical and Diagnostic Equipment Fund	$34,500,000	2%
Public health laboratories	$17,260,800	1%
Provincial psychiatric hospitals divestment	$10,000,000	0.7%
Long-term care programs	$4,812,000	0.3%
Facilities Condition Assessment Program	$2,287,100	0.2%
Integrated health facility programs	$1,317,400	0.1%
Total	$1,450,847,800	100%

Source: 100

Conclusion

The health system's infrastructure includes both the places where care is delivered and the supports for that care. Providing a full picture of the available infrastructure requires not only using data to quantify the amount of infrastructure available (i.e., the capacity available), but also measuring the extent to which capacity in different parts of the system is being used. In developing this picture of infrastructure in the province, we have found that the places of care that tend to be tracked with the most detail (in terms of both the capacity available and its use) are where most government-provided capital is invested in the system (hospitals and to a much lesser extent, community care) and where 'beds' are available (i.e., hospitals and long-term care). In contrast, data regarding the availability and use of supports for care are detailed on some topics (e.g., for telemedicine and EMRs), but in others are reliant on unconfirmed reports by small samples of physicians who may or may not be broadly representative (e.g., for EMRs in the National Physician Survey). In terms of conducting capacity planning to determine what infrastructure is needed in the future, there are formal processes for some of the most capital-intensive parts of health-system infrastructure (e.g., hospitals and regional cancer centres that operate within hospitals). However, many other parts of the system have no formal approach to capacity planning or have some form of capacity planning that is not part of an integrated approach across a region or the system. Perhaps as a result of, or a reason for this, the vast majority of capital expenses for health-system infrastructure in Ontario is directed to hospitals. That said, recent capital investments have been directed to the community sector, which aligns with the shift from having many services traditionally provided in capital-intensive hospitals now being provided in community settings.

References

1. Home Care Ontario. Facts & figures. Publicly funded home care. Toronto: Home Care Ontario; 2016. http://www.homecareontario.ca/home-care-services/facts-figures/publiclyfundedhomecare (accessed 24 August 2016).

2. Legislative Assembly of Ontario. Bill 41, Patients First Act, 2016. Toronto: Queen's Printer for Ontario; 2016. http://www.ontla.on.ca/web/bills/bills_detail.do?locale=en&Intranet=&BillID=4215 (accessed 7 October 2016).

3. Ministry of Health and Long-Term Care. Bringing care home. Report of the Expert Group on Home and Community Care. Toronto Queen's Printer for Ontario; 2015.

4. ConnexOntario. Number of distinct programs in the ConnexOntario database funded by the Ministry of Health and Long-Term Care - Community Mental Health and Addictions Branch by type of program and Local Health Integration Network (LHIN). Toronto: ConnexOntario; 2015.

5. Government of Ontario. Diabetes education program. Toronto: Queen's Printer for Ontario; 2015. https://www.ontario.ca/page/diabetes-education-program (accessed 24 August 2016).

6. HealthForceOntario. Family practice models. Toronto: Queen's Printer for Ontario; 2013. http://www.healthforceontario.ca/en/Home/Physicians/Training_%7C_Practising_in_Ontario/Physician_Roles/Family_Practice_Models (accessed 24 August 2016).

7. Glazier RH, Hutchison B, Kopp A. Comparison of Family Health Teams to other Ontario primary care models, 2004/05 to 2011/12. Toronto: Institute for Clinical Evaluative Sciences; 2015.

8. Association of Ontario Health Centres. Aboriginal Health Access Centres. Toronto: Association of Ontario Health Centres; 2016. https://www.aohc.org/aboriginal-health-access-centres (accessed 24 August 2016).

9. Health Quality Ontario. Measuring up: HQO's 2015 yearly report. Toronto: Queen's Printer for Ontario; 2015. http://www.hqontario.ca/portals/0/Documents/pr/measuring-up-2015-en.pdf (accessed 24 August 2016).

10. Government of Ontario. Pharmacies. Toronto: Queen's Printer for Ontario; 2015. https://www.ontario.ca/page/pharmacies (accessed 24 August 2016).

11. Ontario College of Pharmacists. 2015 annual report. Toronto: Ontario College of Pharmacists; 2016.

12. IBIS World. Pharmacies and drugstores in Canada: Major companies. http://clients1.ibisworld.ca/reports/ca/industry/majorcompanies.aspx?entid=1054 - MP9164 (accessed 14 October 2016).

13. Ministry of Government and Consumer Services. Collaborative procurement in Ontario. Toronto: Queen's Printer for Ontario; 2016. https://www.doingbusiness.mgs.gov.on.ca/mbs/psb/psb.nsf/EN/map-collaborative-procurement (accessed 14 October 2016).

14. Ministry of Health and Long-Term Care. Public Hospitals Act / Loi sur les hôpitaux publics. Toronto: Queen's Printer for Ontario; 2015. http://www.health.gov.on.ca/en/common/system/services/hosp/hospcode.aspx (accessed 25 August 2016).

15. CIHI. OECD interactive tool: International comparisons, peer countries. Ottawa: Canadian Institute for Health Information; 2012. https://www.cihi.ca/en/health-system-performance/performance-reporting/international/oecd-interactive-tool-peer-countries-on (accessed 24 August 2016).

16. Ministry of Health and Long-Term Care. Hospitals. Toronto: Queen's Printer for Ontario; 2014. http://www.health.gov.on.ca/en/common/system/services/hosp/faq.aspx (accessed 25 August 2016).

17. Ministry of Health and Long-Term Care. Emergency health services branch. Toronto: Queen's Printer for Ontario; 2012. http://www.health.gov.on.ca/english/public/program/ehs/ehs_dt.html (accessed 25 August 2016).

18. Ornge. Operations control centre. Mississauga: Ornge; 2012. http://www.ornge.ca/Programs/Pages/OperationsControlCentre.aspx (accessed 24 August 2016).

19. Ornge. Air operations. Mississauga: Ornge; 2012. http://www.ornge.ca/Programs/Pages/AirOperations.aspx (accessed 24 August 2016).

20. Ornge. Critical care land program. Mississauga: Ornge; 2012. http://www.ornge.ca/PROGRAMS/Pages/CriticalCareLandProgram.aspx (accessed 24 August 2016).

21. CIHI. NACRS emergency department visits and length of stay by province/territory, 2014-2015. Table 5: Number of ED visits and length of stay (LOS) in ED by age group, participating provinces/territories, NACRS, 2014–2015 Ottawa: Canadian Institute for Health Information; 2015.

22. Cancer Care Ontario. Regional cancer program and regional cancer centre locations. Toronto: Cancer Care Ontario; 2015. https://www.cancercare.on.ca/pcs/treatment/rcchospitals/ (accessed 24 August 2016).

23. Cancer Care Ontario. Regional cancer programs. Toronto: Cancer Care Ontario; 2015. https://www.cancercare.on.ca/ocs/rcp/ (accessed 24 August 2016).

24. Ministry of Health and Long-Term Care. Designated psychiatric facilities under the Mental Health Act. Toronto: Queen's Printer for Ontario; 2015. http://www.health.gov.on.ca/en/common/system/services/psych/designated.aspx - six (accessed 25 August 2016).

25. Ministry of Health and Long-Term Care. Independent Health Facilities fact sheet. Toronto: Queen's Printer for Ontario; 2014. http://www.health.gov.on.ca/en/public/programs/ihf/docs/ihf_fact.pdf (accessed 25 August 2016).

26. Ministry of Health and Long-Term Care. Independent Health Facilities report. Toronto: Queen's Printer for Ontario; 2015. http://www.health.gov.on.ca/en/public/programs/ihf/docs/ihf_assessment_report.pdf (accessed 25 August 2016).

27. Office of the Auditor General of Ontario. 2012 annual report of the Office of the Auditor General of Ontario. Chapter 3, section 3.06: Independent Health Facilities. Toronto: Office of the Auditor General of Ontario; 2012.

28. Office of the Auditor General of Ontario. 2014 annual report of the Office of the Auditor General of Ontario. Chapter 4, section 4.06: Independent Health Facilities. Toronto: Office of the Auditor General of Ontario; 2014.

29. College of Physicians and Surgeons of Ontario. Submission. The regulation of facilities: Looking forward. Toronto: College of Physicians and Surgeons of Ontario; 2015.

30. College of Physicians and Surgeons of Ontario. Out-of-hospital premises inspection program: Quick facts. Toronto: College of Physicians and Surgeons of Ontario; 2011.

31. Ministry of Health and Long-Term Care. Independent Health Facilities Act. Toronto: Queen's Printer for Ontario; 2014.

32. Ontario Coalition for Lab Reform. Labs in Ontario. Toronto: Ontario Coalition for Lab Reform; 2015. http://labreform.ca/labs-in-ontario/ (accessed 26 August 2016).

33. Ontario Coalition for Lab Reform. Medical laboratory testing in Ontario: A history. Toronto: Ontario Coalition for Lab Reform; 2015. http://labreform.ca/medical-laboratory-testing-in-ontario-timeline (accessed 26 August 2016).

34. Quality Management Partnership. About us. Toronto: Quality Management Partnership; 2016. https://www.qmpontario.ca/ (accessed 14 October 2016).

35. Quality Management Partnership. Building on strong foundations: Inaugural report on quality in colonoscopy, mammography and pathology. Toronto: Quality Management Partnership; 2015.

36. CIHI. Supply, distribution and migration of Canadian physicians, 2013. Spending and health workforce. SMDB data tables, Canada profile. Ottawa: Canadian Institute for Health Information; 2013.

37. CIHI. Table 1: Number of devices and number of devices per million population (rate) of selected imaging technologies, by province/territory, Canada, January 1, 2012. National inventory of selected medical imaging equipment, 2012. Ottawa: Canadian Institute for Health Information; 2013.

38. Cancer Quality Council of Ontario. Access to radiation treatment. Toronto: Cancer Quality Council of Ontario; 2016. http://www.csqi.on.ca/cms/One.aspx?portalId=351209&pageId=354808 (accessed 12 October 2016).

39. Cancer Care Ontario. Radiation treatment capital investment strategy April 2012. Toronto: Cancer Care Ontario; 2012. https://www.cancercare.on.ca/common/pages/UserFile.aspx?fileId=155722 (accessed 24 August 2016).

40. CIHI. Wait times for priority procedures in Canada, 2016. Ottawa: Canadian Institute for Health Information; 2016.

41. Ontario Association of Children's Rehabilitation Services. The voice of children's rehabilitation centres. Toronto: OACRS; 2016. http://www.oacrs.com/en/about (accessed 24 August 2016).

42. Ministry of Health and Long-Term Care. Classification of hospitals. Group E hospitals: General rehabilitation. Toronto: Queen's Printer for Ontario; 2016. http://www.health.gov.on.ca/en/common/system/services/hosp/group_e.aspx (accessed 25 August 2016).

43. Ministry of Health and Long-Term Care. Classification of hospitals. Group J hospitals: Special rehabilitation. Toronto: Queen's Printer for Ontario; 2016. http://www.health.gov.on.ca/en/common/system/services/hosp/group_j.aspx (accessed 26 August 2016).

44. Office of the Auditor General of Ontario. 2013 annual report of the Office of the Auditor General of Ontario. Chapter 3, section 3.08: Rehabilitation services in hospitals. Toronto: Office of the Auditor General of Ontario; 2013.

45. Retirement Homes Regulatory Authority. Annual report 2014-2015. Toronto: Retirement Homes Regulatory Authority; 2015.

46. Government of Ontario. Find a retirement home. Toronto: Queen's Printer for Ontario; 2015. https://www.ontario.ca/page/find-retirement-home?_ga=1.205570707.1245738462.1439332164 (accessed 24 August 2016).

47. Ontario Long Term Care Association. About long-term care in Ontario: Facts and figures. Toronto: Ontario Long Term Care Association; 2016. http://www.oltca.com/oltca/OLTCA/LongTermCare/OLTCA/Public/LongTermCare/FactsFigures.aspx?hkey=b-4823fa8-b615-49e3-8097-e67fa4224d40 - Ontario%27s%20long-term%20care%20homes%20(2015) (accessed 18 October 2016).

48. Ministry of Health and Long-Term Care. Find long-term care homes in Ontario. Toronto: Queen's Printer for Ontario; 2016. http://www.health.gov.on.ca/en/public/programs/ltc/home-finder.aspx (accessed 25 October 2016).

49. Ontario Association of Community Care Access Centres. Long-term care wait times. Toronto: Ontario Association of Community Care Access Centres; 2016. http://oaccac.com/Quality-And-Transparency/Provincial-Wait-Times/long-term-care-wait-times (accessed 12 October 2016).

50. Chartier C. LTC and dementia: Challenges, opportunities and the road ahead. National Conference on Dementia Care; 11-12 June 2015; Toronto. Toronto: National Conference on Dementia Care; 2015.

51. Ontario Medical Association. Ontario physicians supporting patients with dementia: A call for an Ontario dementia strategy. Ontario Medical Review 2016;February: 11.

52. CIHI. Residential long-term care financial data tables. Table 1.1: Selected characteristics of selected residential long-term care facilities, by province and territories, 2012. Ottawa: Canadian Institute for Health Information; 2014.

53. Ministry of Health and Long-Term Care. Complex continuing care co-payment. Toronto: Queen's Printer for Ontario; 2015. http://www.health.gov.on.ca/en/public/publications/chronic/chronic.aspx (accessed 25 August 2016).

54. Ministry of Health and Long-Term Care. Patients first - Reporting back on the proposal to strengthen patient-centred health care in Ontario. Toronto: Queen's Printer for Ontario; 2016. http://www.health.gov.on.ca/en/news/bulletin/2016/docs/patients_first_report_back_20160602.pdf (accessed 25 August 2016).

55. Ministry of Health and Long-Term Care. Health services in your community: Public health units. Toronto: Queen's Printer for Ontario; 2014. http://www.health.gov.on.ca/en/common/system/services/phu/ (accessed 25 August 2016).

56. Ministry of Health and Long-Term Care. Transforming Ontario's health care system. Toronto: Queen's Printer for Ontario; 2016. http://www.health.gov.on.ca/en/pro/programs/transformation/community.aspx (accessed 14 October 2016).

57. Health Quality Ontario. Health Links: Improving integrated care for patients with multiple conditions and complex needs. Toronto: Health Quality Ontario; 2016.

58. Government of Ontario. Get medical advice: Telehealth Ontario. Toronto: Queen's Printer for Ontario; 2016. https://www.ontario.ca/page/get-medical-advice-telehealth-ontario (accessed 24 August 2016).

59. Ontario Telemedicine Network. Connected care across Ontario. OTN; 2016. https://otn.ca/ (accessed 24 August 2016).

60. Ministry of Health and Long-Term Care. Excellent care for all: Telemedicine - Improving access to care through technology. Toronto: Queen's Printer for Ontario; 2014. http://www.health.gov.on.ca/en/pro/programs/ecfa/action/primary/pri_telemedecine.aspx (accessed 25 August 2016).

61. COACH: Canada's Health Informatics Association. 2015 Canadian telehealth report. Toronto: COACH: Canada's Health Informatics Association; 2016.

62. COACH: Canada's Health Informatics Association. 2011 Canadian telehealth report. Toronto: COACH: Canada's Health Informatics Association; 2012.

63. eHealth Ontario. Progress report. It's working for you. Toronto: eHealth Ontario; 2016. http://www.ehealthontario.on.ca/en/progress-report (accessed 25 August 2016).

64. Canada Health Infoway. A conversation about digital health. Annual report 2015-2016. Toronto: Canada Health Infoway; 2016.

65. National Physician Survey. 2014 National Physician Survey. Mississauga: National Physician Survey; 2014. http://nationalphysiciansurvey.ca/result/2014-results-ontario/ (accessed 26 August 2016).

66. MyOSCAR. MyOSCAR - Your connection to health. Hamilton: McMaster University; 2016. http://myoscar.org/ (accessed 4 November 2016).

67. Sunnybrook Health Sciences Centre. MyChart. Toronto: Sunnybrook Health Sciences Centre; 2016. http://sunnybrook.ca/content/?page=mychartlogin-learnmore (accessed 24 August 2016).

68. Group Health Centre. myCARE. Sault Ste. Marie: Group Health Centre; 2015. https://www.ghc.on.ca/article.php?i=MjY (accessed 12 October 2016).

69. MiDASH. MiDASH. 2016. https://midash.ca/miDASHApp/Pages/miDASHHome.aspx (accessed 12 October 2016).

70. LifeLabs. See my results. LifeLabs Medical Laboratories; 2016. http://www.lifelabs.com/patients/Pages/Test-Results.aspx?Province=ON (accessed 24 August 2016).

71. Zelmer J, Hagens S. Understanding the gap between desire for and use of consumer health solutions. Healthcare Papers 2014;13(4): 12.

72. Canada Health Infoway. Electronic Medical Record (EMR). Ottawa: Canada Health Infoway; 2016. https://www.infoway-inforoute.ca/en/home/82-our-partners/vendors/certification-services/240-emr (accessed 24 August 2016).

73. Larsen D. eNotifications: Faster followup for better patient outcomes. Ontario Medical Review 2016;January: 2.

74. Collier R. National physician survey: EMR use at 75%. Canadian Medical Association Journal 2015;187(1): E17-E18.

75. National Physician Survey. 2010 National Physician. Mississauga: National Physician Survey; 2010. http://nationalphysiciansurvey.ca/result/2010-on/ (accessed 26 August 2016).

76. CIHI. How Canada compares: Results from the Commonwealth Fund 2015 international health policy survey of primary care physicians. Ottawa: Canadian Institute for Health Information; 2016.

77. Lavis JN, Wilson MG, Grimshaw JM. Evidence brief: Optimizing clinical practice in Ontario based on data, evidence and guidelines. Hamilton: McMaster Health Forum; 2015.

78. Gray JAM. How to practice population medicine. Oxford: Offox Press; 2011.

79. Health Quality Ontario. Quality improvement plans. Toronto: Health Quality Ontario; 2016. http://www.hqontario.ca/Quality-Improvement/Quality-Improvement-Plans (accessed 14 October 2016).

80. Ministry of Health and Long-Term Care. Long-Term Care Home Quality Inspection Program (LQIP). Toronto: Queen's Printer for Ontario; 2015. http://www.health.gov.on.ca/en/public/programs/ltc/31_pr_inspections.aspx (accessed 14 October 2016).

81. Health Quality Ontario. Quality improvement plans reports. Toronto: Health Quality Ontario; 2016. http://www.hqontario.ca/Quality-Improvement/Quality-Improvement-Plans/Quality-Improvement-Plans-Reports (accessed 14 October 2016).

82. Health Quality Ontario. Measuring up: HQO's 2015 yearly report. Toronto: Queen's Printer for Ontario; 2015.

83. Price D, Baker E, Golden B, Hannam R. Patient care groups: A new model of population based primary health care for Ontario. A report on behalf of the Primary Health Care Expert Advisory Committee. Toronto: Ministry of Health and Long-Term Care; 2015.

84. Ontario Hospital Association. OHA position statement on funding and capacity planning for Ontario's health system and hospitals. Toronto: Ontario Hospital Association; 2011. https://www.oha.com/Documents/OHA Position Statement on Funding and Capacity Planning for Ontario%27s Health System and Hospitals.pdf (accessed 24 August 2016).

85. Ministry of Health and Long-Term Care. Update on the stroke capacity planning project. Toronto: Queen's Printer for Ontario; 2015. http://ontariostrokenetwork.ca/wp-content/uploads/2015/01/Stroke-Capacity-Planning-Update-OSN-Conference-January-9-2015_Final.pdf (accessed 25 August 2016).

86. Ministry of Health and Long-Term Care. Shaping Ontario's physician workforce: Building Ontario's capacity to plan, educate, recruite and retain physicians to meet health needs. Report of the Expert Panel on Health Professional Human Resources. Executive summary. Toronto: Queen's Printer for Ontario; 2015. http://www.health.gov.on.ca/en/common/ministry/publications/reports/workforce/workforce.aspx (accessed 12 October 2016).

87. Women's College Hospital Institute for Health Systems Solutions and Virtual Care. Health system capacity planning: Strengthening health care for Ontario's future. Toronto: Women's College Hospital Institute for Health Systems Solutions and Virtual Care; 2015. http://www.womenscollegehospital.ca/assets/pdf/wihv/Strengthening_Health_Care_for_Ontario%27s_Future_Report_FINAL.PDF (accessed 26 August 2016).

88. Ministry of Health and Long-Term Care. A vision for Ontario. Strategic recommendations for ophthalmology in Ontario. Toronto: Queen's Printer for Ontario; 2013. http://www.health.gov.on.ca/en/requests/namd.aspx (accessed 25 August 2016).

89. eHealth Ontario. Introducing Ontario's eHealth blueprint. Toronto: eHealth Ontario; 2016. http://www.ehealthblueprint.com/en/ (accessed 12 October 2016).

90. Home Care Ontario. Capacity planning: The home care perspective. Toronto: Home Care Ontario; 2016. http://www.homecare-ontario.ca/docs/default-source/position-papers/capacity-planning-apr-8-16-public-home-care-ontario.pdf?sfvrsn=6 (accessed 12 October 2016).

91. Ettelt S, Nolte E, Thomson S, Mays N, International Healthcare Comparisons Network. Capacity planning in health care. A review of the international experience. Geneva: World Health Organization; 2008. http://www.euro.who.int/__data/assets/pdf_file/0003/108966/E91193.pdf?ua=1 (accessed 25 August 2016).

92. Klein DJ, Brown AD, Huynh TM, et al. Capital spending in healthcare: A missed opportunity for improvement? Ottawa: Canadian Foundation for Healthcare Improvement; 2013.

93. CIHI. National health expenditure trends, 1975 to 2015. Series A, table A.3.2.1, private sector health expenditure by use of funds, Canada, 1975 to 2015 - Current dollars. Ottawa: Canadian Institute for Health Information; 2015.

94. CIHI. National health expenditure trends, 1975 to 2015. Series A, table A.3.2.2, private sector health expenditure by use of funds, Canada, 1975 to 2015 - Current dollars. Ottawa: Canadian Institute for Health Information; 2015.

95. CIHI. National health expenditure trends, 1975 to 2015. Series A, table A.3.3.1, public sector health expenditure by use of funds, Canada, 1975 to 2015 - Current dollars. Ottawa: Canadian Institute for Health Information; 2015.

96. CIHI. National health expenditure trends, 1975 to 2015. Series D table D.2.6.1, private sector health expenditure, by use of funds, Ontario, 1975 to 2015 - Current dollars ($' 000,000). Ottawa: Canadian Institute for Health Information; 2015.

97. CIHI. National health expenditure trends, 1975 to 2015. Series D table D.2.6.2, private sector health expenditure, by use of funds, Ontario, 1975 to 2015 - Current dollars (percentage distribution). Ottawa: Canadian Institute for Health Information; 2015.

98. CIHI. National health expenditure trends, 1975 to 2015. Series D table D.3.6.2, public sector health expenditure, by use of funds, Ontario, 1975 to 2015 - Current dollars (percentage distribution). Ottawa: Canadian Institute for Health Information; 2015.

99. CIHI. National health expenditure trends, 1975 to 2015. Series D table D.3.6.1, public sector health expenditure, by use of funds, Ontario, 1975 to 2015 - Current dollars ($' 000,000). Ottawa: Canadian Institute for Health Information; 2015.

100. Government of Ontario. Expenditure estimates for the Ministry of Health and Long-Term Care (2016-17). Toronto: Queen's Printer for Ontario; 2016. https://www.ontario.ca/page/expenditure-estimates-ministry-health-and-long-term-care-2016-17 - vote18 (accessed 24 August 2016).

101. Ministry of Health and Long-Term Care. Ontario making new $345 million investment in hospitals. Toronto: Queen's Printer for Ontario; 2016. https://news.ontario.ca/mohltc/en/2016/02/ontario-making-new-345-million-investment-in-hospitals.html (accessed 14 October 2016).

102. Government of Ontario. Investing in community health infrastructure. Ontario ensuring access to health care services, creating jobs. Toronto: Queen's Printer for Ontario; 2014. https://news.ontario.ca/mof/en/2014/04/investing-in-community-health-infrastructure.html (accessed 24 August 2016).

103. Association of Ontario Health Centres. Annual report 2012-2013. Toronto: Association of Ontario Health Centres; 2013. http://issuu.com/aohc_acso/docs/aohc_annual_report_2013?e=7738038/2899350 (accessed 26 August 2016).

104. Association of Ontario Midwives. Welcome to Ontario midwives. Toronto: Association of Ontario Midwives; 2014. http://www.ontariomidwives.ca/ (accessed 24 August 2016).

105. Ministry of Health and Long-Term Care. Community health centres. Toronto: Queen's Printer for Ontario; 2014. http://www.health.gov.on.ca/en/common/system/services/chc/ (accessed 25 August 2016).

106. Nurse Practitioners' Association of Ontario. Nurse Practioner-Led Clinics. Toronto: Nurse Practitioners' Association of Ontario; 2014. http://npao.org/nurse-practitioners/clinics/ - U7v8X7EXtmo (accessed 26 August 2016).

107. Vakrilova G. Personal communication.

108. Ministry of Health and Long-Term Care. Public health units. Toronto: Queen's Printer for Ontario; 2014. http://www.health.gov.on.ca/en/common/system/services/phu/default.aspx (accessed 25 August 2016).

109. Public Health Ontario. Laboratory services. Toronto: Ontario Agency for Health Protection and Promotion; 2014. http://www.publichealthontario.ca/en/ServicesAndTools/LaboratoryServices/Pages/default.aspx (accessed 24 August 2016).

110. Ministry of Health and Long-Term Care. Publicly-funded physiotherapy: Clinic locations. Toronto: Queen's Printer for Ontario; 2015. http://www.health.gov.on.ca/en/public/programs/physio/pub_clinics.aspx (accessed 25 August 2016).

111. Ontario College of Pharmacists. 2015 annual report. Toronto: Ontario College of Pharmacists; 2016. http://www.ocpinfo.com/library/news/2015-annual-report/ (accessed 24 August 2016).

112. HealthForceOntario. Specialist practice models. Toronto: Queen's Printer for Ontario; 2014. http://www.healthforceontario.ca/en/Home/Physicians/Training_%7C_Practising_in_Ontario/Physician_Roles/Specialist_Practice_Models (accessed 24 August 2016).

113. Ministry of Health and Long-Term Care. Primary health care status report - Signed at June 1, 2016. Toronto: Queen's Printer for Ontario; 2016.

114. CIHI. Continuing Care Reporting System, 2014–2015, quick stats. Table 1: Number of facilities and residents in continuing care facilities submitting to CCRS by province/territory, 2014–2015. Ottawa: Canadian Institute for Health Information; 2015. https://www.cihi.ca/en/ccrs_quickstats_14_15_en.xlsx (accessed 27 October 2016).

115. Office of the Auditor General of Canada. 2015 spring reports of the Auditor General of Canada. Report 4. Access to health services for remote First Nations communities. Ottawa: Office of the Auditor General of Canada; 2015. http://www.oag-bvg.gc.ca/internet/English/parl_oag_201504_04_e_40350.html - ex1 (accessed 24 August 2016).

116. CIHI. Hospital MIS Statistics. CMDB number of hospital inpatient days, inpatient admissions, ambulatory care visits, emergency visits and day/night care visits, by province, territory and Canada, 1999-2000 to 2013-2014. QuickStats. Ottawa: CIHI; 2015.

117. CIHI. Highlights of 2011–2012 emergency department visits and inpatient hospitalizations. Ottawa: Canadian Institute for Health Information; 2013.

118. CIHI. NACRS emergency department visits and length of stay by province/territory, 2014-2015. Table 3: ED length of stay for Canadian Triage and Acuity Scale (CTAS) levels and admitted cases, participating provinces/territories, NACRS, 2014–2015 Ottawa: Canadian Institute for Health Information; 2015.

119. Canadian Agency for Drugs and Technologies in Health. The Canadian medical imaging inventory, 2015. Ottawa: Canadian Agency for Drugs and Technologies in Health; 2016.

120. CIHI. Table 3: Number of magnetic resonance imaging (MRI) and computed tomography (CT) exams, by province/territory, Canada, 2003–2004 to 2011–2012. Ottawa: Canadian Institute for Health Information; 2013. https://www.cihi.ca/sites/default/files/document/stats_mit_2012_en.xlsx (accessed 24 August 2016).

121. Canadian Agency for Drugs and Technologies in Health. The Canadian medical imaging inventory, 2015. Ottawa: Canadian Agency for Drugs and Technologies in Health; 2016. https://www.cadth.ca/canadian-medical-imaging-inventory-2015 (accessed 14 October 2016).

122. CIHI. Residential long-term care financial data tables. Table 2.1: Age and sex of residents in selected residential long-term care facilities, by province and territories, 2012. Ottawa: Canadian Institute for Health Information; 2014.

123. CIHI. Residential long-term care financial data tables. Table 3.1: Expenses ($000) reported by selected residential long-term care facilities, by province and territories, 2012. Ottawa: Canadian Institute for Health Information; 2014.

124. Ministry of Health and Long-Term Care. Ontario wait times. Toronto: Queen's Printer for Ontario; 2016. http://www.ehealthontario.on.ca/en/progress report (accessed 25 August 2016).

125. Cancer Care Ontario. Cancer System Quality Index. Toronto: Cancer Care Ontario; 2016. https://www.cancercare.on.ca/cms/One.aspx?portalId=1377&pageId=8813 (accessed 24 August 2016).

126. Cancer Care Ontario. Ontario's wait times strategy. Toronto: Cancer Care Ontario; 2016. https://www.cancercare.on.ca/ocs/wait-times/ (accessed 24 August 2016).

127. Health Quality Ontario. System performance. Why and how we report on health system performance in Ontario. Toronto: Queen's Printer for Ontario; 2016. http://www.hqontario.ca/System-Performance/Health-System-Performance (accessed 24 August 2016).

128. Local Health Integration Network. Ontario's LHINs. Toronto: Local Health Integration Network; 2016. http://www.lhins.on.ca/ (accessed 24 August 2016).

129. Ontario Renal Network. About Ontario Renal Network. Toronto: Ontario Renal Network; 2016. http://www.renalnetwork.on.ca/about_orn/ - .V32KSVfnKJU (accessed 24 August 2016).

130. Public Health Ontario. Corporate reporting. Toronto: Ontario Agency for Health Protection and Promotion; 2016. https://www.publichealthontario.ca/en/About/Publications/Pages/default.aspx (accessed 24 August 2016).

131. Better Outcomes Registry & Network. About BORN. Toronto: BORN; 2016. https://www.bornontario.ca/en/about-born/ (accessed 24 August 2016).

132. Cancer Quality Council of Ontario. About CQCO. Toronto: Cancer Quality Council of Ontario; 2016. http://www.cqco.ca/cms/One.aspx?portalId=89613&pageId=89831 (accessed 25 August 2016).

133. Cardiac Care Network. About CCN. Toronto: CCN; 2016. http://www.ccn.on.ca/ccn_public/FormsAboutCCN/about.aspx (accessed 25 August 2016).

134. Institute for Clinical Evaluative Sciences. About ICES. Toronto: Institute for Clinical Evaluative Sciences; 2016. http://www.ices.on.ca/About-ICES (accessed 24 August 2016).

135. Provincial Council for Maternal and Child Health. 2015 Ontario maternal-child healthcare system report. Toronto: Provincial Council for Maternal and Child Health; 2015. http://www.pcmch.on.ca/health-care-providers/maternity-care/performance-and-quality-improvement/2015report/ (accessed 24 August 2016).

136. Association of Family Health Teams of Ontario. Strategic direction and reports. Toronto: Association of Family Health Teams of Ontario; 2016. http://www.afhto.ca/about/advocacy-and-issues/ (accessed 26 August 2016).

137. Children's Mental Health Ontario. 2016 report card: Child and youth mental health. Toronto: Children's Mental Health Ontario; 2016. http://www.kidsmentalhealth.ca/about_us/cmho-report-card-2016.php (accessed 24 August 2016).

138. Ontario Association of Community Care Access Centres. Quality and transparency. Toronto: Ontario Association of Community Care Access Centres; 2013. http://oaccac.com/Quality-And-Transparency (accessed 26 August 2016).

139. Ontario Hospital Association. Employee relations services. Toronto: Ontario Hospital Association; 2013. http://www.oha.com/Services/EmployeeRelations/Pages/EmployeeRelations.aspx (accessed 24 August 2016).

140. Ontario Hospital Association. OHA's eHealth Applications Registry. Toronto: Ontario Hospital Association; 2013. http://www.oha.com/CurrentIssues/keyinitiatives/eHealth/Pages/eHealthApplicationsRegistry.aspx (accessed 24 August 2016).

141. Ontario Long Term Care Association. Our mission. Toronto: Ontario Long Term Care Association; 2016. http://www.oltca.com/oltca/OLTCA/AboutUs/OurMission/OLTCA/Public/AboutUs/Mission.aspx?hkey=f78f9822-cc19-49ec-8eed-fa5328e8541a (accessed 24 August 2016).

142. Statistics Canada. Health. Ottawa: Statistics Canada; 2016. http://www5.statcan.gc.ca/subject-sujet/theme-theme?pid=2966&lang=eng&more=0 (accessed 24 August 2016).

143. Canada Health Infoway. Progress in Canada. Toronto: Canada Health Infoway; 2016. https://www.infoway-inforoute.ca/en/what-we-do/progress-in-canada (accessed 24 August 2016).

144. CIHI. Vision and mandate. Ottawa: Canadian Institute for Health Information; 2016. https://www.cihi.ca/en/about-cihi/vision-and-mandate (accessed 24 August 2016).

145. Canadian Partnership Against Cancer. System performance. Toronto: Canadian Partnership Against Cancer; 2016. http://www.partnershipagainstcancer.ca/what-we-do/system-performance (accessed 24 August 2016).

146. Canadian Medical Association. Policies and research. Ottawa: Canadian Medical Association; 2016. https://www.cma.ca/En/pages/policies-research.aspx (accessed 24 August 2016).

5. Delivery arrangements 2: Workforce

Cristina A. Mattison and John N. Lavis

Key messages for citizens

- While a distinction is frequently made between regulated health professionals (e.g., nurses and physicians) and unregulated health workers (e.g., personal support workers and paramedics), there are mechanisms in place to protect and serve the public interest where either group is concerned.

- Over the last decade, there have been substantial increases in the number of health professionals and workers, with particularly noticeable increases among: midwives (244%); social workers (162%); dental hygienists (103%); optometrists (84%); health-information management professionals (77%); respiratory therapists (73%); medical physicists (68%); chiropractors (67%); and dietitians (61%).

- The majority (94%) of Ontarians are registered with a primary-care provider, however, less than half (44%) report that they are able to see their family physician the same- or next-day when they are sick.

- Ontarians living in rural and remote areas continue to experience difficulty in accessing family physicians as well as specialists, despite increases in physician supply.

Key messages for health professionals

- From 2000 (which is near the end of a period of 'belt tightening' by the government) to 2013, the unadjusted workforce per 100,000 population has increased across a range of health professionals, with the exception of registered practical nurses and medical laboratory technologists.

- From 2000 to 2011, training capacity for physicians has grown and the total number of medical-school graduates increased by 62% (with 58% of these graduates in 2011 being female).

- New healthcare roles have been created to complement the existing cadres of health professionals (e.g., physician assistants).

- Registered nurses and physicians are not distributed equitably across geographic areas, with numbers particularly low in rural and remote areas.

Key messages for policymakers

- Projections indicate that the supply of physicians will increase by an additional 23% by 2025.

- Unregulated health workers, particularly personal support workers, are playing an increasingly central role in home and community care and in long-term care.

- Using simple headcounts as a measure of supply ignores differences in working hours across workers (e.g., women versus men) and changes in working hours over time (e.g., reduced 'patient care' hours among family physicians).

- Using unadjusted workforce-to-population ratios as a measure of density, as is typically done, ignores the aging of the population.

. . .

In this chapter we continue our focus on delivery arrangements, but move from a focus on infrastructure (Chapter 4) to the health workforce, which is the final 'building block' of the health system. The health workforce is a key input to the health system, albeit one that is – over the short term at least – relatively fixed. Over the longer term, however, changes to the health workforce are and will remain essential to achieving the 'triple aim' of improving the patient experience, improving population health, and keeping per capita costs manageable. We return to the 'triple aim' in Chapter 11, which is focused on the performance of the health system.

Adjusting the supply (e.g., number) and distribution (e.g., location) of regulated health professionals and unregulated health workers to meet the changing health needs of Ontarians is a key challenge for a responsive and efficient health system, both in general, and in particular geographic locations and among particular (e.g., marginalized) groups. The life expectancy of Ontarians has increased over the past decade, and the proportion of Ontarians aged 65 years and over is increasing and projected to double to 25% by 2041.(1; 2) As the age of the population increases, so too does the number of people living with chronic conditions and complex needs.(3) Understanding the existing health workforce along with shifting health needs is key to planning initiatives.

Policy initiatives can also necessitate adjustments to supply and distribution. For example, the Ministry of Health and Long-Term Care's 2015 Patients First initiative and the *Patients First Act, 2016* aim, at least in part, to improve access to care.(4) One of the main components of 'Patients First' is the plan to create geographically defined populations at a Local Health Integration Network (LHIN) 'sub-region level' (which may range from 40,000 citizens to 350,000 in densely populated urban areas) within each of the province's 14 LHINs, where significant effort would be devoted to coordinating and integrating home and community care and primary care (and to some extent public health).(5) Workforce planning and the strategic use of policy levers will be critical to ensuring that the health workforce is aligned with this policy initiative.

In this chapter we describe the workforce in general terms – both regulated health professionals (e.g., nurses and physicians) and unregulated health workers (e.g., personal support workers) – and present profiles of select professions. We also describe the Government of Ontario's strategies to maintain and, where necessary, adjust the supply and distribution of the health workforce, as well as the education and training initiatives and other policy levers being used in the province.

Health workforce supply, density and distribution

Twenty-eight regulated health professions and many categories of unregulated health workers contribute to the health system. Twenty-six regulatory colleges oversee the regulated health professions (see Chapter 2). To illustrate this diversity, we selected 15 of these professions and categories based on the size of the workforce and, for each one, we provide both the definition used by the Canadian Institute for Health Information in tracking the profession's or category's size, and the sector(s) where they commonly work (Table 5.1). While the Canadian Institute for Health Information does not have data available on personal support workers, we include this category of unregulated health workers in Table 5.1 and utilize workforce estimates by the Ministry of Health and Long-Term Care.

Table 5.1: Select regulated health professions and categories of unregulated health workers, and the sectors where they commonly work

Profession or category	Home and community care	Primary care	Specialty care	Long-term care	Public health
Nurses • Regulated health profession that includes registered nurses and registered practical nurses who are engaged in both health promotion and care delivery, either with other health professions or independently • Nurses hold four-year degrees and care for patients with a wide range of complexity and predictability of outcomes • Registered practical nurses hold two-year diplomas and care for less complex patients with more predictable outcomes • Nurse practitioners are a subset of registered nurses and have additional training and a wider scope of practice (e.g., ordering and interpreting diagnostic tests, as well as writing some prescriptions)	✓	✓	✓	✓	✓
Personal support workers • Category of unregulated health workers who provide (often in-home) care and support with a range of personal support services	✓		✓	✓	
Physicians • Regulated health profession that includes family physicians and specialists • Family physicians provide primary care ranging from disease prevention to medical care, disease management, and coordination of care • Specialists have additional training and work in defined areas (e.g., internal medicine, surgery and laboratory medicine)		✓	✓		✓
Social workers • Regulated health profession that provides assessment services as well as a range of psycho-social supports	✓	✓	✓	✓	✓
Dental hygienists • Regulated health profession involved in oral health promotion		✓			✓
Pharmacists • Regulated health profession that dispenses prescription drugs • Expanded scope of practice (as part of the *Regulated Health Professions Statute Law Amendment Act, 2009*) includes renewing and adapting prescriptions, prescribing certain smoking cessation drugs, and administering influenza vaccinations, among other things	✓	✓	✓	✓	

Continued on next page

Profession or category	Home and community care	Primary care	Specialty care	Long-term care	Public health
Dentists • Regulated health profession supporting oral health through both prevention and treatment		✓	✓		✓
Paramedics • Category of unregulated health workers providing land and air ambulance services			✓		
Physiotherapists • Regulated health profession providing rehabilitation services to those with an injury or disease	✓	✓	✓	✓	
Medical radiation technologists • Regulated health profession operating radiographic equipment			✓		
Medical laboratory technologists • Regulated health profession conducting laboratory analyses			✓		✓
Occupational therapists • Regulated health profession providing rehabilitation services focused on skill development in daily activities	✓	✓	✓	✓	
Chiropractors • Regulated health profession providing care related to the musculoskeletal system, with a specific focus on the spine		✓			
Psychologists • Regulated health profession providing care for behavioural and mental health and addiction issues		✓	✓		
Dietitians • Regulated health profession providing nutrition related care	✓	✓	✓	✓	✓

Sources: 57-68

The World Health Organization outlines a series of indicators for the health workforce 'building block,' which include: 1) supply (e.g., number of regulated health professionals and unregulated health workers, and annual number of graduates of professionals and workers from educational institutions); 2) density (e.g., health workforce per 100,000 population); and 3) distribution of the health workforce (e.g., occupation/specialization, gender and location).(6) All of these indicators have their challenges. For example, using simple headcounts as a measure of supply ignores differences in working hours across workers (e.g., women versus men) and changes in working hours over time (e.g., reduced 'patient care' hours among family physicians).(7) Using unadjusted workforce-to-population ratios as a measure of density ignores the aging of the population. Also, changes in these indicators over time depend on the base year, and we have chosen the year 2000, which is near the end of a period of 'belt tightening' by the government. These considerations need to be borne in mind when reviewing the numbers that follow.

Overall, the health workforce in Ontario has grown substantially between 2000 and 2013 (Table 5.2). With the exception of medical laboratory technologists (for whom there was a 9% decrease), all of the regulated health professionals and unregulated health workers listed have increased in number. Of particular note are the increases in:

- midwives (244%);
- social workers (162%);
- dental hygienists (103%);
- optometrists (84%);
- health information-management professionals (77%);
- respiratory therapists (73%);
- medical physicists (68%);
- chiropractors (67%); and
- dietitians (61%).

Physician supply has increased significantly over the same time period, and the Ministry of Health and Long-Term Care states that it has "stabilized."(8) Between 2002 and 2012 (which are slightly different than the years used in Table 5.2) the physician workforce increased by 33% while the population increased by 13%.(8) Through the use of service-utilization models, the ministry estimates that the supply of physicians will increase by an additional 23% by 2025, outpacing anticipated service utilization increases by 8%.(8) However, this upward trajectory is just part of a long-term cycle that reflects the government's willingness and ability to pay for physician services (and its tendency to adjust physician numbers not physician pay, particularly during difficult economic times, such as the late 1990s).

Table 5.2: Number of regulated health professionals and unregulated health workers, 2000, 2010 and 2013[1]

Profession or category	Number				Percentage distribution[2]	13-year percentage change
	Ontario			Canada	Ontario	Ontario
	2000	2010	2013	2013	2013	
Nurses	114,750	125,608	131,408	375,843	35%	15%
Registered nurses[3]	81,679	95,185	96,148	276,914	35%	18%
Nurse practitioners	—	1,518	2,158	3,655	59%	42%
Registered practical nurses	33,071	30,423	35,260	93,656	38%	7%
Physicians[4]	21,176	25,044	28,422	77,674	37%	34%
Specialists	11,202	12,874	14,449	38,282	38%	29%
Family medicine	9,974	12,170	13,973	39,392	35%	40%
Social workers	5,449	12,628	14,264	43,800	33%	162%
Dental hygienists	6,540	11,998	13,271	28,495	47%	103%
Pharmacists	8,490	10,564	12,630	35,337	36%	49%
Dentists[5]	7,095	8,472	9,050	21,731	42%	28%
Paramedics[6]	—	—	7,534	—	—	—
Physiotherapists	5,210	5,597	6,950	19,253	36%	33%
Medical radiation technologists	5,306	6,338	6,651	18,850	35%	25%
Medical laboratory technologists	7,023	6,819	6,411	—	—	-9%
Occupational therapists	3,196	4,337	4,892	14,351	34%	53%
Chiropractors	2,708	4,062	4,515	8,745	52%	67%
Psychologists	2,575	3,367	3,692	17,133	22%	43%
Dietitians	2,202	3,180	3,545	10,847	33%	61%
Respiratory therapists	1,816	2,858	3,137	11,013	28%	73%
Speech-language pathologists	—	2,822	3,014	8,973	34%	7%
Opticians	—	—	2,552	7,700	33%	—
Optometrists	1,178	1,879	2,167	5,425	40%	84%
Health information-management professionals[6]	1,086	1,698	1,924	4,716	41%	77%
Environmental public health[6]	433	619	681	1,621	42%	57%
Midwives	177	471	608	1,173	52%	244%
Audiologists	—	591	657	1,759	37%	11%
Medical physicists[6]	118	181	198	443	45%	68%
Genetic counsellors[6]	—	—	107	258	41%	—

Sources: 69-95

Notes:
[1] Data not available for the specific reference period are denoted by —.
[2] Percentage distribution is the proportion of the profession or category in Ontario
[3] Includes nurse practitioners
[4] Excludes residents
[5] Includes licensed general practitioner and certified dental specialists
[6] No provincial regulatory body (i.e., category of unregulated health workers)

When we examine the numbers of health professionals and unregulated health workers relative to the size of the population (per 100,000), we get a measure of their density and hence some sense of the ease with which we can access them (Table 5.3). Workforce density is still relatively small for some professions (e.g., midwives) and greater for others (e.g., nurses and physicians). Between 2000 and 2013, health workforce density increased across all regulated health professionals and unregulated health workers, with the exception of registered practical nurses and medical laboratory technologists (although as we note below a slightly different pattern emerges with registered practical nurses when data up to 2015 are included).

Table 5.3: Health workforce density, 2000, 2010 and 2013[1]

| Profession or category | Workforce per 100,000 population | | | |
| | Ontario | | | Canada |
	2000[2]	2010[2]	2013	2013
Nurses	982	956	970	1,069
Registered nurses[3]	699	725	710	788
Nurse practitioners	—	11	16	10
Registered practical nurses	283	230	260	266
Physicians[4]	180	188	210	221
Specialists	95	97	107	109
Family medicine	85	92	103	112
Social workers	47	96	105	125
Dental hygienists	56	90	98	81
Pharmacists	73	80	93	101
Dentists	61	64	67	62
Paramedics	—	—	56	—
Physiotherapists	45	42	51	55
Medical radiation technologists	45	48	49	54
Medical laboratory technologists	60	52	47	—
Occupational therapists	27	33	36	41
Chiropractors	23	31	33	25
Psychologists	19	25	27	49
Dietitians	19	24	26	31
Respiratory therapists	16	22	23	31
Speech-language pathologists	—	21	22	26
Opticians	—	—	19	22
Optometrists	8	14	16	15
Health information-management professionals	9	13	14	13
Environmental public health	4	5	5	5

Continued on next page

Profession or category	Workforce per 100,000 population			
	Ontario			Canada
	2000[2]	2010[2]	2013	2013
Midwives	2	4	4	3
Audiologists	—	4	3	5
Medical physicists	1	1	1	1
Genetic counsellors	—	—	1	1

Sources: 69-106

Notes:
[1] Data not available for the specific reference period are denoted by —.
[2] Some densities were calculated manually. Figures are based on health workforce estimates from 2000 and 2010, taken from the Canadian Institute for Health Information's Health Personnel Database. The population of Ontario in 2000 and 2013 is based on Statistics Canada's population estimates, CANSIM table 051-0001. Workforce per 100,000 is calculated by dividing the number of health professionals by the population of Ontario in 100,000's (e.g., registered nurses per 100,000 population = 81,679 / (11,683,290/100,000)).
[3] Includes nurse practitioners
[4] Excludes residents

The geographic distribution of the health workforce continues to present a challenge for rural, northern and remote communities. As noted in Chapter 1, the Ministry of Health and Long-Term Care's Rural and Northern Health Care Framework defines: 1) rural communities as those with a population of less than 30,000 and over 30 minutes away from a community with a population over 30,000; 2) northern communities as those within 10 territorial districts (145 municipalities) and constituting 90% of Ontario's land area; and 3) remote communities as those that do not have year-round road access or rely on a third party (e.g., airplane or ferry) for transportation to a larger community.(9) As one example of the distribution challenge, approximately 6% of registered nurses were working in rural and remote areas in 2015, whereas 14% of the population lives in rural areas and more live in remote areas (based on the 2011 census).(10; 11) Moreover, the proportion of registered nurses working in rural and remote areas has declined in the province, whereas the registered practical nurse-to-population ratio in rural and remote areas has increased.(12; 13) Similarly, despite high demand, the supply of physicians is not distributed equitably across geographic areas, and only 5% of physicians practice in rural areas.(14)

Regulated health professionals

In this section we focus on nurses and physicians, as they form the two largest regulated health professions in Ontario. Nurses are the largest health profession and there are two types of regulated nursing professions in the province: 1) registered nurses; and 2) registered practical nurses (who are called licensed practical nurses in some other parts of Canada).(12; 15; 16) Nurse practitioners, a subset of registered nurses, have a broader scope of practice and can diagnose, order and interpret diagnostic tests, and prescribe certain drugs. Physicians are the second largest regulated health profession and are typically considered in two broad categories – family physicians and specialists.

Nurses

Key observations about the province's nursing profile from 2010 to 2015 (Table 5.4) include:

- the overall registered nurse supply (the number of registered nurses eligible to practise in a given year) has decreased by 2% while the nurse practitioner supply has increased by 66% (although it remains small in absolute terms) and the registered practical nurse supply has increased by 25%;
- as of 2015, the majority of registered nurses are female (94%), middle aged (with an average age of 46), and trained in Canada (88%);
- the registered nursing workforce (the number of registered nurses who were employed at the time of annual registration) has increased by 3% (and nurse practitioners by 62%) and the registered practical nurse workforce has increased by 28%;
- as of 2015, the majority of the registered nursing workforce is employed full time (67%), works in a hospital setting (63%), and works in a staff nurse position (74%); and
- as of the same year, 94% of the registered nursing workforce is working in urban areas.

Table 5.4: Nurse profile, 2010 and 2015

Characterisic	Number			%	
	Ontario		Canada	Ontario	Canada
	2010[1]	2015	2015	2015	
Supply (eligible to practise)[2]					
Registered nurses[3]	106,959	105,010	296,731		
Nurse practitioners	1,518	2,520	4,353		
Registered practical nurses	34,917	43,656	113,367		

Continued on next page

Characterisic	Number			%	
	Ontario		Canada	Ontario	Canada
	2010[1]	2015	2015	2015	
Registered nurses					
Gender					
Female	101,766	98,448	274,265	94%	92%
Male	5,193	6,562	22,466	6%	8%
Average age	47	46	45		
Age					
<30	—	13,248	42,349	13%	14%
30-34	—	10,945	36,898	10%	12%
35-39	—	9,957	32,475	9%	11%
40-44	—	11,731	34,045	11%	11%
45-49	—	12,858	35,739	12%	12%
50-54	—	14,949	39,763	14%	13%
55-59	—	13,126	35,589	12%	12%
60-64	—	11,540	26,107	11%	9%
65-69	—	4,897	10,243	5%	3%
70+	—	1,758	3,522	2%	1%
Highest level of education in nursing					
Diploma	64,144	47,947	140,188	46%	47%
Baccalaureate	38,805	49,991	142,394	48%	48%
Master's/doctorate	4,010	7,072	14,026	7%	5%
Location of graduation					
Canada	94,218	92,915	269,509	88%	91%
Outside Canada	12,608	11,830	26,474	11%	9%
Years since graduation					
0-10	22,109	28,335	94,841	27%	32%
11-20	2,905	2,329	61,727	2%	21%
21-30	25,564	24,683	66,579	24%	22%
31+	34,682	29,803	71,817	28%	24%
Workforce (employed)[2]					
Registered nurses	95,185	98,064	283,575		
Nurse practitioners	1,482	2,405	4,090		
Registered practical nurses	30,423	39,069	101,319		
Registered nurses					
Employment status					
Full time	62,602	65,635	172,125	67%	61%
Part time	24,742	25,553	81,661	26%	29%
Casual	7,841	6,876	29,267	7%	10%
Place of work					
Hospital	61,449	62,018	178,359	63%	63%

Continued on next page

Characterisic	Number			%	
	Ontario		Canada	Ontario	Canada
	2010[1]	2015	2015	2015	
Registered nurses – continued					
Community health	18,356	16,877	44,121	17%	16%
Long-term care home	7,854	7,923	26,086	8%	9%
Other place of work	6,483	11,246	33,192	11%	12%
Position					
Staff nurse	72,249	72,601	217,088	74%	77%
Manager	5,522	5,512	18,053	6%	6%
Other positions[4]	16,715	19,951	46,359	20%	16%
Location					
Urban	89,157	91,945	253,177	94%	89%
Rural/remote	6,028	6,118	30,284	6%	11%

Sources: 10; 15; 107-119

Notes:
[1] Data not available for the specific reference period are denoted by —.
[2] Supply refers to all nurses eligible to practice, including those employed or unemployed at time of registration. Workforce refers to nurses who were employed at time of registration.
[3] Includes nurse practitioners
[4] For example, instructor/professor/educator, researcher, consultant, clinical specialist, nurse midwife, and nurse practitioner

The ratio of registered nurses to registered practical nurses has changed over the past decade, from 3:1 in 2005-10 to 2.3:1 in 2015.(17) The registered nursing supply peaked in 2013 with 108,705 registered nurses, and has since dropped by 3% to 105,010 in 2015.(15) The change reflects a shift away from registered nurse employment to registered practical nurse employment, primarily in hospital settings.(16) The decrease in the number of registered nurses can also be attributed to the 2014 Declaration of Practice, a requirement by the College of Nurses of Ontario, according to which members must declare whether they have practised in Ontario within the previous three years as part of membership renewal.(18)

Physicians

Key observations about the province's physician profile from 2010 to 2014 (Table 5.5) include:

- the total number of physicians has increased by 17% (family medicine by 21% and specialists by 14%);
- as of 2014, the average physician age is 51;
- as of the same year, 62% of physicians are male, however, the number of female physicians has increased from 2010 to 2014 by 26% (family

Table 5.5: Physician profile, 2010 and 2014

Characterisic	Number			%	
	Ontario		Canada	Ontario	Canada
	2010	2014	2014	2014	
Total number of physicians	25,044	29,368	79,905		
Family medicine	12,170	14,695	40,781		
Specialists	12,874	14,673	39,124		
Average age	51	51	50		
Family medicine	51	51	50		
Specialists	51	52	50		
Gender					
Male	16,305	18,346	48,727	62%	61%
Family medicine	7,306	8,482	22,889	46%	47%
Specialists	8,999	9,864	25,838	54%	53%
Female	8,737	11,018	31,148	38%	64%
Family medicine	4,862	6,209	17,867	56%	57%
Specialists	3,875	4,809	13,281	44%	43%
Specialty					
Family medicine	12,170	14,695	40,781	50%	51%
Medical specialists					
Clinical specialists	9,120	10,465	27,531	36%	34%
Laboratory specialists	546	603	1,832	2%	2%
Surgical specialists	3,197	3,595	9,735	12%	12%
Medical scientists	11	10	26	0.03%	0.03%
Years since MD graduation					
<6	925	1,386	4,482	5%	6%
6–10	2,709	3,566	9,977	12%	12%
11–25	9,873	10,690	29,073	36%	36%
26–30	3,501	3,474	9,810	12%	12%
31–35	3,016	3,528	9,313	12%	12%
36+	5,008	6,698	16,787	23%	21%
Place of MD graduation					
Canada	18,566	21,033	59,151	72%	74%
Family medicine	9,055	10,158	28,959	48%	49%
Specialists	9,511	10,875	30,192	52%	51%
Outside Canada	6,471	8,318	20,295	28%	25%
Family medicine	3,111	4,520	11,549	54%	57%
Specialists	3,360	3,798	8,746	46%	43%

Continued on next page

Characterisic	Number			%	
	Ontario		Canada	Ontario	Canada
	2010	2014	2014	2014	2014
Location[1]					
Urban	23,833	27,914	73,192	95%	92%
Family medicine	11,103	13,430	35,045	48%	48%
Specialists	12,730	14,484	38,147	52%	52%
Rural	1,199	1,396	6,577	5%	8%
Family medicine	1,061	1,230	5,646	88%	86%
Specialists	138	166	931	12%	14%

Source: 14

Note:
[1] Urban and rural areas were assigned based on Statistics Canada's definitions.

medicine by 28% and specialists by 24%);
- as of 2014, roughly half of physicians practise family medicine (50%), with specialists including clinical specialists (36%), surgical specialists (12%), and laboratory specialists (2%);
- as of the same year, nearly three quarters of physicians graduated from a Canadian medical school (72%); and
- as of 2014, 95% of physicians (and 92% of family physicians) practise in urban areas, however, the number of physicians practising in rural areas has increased by 16% from 2010 to 2014.

Family physicians

Most Ontarians (94%) now report having access to a family physician, however less than half (44%) report that they are able to see their family physician the same or next day when they are sick.(19) Key findings for Ontarians from the Commonwealth Fund's 2015 International Health Policy Survey of Primary Care Physicians include:
- 66% of family physicians were able to provide same- or next-day appointments almost all or most of the time to their patients (versus 56% in B.C. and 34% in Quebec);
- 67% of family physicians have an arrangement where patients can access after-hours care, through a nurse or physician, to avoid going to the hospital or emergency department (versus 31% in B.C. and 37% in Quebec);
- 60% of family physicians thought their patients experience long wait times to see a specialist after referral (versus 75% in B.C. and 81% in Quebec);

- 20% of family physicians thought their patients experience long wait times for treatment after diagnosis (versus 32% in B.C. and 20% in Quebec);
- 53% of family physicians reported that they or someone in their practice frequently coordinates care with social services or other types of care in the community (versus 44% in B.C. and 46% in Quebec); and
- 36% of family physicians thought it was easy to coordinate care for a patient with social services or other community supports, such as housing and transportation (versus 32% in B.C. and 32% in Quebec).(20; 21)

Specialists

While government initiatives, including those designed to increase medical-school enrolment, postgraduate-training positions and recruitment to underserved communities, have increased the total number of physicians in Ontario, challenges remain with specialist retention and distribution. Retention rates are the lowest among specialist graduates for surgeons, with 33% leaving the province between 2005 and 2011.(8) This has been attributed to a lack of full-time employment opportunities for certain specialties (neurosurgeons and cardiac, orthopedic, pediatric and general surgeons) despite long wait times for some services provided by these specialties (e.g., 312 day wait time for lumbar disc surgery).(22; 23) The geographic distribution of specialists is particularly low, with less than 1% of specialists working in rural communities (Table 5.5).

The Government of Ontario spent $438 million on specialist education in 2011, a 63% increase since 2005.(22) On average it costs $780,000 for each specialist trained, which includes a three-or-four-year undergraduate degree, two-to-five years of postgraduate residency training, and resident salary and benefits.(22) However, 'public dollars' are also spent on many professional degree holders (e.g., engineering) and the dollars spent on resident salary and benefits include remuneration for many services that would cost much more if they had to be provided by a fully trained specialist.

Training capacity

The training capacity of physicians has grown substantially in the province (Table 5.6). Between 2000 and 2011, training capacity grew to 965 medical-school positions, and the total number of graduates increased by

Table 5.6: Number of graduates from medical education programs and training capacity, 2000, 2010 and 2011

School	Graduates			Training capacity
	2000	2010	2011	2011
University of Toronto	167	223	223	259
Males	104	95	97	
Females	63	128	126	
McMaster University	103	156	181	203
Males	37	67	64	
Females	66	89	117	
Western University	101	139	144	171
Males	62	74	73	
Females	39	65	71	
University of Ottawa[1]	84	147	152	168
Males	37	53	60	
Females	47	94	92	
Queen's University	75	99	97	100
Males	46	47	51	
Females	29	52	46	
Northern Ontario School of Medicine[2]	n/a	52	59	64
Males	n/a	23	16	
Females	n/a	29	43	
Total	530	816	856	965
Males	286	359	361	
Females	244	457	495	

Sources: 24; 25

Notes:
[1] Program is offered in both English and French.
[2] Collaborative program between Laurentian University and Lakehead University

62%. In 2011, 58% of the graduates were female.(24; 25) In addition, the number of first-year postgraduate residents increased by 122% (from 557 to 1,237) between 2000 and 2014.(8)

While the number of medical-school positions has grown in the province, the number of residency positions has decreased recently. In 2016 the government cut 25 residency positions and had plans to cut an additional 25 positions in 2017, although the latter has been placed on hold until at least 2018-19.(26) There were a total of 5,137 residents in 2015-16, of which 4,855 are funded by the Ministry of Health and Long-Term Care.(27; 28) In 2016 there were a total of 1,194 R-1 (entry-level postgraduate) residency positions available, with 994 for Canadian medical graduates (of which 966 were filled) and 200 for international medical graduates (of which 179 were filled).(29) Examples of the distribution of filled positions for Canadian medical graduates (and international medical graduates) include: 424 (and 64) in family medicine, 142 (and 32) in internal medicine, 61 (and 15) in psychiatry, 32 (and four) in general surgery, and seven (and one) in public health and preventive medicine.(29)

International medical graduates

Ontario has the largest number of postgraduate medical training positions for international medical graduates in the country, and offers 200 of the available 340 training and assessment places each year.(30) The program enables physicians trained outside of Canada to train and practise in the province. Of the 200 positions offered, half are two-year residencies in family medicine and the other half are for specialties requiring at least four years of residency.(30) As part of the program, physicians sign a return-of-service agreement with the Ministry of Health and Long-Term Care for five years of full-time services in eligible communities, which are communities in need of physicians.(30)

Title of 'doctor'

As noted in Chapter 2, the *Regulated Health Professions Act, 1991* states that only certain regulated health professionals can use the title of 'doctor' when providing (or offering to provide) health services to individuals. In addition to physicians, which are our focus here, the list includes chiropractors, dentists, optometrists, and psychologists, as well as (with certain conditions and restrictions) naturopaths and practitioners of traditional Chinese medicine.

Unregulated health workers

Unregulated health workers are also contributing significantly to the growth of the health workforce. Despite the lack of a self-regulation regime governing these workers, there are mechanisms in place to protect and serve the public interest where most categories of them are concerned (e.g., regulations, contracts and other arrangements with their employers). While we focus here on two types of workers, we recognize that there are many others (e.g., paramedics and dental assistants). First, we focus on personal support workers, who play a central role in home and community care. The home and community care sector is a major focus of the Patients First initiative, and care is increasingly being shifted from traditional hospital settings to community-based settings.(31) Second, we focus on physician assistants, who have been a more recent and contested addition to the health workforce.(32)

Personal support workers

Personal support workers deliver a range of personal support services, typically under the direction of a registered nurse or registered practical nurse, and primarily in the home and community care sector (e.g., private homes) and long-term care sector (i.e., long-term care homes), and to a lesser extent in hospitals (e.g., rehabilitation and palliative care).(33; 34) There is limited information available on the personal support worker workforce in Ontario and no statistics available through the Canadian Institute for Health Information. In 2011, the Ministry of Health and Long-Term Care created a registry to recognize and collect information on the profession, however, the registry was subsequently closed in February 2016.(35; 36)

The Ministry of Health and Long-Term Care estimates that there are approximately 100,000 personal support workers working in Ontario, of which approximately 57,000 work in long-term care homes, over 34,000 work in the home and community care sector, and 7,000 provide care in hospitals.(36; 37) Their base hourly wage has been increased by $4.00, and as of 2015 publicly funded personal support workers earn a minimum base wage of $16.50 per hour.(37) The Ministry's Personal Support Worker Workforce Stabilization Strategy currently focuses on: 1) creating full-time/permanent employment; 2) assisting recent graduates; 3) supporting leadership among personal support workers; and 4) recruiting and retaining them.(37)

Physician assistants

Physician assistants are a category of unregulated health worker that has recently been added to Ontario's health system. Established in 2007, physician assistants support and extend the reach of physicians, often in interprofessional teams, and work primarily in emergency medicine and primary care.(38) The aim in introducing physician assistants was to improve patient access and reduce wait times (e.g., in emergency room departments). In 2016 there were 200 physician assistants working in over 100 sites.(39) Two universities in the province offer education programs: McMaster University and the University of Toronto (in collaboration with the Northern Ontario School of Medicine and The Michener Institute for Applied Health Sciences).(39)

Planning, education and training, and other policy levers

Several organizations are involved in planning, education and training, and other initiatives related to the health workforce (Table 5.7). The Health Professions Regulatory Advisory Council (established by the *Regulated Health Professions Act, 1991*) advises and makes recommendations to the Minister of Health and Long-Term Care on whether unregulated health workers should be regulated and whether amendments to the act should be made.(40) HealthForceOntario was created in 2006 to address workforce planning, as a combined initiative of the Ministry of Health and Long-Term Care and the Ministry of Advanced Education and Skills Development (formerly the Ministry of Training, Colleges and Universities).(41; 42) HealthForceOntario's strategy includes introducing new and expanding healthcare provider roles. HealthForceOntario Marketing and Recruitment Agency was created in 2007 and focuses on the recruitment, retention and distribution of regulated health professionals and unregulated health workers.(43) The budget for HealthForceOntario's strategy has grown from $448 million in 2006 to $738.5 million in 2013, a 65% increase.(22)

Table 5.7: Health workforce: Planning, education and training, and related initiatives

Planning
HealthForceOntario's 2014 strategic directions include:(120) • delivering health workforce solutions through supporting recruitment and retention as well as efforts related to distribution of health human resources; • building strategic partnerships through outcome-based partnerships; and • improving processes by maximizing opportunities for efficiencies and integration of leading practice tools. HealthForceOntario has created a strategy specific to nurses to address the instability in the nursing workforce.(121) The strategy focuses on: • full-time employment; • recruitment and retention; and • creating positive and rewarding work environments.

Continued on next page

Health human resource forecasting models (22)
- Planning for physician human resources in Ontario has traditionally been utilization-based. In 2007, the Ministry of Health and Long-Term Care in conjunction with the Ontario Medical Association contracted the Conference Board of Canada to develop a needs-based model. The model compares the supply of physician services to the population's need for health services in order to quantify the gap in services as well as physician requirements. Some limitations exist with the model as a result of data-availability issues.
- In 2008 the Ministry of Health and Long-Term Care engaged in a similar process to develop a needs-based nursing model. However, there were various issues, including problems with the understatement of first-year enrolment, which have limited the applicability of the model.

Education and training

Nursing education (122)
- The College of Nurses of Ontario is the regulatory body and sets the requirements for entry-to-practice as well as practice standards.
- There are three types of nursing programs:(123)

  1. registered nurses, which is a university (baccalaureate) degree program offered either through a collaborative college-university program or a four-year university program;
  2. nurse practitioners, which is an advanced university education program for registered nurses, delivered by a consortium of nine universities, and overseen by the Council of Ontario University Programs in Nursing; and
  3. registered practical nurses, which is a two-year college diploma program.

Medical education (22)
- The College of Physicians and Surgeons of Ontario regulates the practice of medicine in the province.
- Both undergraduate and postgraduate medical education is offered at the six universities listed in Table 5.6.

Continuing professional development (50)
- Continuing professional development programs are available through universities, hospitals, professional associations, and regulatory colleges.
- Continuing medical education is monitored through the College of Family Physicians of Canada and the Royal College of Physicians and Surgeons of Canada.

Related initiatives

Nursing initiatives:(48)

9,000 Nurses Commitment (22)
- In 2007, the government made a commitment to hiring 9,000 more nurses over four years. However, the initiative has been extended in order to reach the goal and data are not available to determine the number of nursing positions that were created through the initiative.

Late Career Nurse Initiative
- For nurses aged 55 and older who spend a portion of time in less physically demanding activities (e.g., mentoring and teaching).

Nursing Graduate Guarantee Initiative
- The initiative supports new nurses through full-time job opportunities.

Nursing Career OrIENtation
- The program provides full-time employment to internationally educated nurses who are newly registered in Ontario.

Tuition Support Program for Nurses
- The program provides tuition reimbursement for graduating nurses from rural and remote communities in exchange for signing a return-of-service agreement.

Continued on next page

From 2005 to 2012, the Ministry of Training, Colleges and Universities worked with the Ministry of Health and Long-Term Care to increase enrolment in physician training programs by the following amounts:(22)
- 22% increase in first-year undergraduate medical-school enrolment;
- 60% increase in first-year postgraduate trainees;
- 67% increase in family medicine first-year postgraduate trainees;
- 56% increase in specialist first-year postgraduate trainees; and
- 48% increase in international medical graduates in residency training.

Physician initiatives:(124)

Northeastern Ontario Health Professional Development Program
- Targeted to health professionals in northeastern Ontario to increase access to educational opportunities.

Ontario Physician Locum Programs
- The Emergency Department Locum Programs provide emergency department locum coverage for designated hospitals with difficulties filling emergency department shifts.

- Northern Specialist Locum Programs – Urgent Locum Tenens Program and the Respite Locum Tenens Program – are designed specifically for northern Ontario communities.

- The Rural Family Medicine Locum Program provides temporary, short-term replacement coverage for practising rural family physicians.

Physician Outreach Program for General/Family Practitioners
- As part of the Northern Health Programs, the program provides primary-care clinics and physician telephone back-up services to underserviced areas.

Sources: 22; 50; 120-122; 125-129

Planning

Health workforce planning provides the foundation for considering and making changes to the supply and distribution of the workforce. There are three main approaches to planning: 1) utilization-based, 2) needs-based, and 3) effective demand-based.(44) Utilization-based planning incorporates the number, mix and population distribution of health professionals and health workers to create baseline estimates for future planning. Needs-based planning differs in that workforce decisions are based on projected population-health needs and the mix, supply and distribution of workers required to address these needs. Effective demand-based planning incorporates population-health needs as well as societal economic considerations, taking into account that resource constraints limit the extent to which health needs can be met.(44)

The Ministry of Health and Long-Term Care has relatively recently transitioned from a utilization-based approach to workforce planning to a mixed approach that incorporates elements of needs-based planning and shifts from a sole focus on physicians to a focus on both physicians and nurses. Historically, the ministry focused on estimating medical workforce needs based on the number and geographic distribution of physicians in the province (e.g., using physician-to-population ratios).(44) In 2007, the ministry, in collaboration with the Ontario Medical Association (OMA), contracted the Conference Board of Canada to create a needs-based model for physician workforce planning.(45) The model helped to project the population-health needs for physician services by taking into account disease incidence and prevalence, socio-economic and lifestyle factors, and population demographics.(45) The model was found to have limited reliability due to data availability and quality issues.(8)

In 2008, the ministry contracted with an external consultant to develop a similar needs-based model for nursing workforce planning.(22) The model had limitations both in the assumptions being used (e.g., understating first-year enrolment data and rate of direct patient care) and in forecasting any gaps between supply and need at the regional level.(22)

To support health workforce planning for nurses, the College of Nurses of Ontario created the three-factor framework to account for the factors that influence decision-making related to the category of nurse assignment (registered nurse or registered practical nurse).(46) The level of autonomy and scope of practice between the different nursing professions varies based on the education and training demanded, and the framework guides employers to make decisions on nurse utilization based on three factors:

1) client factors, including complexity of the client's condition, predictability of the client's outcomes, and likelihood that the client will experience negative outcomes;
2) nurse factors, consisting of efficient consultation, transferring an element of the care or transferring all care; and
3) environment factors, including practice supports (e.g., policies and protocols), consultation resources, and the stability/predictability of the environment.(46)

The three factors are placed on a continuum such that registered practical nurses or registered nurses autonomously provide care for clients with cases that are less complex, predictable, and at lower risk for negative outcomes. (46) As the complexity increases, care moves away from registered practical nurses to registered nurses and the need for registered nurses to consult and collaborate with other health professionals increases.

Education and training

Nursing education in the province ranges from a two-year college diploma (registered practical nurses) to an advanced university education (nurse practitioners) (Table 5.7). The College of Nurses of Ontario, as the regulatory body for the profession, sets the requirements for entry-to-practice as well as practice standards. In 2014, there were 4,034 registered nursing graduates ready for entry to practice (which includes pre-licensure nursing education that entitles successful graduates to apply for licensure), of whom 239 were nurse practitioners.(47) The Nursing Education Initiative provides $1,500 professional-development grants to registered nurses and registered practical nurses, and focuses on supporting nursing knowledge and skill development.(48) The program is funded by the Ministry of Health and Long-Term Care and administered by the Registered Nurses' Association of Ontario.

Six universities offer undergraduate and postgraduate medical education programs: University of Toronto, McMaster University, Western University, University of Ottawa, Queen's University, and Northern Ontario School of Medicine (Table 5.6). The University of Ottawa is the only program that is offered in both English and French, however, the Northern Ontario School of Medicine offers opportunities for learning in French for Francophone students. The Ministry of Advanced Education and Skills Development provides funding for universities and undergraduate positions, and the Ministry of Health and Long-Term Care funds postgraduate training. In the 2011-12 fiscal year, $485 million was spent on physician initiatives, including $315 million on medical schools and resident salaries, and $107 million on medical schools to support academic activities.(22)

All physicians in the province are required to participate in continuing professional development and report their activities to either the College of Family Physicians of Canada (for family physicians) or the Royal College of Physicians and Surgeons of Canada (for specialists).(49) Continuing professional development programs are available through universities, hospitals, professional associations, regulatory colleges, and national professional bodies. Continuing medical education is offered through the six universities listed above, many hospitals, the OMA, the Ontario College of Family Physicians, the College of Family Physicians of Canada, and the Royal College of Physicians and Surgeons of Canada.(50)

Education and training for leadership roles in the health system is less formalized. The 'LEADS in a Caring Environment Capabilities Framework' is generally well accepted as a guide to understanding and defining health leadership, and many education and training programs (and related resources and tools) are available in the province. Despite the existing and nascent leadership capacity in the system, consulting firms are frequently drawn upon to supplement this capacity.(51; 52)

Other policy levers

There are a variety of policy levers that can be used in order to make adjustments to the supply and distribution of the health workforce. For example, other 'building blocks' can be harnessed, such as governance arrangements to expand scopes of practice, financial arrangements to incentivize specific behaviours, and delivery arrangements to change the skill mix within interprofessional teams. Having pharmacists administer many types of vaccinations and allowing nurses to prescribe, as are currently being considered, would require a change to their respective scopes of practice (a governance arrangement), an appropriate remuneration mechanism (a financial arrangement), and adjustments to policies related to interprofessional models like Family Health Teams (a delivery arrangement). Evidence about the effectiveness of policy levers can be found by searching Health Systems Evidence (www.healthsystemsevidence.org).

A key policy lever for much of the health workforce are collective agreements. In the case of nurses, the Ontario Nurses' Association is the union that bargains with employers on behalf of nurses, whereas the Registered Nurses' Association of Ontario and the Registered Practical Nurses Association of Ontario act as professional associations, not unions. In the case of physicians, on the other hand, the OMA is not a union and it negotiates a Physician Services Agreement (not a collective agreement) with government on behalf of physicians (who are prohibited by the *Labour Relations Act, 1995* from unionizing).(53) The Physician Services Agreement expired in 2014 and a newly negotiated agreement was voted down by OMA members in 2016.

The use of policy levers to make adjustments to the supply and distribution of the health workforce can be fraught, just as it can be with some other types of professionals. Health professionals are highly knowledgeable and skilled, which leads them (among other factors) to place great value on their professional autonomy. And many health professionals, particularly physicians, have made significant investments in their private practices, which are in many cases essentially small (and sometimes very large) businesses. So the use of policy levers requires that consideration be given to whether and when resistance to particular policy levers is sufficiently justified that the government and voters are willing to sacrifice some or all elements of the health system's 'triple aim.' To add 'improving the provider experience' as a fourth aim, as some have suggested, may not make a decision about trade-offs any easier.

Key health workforce initiatives

There are a number of other initiatives targeting the health workforce, the majority of which are oriented towards increasing access to healthcare in rural and remote communities, by creating opportunities for and incentivizing healthcare providers to practise in these areas (often as a complement to efforts to recruit candidates from and train them in the areas where they will be needed). The Northern Health Programs are provided through the Ministry of Health and Long-Term Care and include programs ranging from recruitment and retention initiatives to tuition support for nurses.(54)

As part of HealthForceOntario's strategy, goals were set to hire 9,000 new nurses and increase the share of nurses working full time in the province to 70% from 64%, over the four-year period of 2008 to 2012.(22; 55) The 9,000 Nurses Commitment had a budget of $309 million to hire the nurses. A review of the program showed that the number of nurses increased by 7,300, which is short of the original goal.(22) Full-time employment goals also fell slightly short of the set goals and by the end of 2011, 67% of nurses were employed full time.(22)

In addition to the recruitment and retention initiatives, HealthForceOntario's strategy established three new healthcare roles in the province. In addition to physician assistants (covered in the unregulated health workers section of this chapter), clinical specialist radiation therapist and anesthesia assistant roles have been created.(56) These new healthcare roles were created to address areas of high need. Clinical specialist radiation therapists are medical radiation technologists with advanced training who work in interprofessional teams in cancer-care settings. Anesthesia assistants are respiratory therapists and registered nurses with additional training to support anesthesiologists in the care of surgical patients during anesthesia.

Conclusion

Over the past decade the health workforce in Ontario has continued to grow, which has led to some tangible improvements for Ontarians (e.g., the majority of Ontarians are now registered with a primary-care provider). While the health workforce has grown, the trends in workforce supply are not necessarily aligning with the needs of the population. The health system is facing challenges: Ontarians are living longer and experiencing more chronic conditions and complex needs. In addition, Ontarians living in rural and remote areas continue to have trouble accessing care. In order to meet the needs of Ontarians, new approaches to health workforce planning are being applied. These include needs-based modelling, expanding scopes of practice, and the creation of new healthcare roles. Future health workforce considerations that move beyond nurses and physicians include interprofessional teams and fully engaging the range of regulated health professionals and unregulated health workers in the health system and across sectors.

References

1. Health Quality Ontario. Measuring up: HQO's 2015 yearly report. Toronto: Queen's Printer for Ontario; 2015. http://www.hqontario.ca/portals/0/Documents/pr/measuring-up-2015-en.pdf (accessed 24 August 2016).

2. Ministry of Finance. Ontario population projections update, 2015–2041. Toronto: Queen's Printer for Ontario; 2016. http://www.fin.gov.on.ca/en/economy/demographics/projections/ (accessed 25 August 2016).

3. CIHI. Seniors and the health care system: What is the impact of multiple chronic conditions. Ottawa: Canadian Institute for Health Information; 2011.

4. Government of Ontario. Ontario introduces legislation to further improve patient access and experience. Toronto: Queen's Printer for Ontario; 2016. https://news.ontario.ca/mohltc/en/2016/06/ontario-introduces-legislation-to-further-improve-patient-access-and-experience.html (accessed 25 August 2016).

5. Ministry of Health and Long-Term Care. Patients first: A proposal to strengthen patient-centred health care in Ontario. A discussion paper. Toronto: Queen's Printer for Ontario; 2015.

6. World Health Organization. Monitoring the building blocks of health systems: A handbook of indicators and their measurement strategies. Geneva: World Health Organization; 2010.

7. Crossley TF, Hurley J, Jeon SH. Physician labour supply in Canada: A cohort analysis. Department of Economics working paper series. Hamilton: McMaster University; 2006.

8. Office of the Auditor General of Ontario. 2015 annual report of the Office of the Auditor General of Ontario. Chapter 4, section 4.02: Health human resources. Toronto: Office of the Auditor General of Ontario; 2015.

9. Ministry of Health and Long-Term Care. Rural and northern health care framework. Stage 1 report. Toronto: Queen's Printer for Ontario; 2011.

10. CIHI. Regulated nurses, 2015: RN/NP data tables. Table 21 - Registered nursing workforce, by urban or rural/remote designation and jurisdiction, Canada, 2006 to 2015. Ottawa: Canadian Institute for Health Information; 2016.

11. Statistics Canada. Population, urban and rural, by province and territory (Ontario). Ottawa: Statistics Canada; 2011. http://www.statcan.gc.ca/tables-tableaux/sum-som/l01/cst01/demo62g-eng.htm (accessed 24 August 2016).

12. CIHI. Regulated nurses, 2015. Ottawa: Canadian Institute for Health Information; 2016.

13. Registered Nurses' Association of Ontario. Coming together, moving forward: Building the next chapter of Ontario's rural, remote and northern nursing workforce. Toronto: Registered Nurses' Association of Ontario; 2015.

14. CIHI. Supply, distribution and migration of Canadian physicians, 2014: Data tables. Ontario - Profile. Ottawa: Canadian Institute for Health Information; 2015.

15. CIHI. Regulated nurses, 2015: RN/NP data tables. Table 5 - Registered nursing supply, by jurisdiction, Canada, 2006 to 2015. Ottawa: Canadian Institute for Health Information; 2016.

16. Grinspun D, Harripaul-Yhap A, Jarvi K, Lenartowych T. Mind the safety gap in health system transformation: Reclaiming the role of the RN. Toronto: Registered Nurses' Association of Ontario; 2016.

17. Registered Nurses' Association of Ontario. Registered nurse/nurse practitioner workforce backgrounder. Toronto: Registered Nurses' Association of Ontario; 2016.

18. College of Nurses of Ontario. FAQ: Declaration of practice. Toronto: College of Nurses of Ontario; 2014. http://www.cno.org/en/maintain-your-membership1/declaration-of-practice/ (accessed 25 August 2016).

19. Health Quality Ontario. Quality in primary care: Setting a foundation for monitoring and reporting in Ontario. Toronto: Queen's Printer for Ontario; 2015.

20. CIHI. How Canada compares: Results from the Commonwealth Fund 2015 international health policy survey of primary care physicians. Ottawa: Canadian Institute for Health Information; 2016.

21. Osborn R, Moulds D, Schneider EC, Doty MM, Squires D, Sarnak DO. Primary care physicians in ten countries report challenges caring for patients with complex health needs. Health Affairs 2015;34(12): 2104-12.

22. Office of the Auditor General of Ontario. 2013 annual report of the Office of the Auditor General of Ontario. Chapter 3, section 3.02: Health human resources. Toronto: Office of the Auditor General of Ontario; 2013.

23. Ministry of Health and Long-Term Care. Orthopaedic surgery (bone/spine). Toronto: Ministry of Health and Long-Term Care; 2016. http://www.ontariowaittimes.com/Surgerydi/en/Service_Data.aspx?View=0&Type=0&Modality=2&ModalityString=2&ModalityType=2&ModalityTypeString=2&LHIN=&city=&pc=&dist=0&hosptID=619&str=B&period=0 (accessed 24 August 2016).

24. CIHI. Health personnel database. Canada's healthcare providers, 1997 to 2011 - A reference guide. Table 4, number of graduates of medical education programs, by school of graduation and sex, Canada, 1997 and 2011. Ottawa: Canadian Institute for Health Information; 2011.

25. CIHI. Health personnel database. Canada's healthcare providers, 1997 to 2011 - A reference guide. Table 1, list of accredited medical education programs, by school, Canada, 2010 and 2011. Ottawa: Canadian Institute for Health Information; 2011.

26. Ontario Medical Association. Government decision to cut residency spots short-sighted: Ontario's doctors. Toronto: Ontario Medical Association; 2016. https://www.oma.org/Mediaroom/PressReleases/Pages/residencyspots.aspx (accessed 24 August 2016).

27. CAPER. Table A-1i Field of post-M.D. training by faculty of medicine providing post-M.D. training, by province of location of Faculty of Medicine providing post-M.D. training (regular ministry-funded trainees only) Ottawa: Canadian Post-MD Education Registry; 2016.

28. CAPER. Table A-1ii Field of post-M.D. training by faculty of medicine providing post-M.D. training (residents only) Ottawa: Canadian Post-MD Education Registry; 2016.

29. Canadian Resident Matching Service. 2016 R-1 match positions available, positions filled in Ontario. Ottawa: Canadian Resident Matching Service; 2016.

30. Ministry of Health and Long-Term Care. Health Workforce Planning and Regulatory Affairs Division. International medical graduates. Toronto: Queen's Printer for Ontario; 2016. http://www.health.gov.on.ca/en/pro/programs/hhrsd/physicians/international_medical_graduates.aspx (accessed 25 August 2016).

31. Ministry of Health and Long-Term Care. Patients first: A roadmap to strengthen home and community care. Toronto: Queen's Printer for Ontario; 2015.

32. Vanstone M, Boesveld S, Burrows K. Introducing physician assistants to Ontario. Health Reform Observer - Observatoire des Réformes de Santé 2014;2(1): 4.

33. Ministry of Health and Long-Term Care. Health Workforce Planning and Regulatory Affairs Division. Other health providers. Toronto: Queen's Printer for Ontario; 2016. http://www.health.gov.on.ca/en/pro/programs/hhrsd/other/ (accessed 25 August 2016).

34. Ontario Personal Support Worker Association. What is a personal support worker? Ontario Personal Support Worker Association; 2016. http://opswa.webs.com/what-is-a-psw (accessed 21 September 2016).

35. PSW Registry Ontario. The Ontario PSW Registry - closing. Toronto: Ontario Communisty Support Association; 2016. http://www.pswregistry.org (accessed 24 August 2016).

36. Government of Ontario. Ontario creating registry for personal support workers. Toronto: Queen's Printer for Ontario; 2011. https://news.ontario.ca/mohltc/en/2011/05/ontario-creating-registry-for-personal-support-workers.html?_ga=1.151103737.1103199844.1444060626 (accessed 24 August 2016).

37. Ministry of Health and Long-Term Care. Health Bulletins. Ontario increasing wages for personal support workers. Toronto: Queen's Printer for Ontario; 2015. http://health.gov.on.ca/en/news/bulletin/2015/hb_20150622.aspx (accessed 26 August 2016).

38. HealthForceOntario Marketing and Recruitment Agency. Physician assistants in Ontario. Toronto: Queen's Printer for Ontario; 2015. http://www.healthforceontario.ca/en/M4/Ontario's_Physician_Assistant_Initiative (accessed 24 August 2016).

39. HealthForceOntario Marketing and Recruitment Agency. Physician assistants in Ontario. Frequently asked questions. Toronto: Queen's Printer for Ontario; 2016. http://www.healthforceontario.ca/en/M4/Ontario%27s_Physician_Assistant_Initiative/Frequently_Asked_Questions (accessed 24 August 2016).

40. Health Professions Regulatory Advisory Council. Mandate. Toronto: Queen's Printer for Ontario; 2013. http://www.hprac.org/en/about/mandate.asp (accessed 24 August 2016).

41. HealthForceOntario. About us. Toronto: Queen's Printer for Ontario; 2016. http://www.healthforceontario.ca/en/M1/About_Us (accessed 24 August 2016).

42. HealthForceOntario. HealthForceOntario (HFO). Toronto: Queen's Printer for Ontario; 2016. http://www.healthforceontario.ca/en/M1/About_Us/HealthForceOntario_%28HFO%29 (accessed 24 August 2016).

43. HealthForceOntario. HealthForceOntario marketing and recruitment agency. Toronto: Queen's Printer for Ontario; 2016. http://www.healthforceontario.ca/en/M1/About_Us/HealthForceOntario_Marketing_and_Recruitment_Agency_%28HFO_MRA%29 (accessed 24 August 2016).

44. Moat KA, Waddell K, Lavis JN. Evidence brief: Planning for the future health workforce of Ontario. Hamilton: McMaster Health Forum; 2016.

45. HealthForceOntario. Ontario population needs-based physician simulation model. Toronto: Queen's Printer for Ontario; 2010.

46. College of Nurses of Ontario. Practice guideline. RN and RPN practice: The client, the nurse and the environment. Toronto: College of Nurses of Ontario; 2014.

47. CIHI. Regulated nurses, 2015: RN/NP data tables. Table 1 - Number of registered nursing graduates (entry to practice) and nurse practitioner graduates by jurisdiction, Canada, 2005 to 2014. Ottawa: Canadian Institute for Health Information; 2016.

48. HealthForceOntario. Government support for nurses. Toronto: Queen's Printer for Ontario; 2016. http://www.healthforceontario.ca/en/Home/Nurses/Training_%7C_Practising_Outside_Ontario/Nursing_Strategy/Government_Support (accessed 25 August 2016).

49. College of Physicians and Surgeons of Ontario. Continuing professional development. Frequently asked questions. Toronto: College of Physicians and Surgeons of Ontario; 2016. http://www.cpso.on.ca/CPSO/media/documents/CPSO Members/Resources/CPD_FAQs.pdf (accessed 25 August 2016).

50. HealthForceOntario. Continuing medical education. Toronto: Queen's Printer for Ontario; 2014. http://www.healthforceontario.ca/en/Home/Physicians/Training_%7C_Practising_in_Ontario/Continuing_Medical_Education (accessed 25 August 2016).

51. Dickson G, Lindstrom R. Systems transformation: LEADS in a caring environment - Leadership Capabilities Framework. Victoria: Leaders for Life; 2010.

52. Lavis JN, Moat KA, Tapp C, Young C. Evidence brief: Improving leadership capacity in primary and community care in Ontario. Hamilton: McMaster Health Forum; 2015.

53. Simpson J. The OMA compared to unions: Ontario labour relation statutes, binding arbitration and unilateral action. Ontario Medical Review 2016;83(2): 9-11.

54. Ministry of Health and Long-Term Care. Northern Health Programs. Toronto: Queen's Printer for Ontario; 2016. http://www.health.gov.on.ca/en/pro/programs/northernhealth/ (accessed 25 August 2016).

55. HealthForceOntario. Ontario's comprehensive nursing strategy. Toronto: Queen's Printer for Ontario; 2010. https://www.healthforceontario.ca/UserFiles/file/Floating/Program/Marketing/nursing-strategy-symposium-june-2010-en.pdf (accessed 21 September 2016).

56. HealthForceOntario. New roles in health care. Toronto: Queen's Printer for Ontario; 2016. http://www.healthforceontario.ca/en/Home/Other_Regulated_Health_Professionals/Training_%7C_Practising_In_Ontario/New_Roles_in_Health_Care (accessed 25 August 2016).

57. College of Nurses of Ontario. Legislation and regulation RHPA: Scope of practice, controlled acts model. Toronto: College of Nurses of Ontario; 2014.

58. Ontario College of Social Workers and Social Service Workers. Position paper on scopes of practice. Toronto: Ontario College of Social Workers and Social Service Workers; 2008.

59. CIHI. Canada's health care providers—2011 provincial profiles: A look at 27 health professions. About medical laboratory technologists. Ottawa: Canadian Institute for Health Information; 2012.

60. CIHI. Canada's health care providers—2011 provincial profiles: A look at 27 health professions. About medical radiation technologists. Ottawa: Canadian Institute for Health Information; 2012.

61. Registered Nurses' Association of Ontario. Primary solutions for primary care. Maximizing and expanding the role of the primary care nurse in Ontario. Toronto: Registered Nurses' Association of Ontario; 2012.

62. Canadian Physiotherapy Association. About physiotherapy. Ottawa: Canadian Physiotherapy Association; 2016. https://www.physiotherapy.ca/About-Physiotherapy (accessed 24 August 2016).

63. College of Occupational Therapists of Ontario. Public/employer information. Toronto: College of Occupational Therapists of Ontario; 2006. http://www.coto.org/public/default.asp (accessed 25 August 2016).

64. Ontario Association of Optometrists. About us. Toronto: Ontario Association of Optometrists; 2016. http://www.optom.on.ca/OAO/About_Us/About_Us/OAO/About_Us/About_Us.aspx?hkey=f2f85663-444f-4387-aac6-e409bc77ce63 (accessed 24 August 2016).

65. Ontario Paramedic Association. Paramedics. Blind River: Ontario Paramedic Association; 2016. https://www.ontarioparamedic.ca/paramedics/ (accessed 24 August 2016).

66. Ontario Pharmacists Association. Scope of practice. Toronto: Ontario Pharmacists Association; 2016. https://www.opatoday.com/professional/advocacy/scope-of-practice (accessed 24 August 2016).

67. College of Physicians and Surgeons of Ontario. The changing scope of practice. Toronto: College of Physicians and Surgeons of Ontario; 2015. http://www.cpso.on.ca/policies-publications/policy/changing-scope-of-practice (accessed 25 August 2016).

68. College of Psychologists of Ontario. About psychology. Toronto: College of Psychologists of Ontario; 2013. http://www.cpo.on.ca/faqs.aspx (accessed 25 August 2016).

69. CIHI. Health personnel database. Canada's healthcare providers, 1997 to 2011 - A reference guide. Supply trends, table 2, number of active registered dentists, by province/territory, Canada, 1997 to 2011. Ottawa: Canadian Institute for Health Information; 2011.

70. CIHI. Health personnel database. Canada's healthcare providers, 1997 to 2011 - A reference guide. Supply trends, table 2, number of registered dental hygienists, by province/territory, Canada, 1997 to 2011. Ottawa: Canadian Institute for Health Information; 2011.

71. CIHI. Health personnel database. Canada's healthcare providers, 1997 to 2011 - A reference guide. Supply trends, table 2, number of pharmacists, by province/territory, Canada, 1997 to 2011. Ottawa: Canadian Institute for Health Information; 2011.

72. CIHI. Health personnel database. Canada's healthcare providers, 1997 to 2011 - A reference guide. Supply trends, table 2, number of registered opticians, by province, Canada, 2011. Ottawa: Canadian Institute for Health Information; 2011.

73. CIHI. Health personnel database. Canada's healthcare providers, 1997 to 2011 - A reference guide. Supply trends, table 2, number of active registered optometrists, by province/territory, Canada, 1997 to 2011. Ottawa: Canadian Institute for Health Information; 2011.

74. CIHI. Health personnel database. Canada's healthcare providers, 1997 to 2011 - A reference guide. Supply trends, table 2, number of active registered midwives, by province/territory, Canada, 1997 to 2011. Ottawa: Canadian Institute for Health Information; 2011.

75. CIHI. Health personnel database. Canada's healthcare providers, 1997 to 2011 - A reference guide. Supply trends, table 2, number of medical radiation technologists, by province/territory, Canada, 1997 to 2011. Ottawa: Canadian Institute for Health Information; 2011.

76. CIHI. Health personnel database. Canada's healthcare providers, 1997 to 2011 - A reference guide. Supply trends, table 2, number of registered chiropractors, by province/territory, Canada, 1997 to 2011. Ottawa: Canadian Institute for Health Information; 2011.

77. CIHI. Health personnel database. Canada's healthcare providers, 1997 to 2011 - A reference guide. Supply trends, table 2, number of registered dieticians, by province/territory, Canada, 1997 to 2011. Ottawa: Canadian Institute for Health Information; 2011.

78. CIHI. Health personnel database. Canada's healthcare providers, 1997 to 2011 - A reference guide. Supply trends, table 2, number of active registered health information management professionals, by province/territory, Canada, 1997 to 2011. Ottawa: Canadian Institute for Health Information; 2011.

79. CIHI. Health personnel database. Canada's healthcare providers, 1997 to 2011 - A reference guide. Supply trends, table 2, number of active registered environmental public health professionals, by province/territory, Canada, 1997 to 2011. Ottawa: Canadian Institute for Health Information; 2011.

80. CIHI. Health personnel database. Canada's healthcare providers, 1997 to 2011 - A reference guide. Supply trends, table 2, number of medical laboratory technologists, by province/territory, Canada, 1997 to 2011. Ottawa: Canadian Institute for Health Information; 2011. CIHI. Health personnel database. Canada's healthcare providers, 1997 to 2011 - A reference guide. Supply trends, table 2, number of active registered members of the Canadian Organization of Medical Physicists, by province, Canada, 1997 to 2011. Ottawa: Canadian Institute for Health Information; 2011.

81. CIHI. Health personnel database. Canada's healthcare providers, 1997 to 2011 - A reference guide. Supply trends, table 2, number of registered audiologists, by province/territory, Canada, 2001 to 2011. Ottawa: Canadian Institute for Health Information; 2011.

82. CIHI. Health personnel database. Canada's healthcare providers, 1997 to 2011 - A reference guide. Supply trends, table 2, number of occupational therapists, by province/territory, Canada, 2001 to 2011. Ottawa: Canadian Institute for Health Information; 2011.

83. CIHI. Health personnel database. Canada's healthcare providers, 1997 to 2011 - A reference guide. Supply trends, table 2, number of registered paramedics, by province, Canada, 2011. Ottawa: Canadian Institute for Health Information; 2011.

84. CIHI. Health personnel database. Canada's healthcare providers, 1997 to 2011 - A reference guide. Supply trends, table 2, number of physiotherapists, by province/territory, Canada, 1997 to 2011. Ottawa: Canadian Institute for Health Information; 2011.

85. CIHI. Health personnel database. Canada's healthcare providers, 1997 to 2011 - A reference guide. Supply trends, table 2, number of active registered psychologists, by province/territory, Canada, 1997 to 2011. Ottawa: Canadian Institute for Health Information; 2011.

86. CIHI. Health personnel database. Canada's healthcare providers, 1997 to 2011 - A reference guide. Supply trends, table 2, number of registered respiratory therapists, by province/territory, Canada, 1997 to 2011. Ottawa: Canadian Institute for Health Information; 2011.

87. CIHI. Health personnel database. Canada's healthcare providers, 1997 to 2011 - A reference guide. Supply trends, table 2, number of registered social workers, by province/territory, Canada, 1997 to 2011. Ottawa: Canadian Institute for Health Information; 2011.

88. CIHI. Health personnel database. Canada's healthcare providers, 1997 to 2011 - A reference guide. Supply trends, table 2, number of registered speech-language pathologists, by province/territory, Canada, 2001 to 2011. Ottawa: Canadian Institute for Health Information; 2011.

89. CIHI. Health personnel database. Canada's healthcare providers, 1997 to 2011 - A reference guide. Supply trends, table 3, number of active registered physicians, including residents, by province/territory, Canada, 1997 to 2011. Ottawa: Canadian Institute for Health Information; 2011.

90. CIHI. Canada's health care providers: Provincial profiles - 2013. Table 1 - Number of providers in selected health professions, Canada, 2009 to 2013. Ottawa: Canadian Institute for Health Information; 2013.

91. CIHI. Canada's health care providers: Provincial profiles - 2013. Table 7 Number of providers in selected health professions, Ontario, 2009 to 2013. Ottawa: Canadian Institute for Health Information; 2013.

92. CIHI. Health personnel database. Canada's healthcare providers, 1997 to 2011 - A reference guide. Supply trends, table 2, number of employed active registered nurses, by province/territory, Canada, 1997 to 2011. Ottawa: Canadian Institute for Health Information; 2011.

93. CIHI. Health personnel database. Canada's healthcare providers, 1997 to 2011 - A reference guide. Supply trends, table 2, number of licensed practical nurses, by province/territory, Canada, 1997 to 2011. Ottawa: Canadian Institute for Health Information; 2011.

94. CIHI. Health personnel database. Canada's healthcare providers, 1997 to 2011 - A reference guide. Supply trends, table 2, number of active registered physicians, excluding residents, by province/territory, Canada, 1997 to 2011. Ottawa: Canadian Institute for Health Information; 2011.

95. CIHI. Nursing database. Regulated nursing workforce, 2012. Table 4, registered nursing workforce per 100,000 population, by jurisdiction, Canada, 2008 to 2012. Ottawa: Canadian Institute for Health Information; 2012.

96. CIHI. Nursing database. Regulated nursing workforce, 2012. Table 18, nurse practitioner workforce per 100,000 population, by jurisdiction, Canada, 2008 to 2012. Ottawa: Canadian Institute for Health Information; 2012.

97. CIHI. Nursing database. Regulated nursing workforce, 2012. Table 27, licensed practical nursing workforce per 100,000, by jurisdiction, Canada, 2008 to 2012. Ottawa: Canadian Institute for Health Information; 2012.

98. CIHI. Physiotherapist workforce, 2012. Physiotherapist database. Physiotherapist workforce profile, Canada, 2008 to 2012. Ottawa: Canadian Institute for Health Information; 2012.

100. CIHI. Physiotherapist workforce, 2012. Physiotherapist database. Physiotherapist workforce profile, Ontario, 2008 to 2012. Ottawa: Canadian Institute for Health Information; 2012.

101. CIHI. Occupational therapist workforce, 2012. Occupational therapist database. Occupational therapists workforce by count, percentage and per 100,000 population by province or territories of registration, 2006 to 2012. Ottawa: Canadian Institute for Health Information; 2012.

102. CIHI. Pharmacist workforce, 2012. Pharmacist database. Pharmacist workforce by count, percentage and per 100,000 population by province or territories of registration, 2008 to 2012. Ottawa: Canadian Institute for Health Information; 2012.

103. CIHI. Canada's health care providers—2010 provincial profiles: A look at 24 health occupations. Ottawa: Canadian Institute for Health Information; 2010.

104. CIHI. Ontario, number of health personnel in selected profession, by registration status, 2004. Health personnel database, population estimates from Statistics Canada, 2004. Ottawa: Canadian Institute for Health Information; 2006.

105. CIHI. Canada's health care providers—2011 provincial profiles: A look at 27 health professions. Ontario, number of health personnel in selected health professions, by registration status, 2011. Ottawa: Canadian Institute for Health Information; 2012.

106. Statistics Canada. Table 051-0001 - Estimates of population, by age group and sex for July 1, Canada, provinces and territories, annual, CANSIM (database). Ottawa: Statistics Canada; 2013. http://www.statcan.gc.ca/tables-tableaux/sum-som/l01/cst01/health21a-eng.htm (accessed 24 August 2016).

107. CIHI. Regulated nurses, 2015: LPN data tables. Table 14 - Licensed practical nursing workforce, by jurisdiction, Canada, 2006 to 2015. Ottawa: Canadian Institute for Health Information; 2016.

108. CIHI. Regulated nurses, 2015: RN/NP data tables. Table 8 - Registered nursing supply, by sex and jurisdiction, Canada, 2006 to 2015. Ottawa: Canadian Institute for Health Information; 2016.

109. CIHI. Regulated nurses, 2015: RN/NP data tables. Table 9 - Registered nursing supply, average age, by jurisdiction, Canada, 2006 to 2015. Ottawa: Canadian Institute for Health Information; 2016.

110. CIHI. Regulated nurses, 2015: RN/NP data tables. Table 10 - Registered nursing supply, by age group and jurisdiction, Canada, 2011 to 2015. Ottawa: Canadian Institute for Health Information; 2016.

111. CIHI. Regulated nurses, 2015: RN/NP data tables. Table 11 - Registered nursing supply, by years since graduation and jurisdiction, Canada, 2006 to 2015. Ottawa: Canadian Institute for Health Information; 2016.

112. CIHI. Regulated nurses, 2015: RN/NP data tables. Table 12 - Registered nursing supply, by location of graduation (Canada and international) and jurisdiction of registration, Canada, 2006 to 2015. Ottawa: Canadian Institute for Health Information; 2016.

113. CIHI. Regulated nurses, 2015: RN/NP data tables. Table 14 - Registered nursing supply, by highest level of education in nursing and jurisdiction, Canada, 2006 to 2015. Ottawa: Canadian Institute for Health Information; 2016.

114. CIHI. Regulated nurses, 2015: RN/NP data tables. Table 15 - Registered nursing workforce, by jurisdiction, Canada, 2006 to 2015. Ottawa: Canadian Institute for Health Information; 2016.

115. CIHI. Regulated nurses, 2015: RN/NP data tables. Table 16 - Registered nursing workforce, by employment status and jurisdiction, Canada, 2006 to 2015. Ottawa: Canadian Institute for Health Information; 2016.

116. CIHI. Regulated nurses, 2015: RN/NP data tables. Table 17 - Registered nursing workforce, by place of work and jurisdiction, Canada, 2006 to 2015. Ottawa: Canadian Institute for Health Information; 2016.

117. CIHI. Regulated nurses, 2015: RN/NP data tables. Table 24 - Nurse practitioner supply, by jurisdiction, Canada, 2006 to 2015. Ottawa: Canadian Institute for Health Information; 2016.

118. CIHI. Regulated nurses, 2015: RN/NP data tables. Table 28 - Nurse practitioner workforce, by jurisdiction, Canada, 2006 to 2015. Ottawa: Canadian Institute for Health Information; 2016.

119. CIHI. Regulated nurses, 2015: LPN data tables. Table 4 - Licensed practical nursing supply, by jurisdiction, Canada, 2006 to 2015. Ottawa: Canadian Institute for Health Information; 2016.

120. HealthForceOntario Marketing and Recruitment Agency. Strategic plan. Toronto: Queen's Printer for Ontario; 2014.

121. HealthForceOntario. Nursing strategy. Toronto: Queen's Printer for Ontario; 2014. http://www.healthforceontario.ca/en/Home/Nurses/Training_%7C_Practising_In_Ontario/Nursing_Strategy (accessed 25 August 2016).

122. College of Nurses of Ontario. Become a nurse. Approved nursing programs. Toronto: College of Nurses of Ontario; 2013. http://www.cno.org/en/become-a-nurse/approved-nursing-programs/ (accessed 25 August 2016).

123. Registered Nurses' Association of Ontario. Types of nursing. Toronto: Registered Nurses' Association of Ontario; 2014. http://careersinnursing.ca/new-nursing-and-students/career-options/types-nursing (accessed 26 August 2016).

124. HealthForceOntario. Government support for physicians. Toronto: Queen's Printer for Ontario; 2016. http://www.healthforceontario.ca/en/Home/Physicians/Training_%7C_Practising_in_Ontario/Government_Support (accessed 25 August 2016).

125. HealthForceOntario. Nursing graduate guarantee initiative for new graduate nurses educated in Canada. Toronto: Queen's Printer for Ontario; 2014. http://www.healthforceontario.ca/en/Home/Nurses/Training_%7C_Practising_In_Ontario/Nursing_Strategy/Nursing_Graduate_Guarantee (accessed 25 August 2016).

126. HealthForceOntario. Nursing Career OrIENtation Initiative for internationally-educated nurses. Toronto: Queen's Printer for Ontario; 2014. http://www.healthforceontario.ca/en/Home/Nurses/Training_%7C_Practising_In_Ontario/Nursing_Strategy/Nursing_Career_OrIENtation (accessed 25 August 2016).

127. HealthForceOntario. Ontario physician locum programs. Toronto: Queen's Printer for Ontario; 2014. http://www.healthforceontario.ca/en/M4/Ontario_Physician_Locum_Programs (accessed 24 August 2016).

128. Ministry of Health and Long-Term Care. Ontario population needs-based physician simulation model. Toronto: Queen's Printer for Ontario; 2010.

129. Registered Practical Nurses Association of Ontario. Nursing education initiative. Mississauga: Registered Practical Nurses Association of Ontario; 2013. http://www.rpnao.org/practice-education/nursing-education-initiative (accessed 24 August 2016).

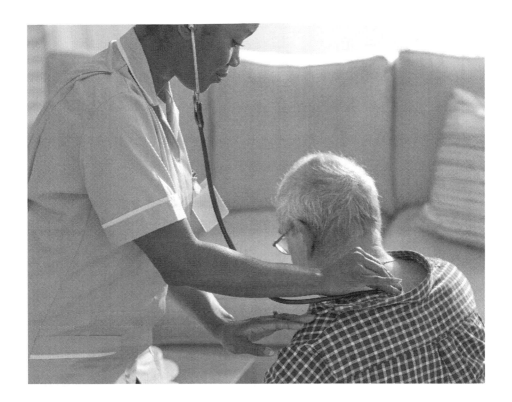

6. Care by sector

John N. Lavis and Amanda C. Hammill

Key messages for citizens

- Community Care Access Centres are the gateway to government-funded home care and long-term care homes, and a source of information about care that is not publicly funded.

- In primary care, teams are increasingly common, typically with a family physician as the 'most responsible' provider.

- Private not-for profit hospitals remain the cornerstone of acute specialty care.

- Rehabilitation care is less a sector in its own right than an element of many other sectors.

- Long-term care homes (or nursing homes) are where adults can live and both receive help with daily activities and have access to 24-hour nursing and personal support services.

- The province's 36 local public health agencies aim to improve the health of Ontarians using strategies that are both population-based (e.g., smoking by-laws) and individually targeted.

Key messages for professionals

- Home care includes professional (e.g., nursing) services, personal support services (e.g., bathing), and homemaking services (e.g., meals).

- Key pillars of a 'primary-care home' include team-based and patient-centred care, same-day appointments, comprehensive and coordinated care, and continuity of care.

- While acute specialty care is still provided in hospitals, Independent Health Facilities and Out of Hospital Premises increasingly provide lower risk diagnostic and therapeutic procedures.

- Payment for rehabilitation care depends on whether citizens are eligible for government-funded care, were injured in an automobile accident or have a work-related injury or disease.

- Long-term care homes provide long-term nursing and personal care, and short-term convalescent and respite care.

- Local public health agencies operate programs in five areas: family health, infectious diseases prevention and control, chronic disease and injuries, environmental health, and emergency preparedness.

Key messages for policymakers

- Community Care Access Centres are funded by Local Health Integration Networks, and will soon become part of them, and support access to home and community care.

- Primary care has been evolving from a sector dominated by family physicians operating as small business owners and paid on a fee-for-service basis by the Ontario Health Insurance Plan to interprofessional primary-care teams paid through an array of funding models.

- A transition is underway from hospitals to community-based specialty clinics as the primary site for lower risk diagnostic and therapeutic procedures.

- Depending on the circumstances of the patient and care, rehabilitation care is governed by several parts of government and paid for directly by patients, or indirectly by government and those paying automobile, health insurance or workers' compensation premiums.

- Most healthcare in a long-term care home is paid for by government, but clients pay standardized charges for accommodation.

- Local public health agencies are governed at the municipal level by a local board of health and funded by provincial and municipal governments to promote health and prevent disease.

. . .

In the first of four chapters focused on using the building blocks to provide care, we examine care by sector. The six sectors include home and community care, primary care, specialty care, rehabilitation care, long-term care, and public health. Syntheses of the available research evidence about each of these sectors can be identified by searching Health Systems Evidence (www.healthsystemsevidence.org) and using the 'Sectors' filter in the 'advanced search.' These sectors can be described in two ways: 1) by the policies that govern them, the programs and services offered within them, the places where programs and services are provided, and the people who provide the programs and services (i.e., by the 4Ps); and 2) by the governance, financial and delivery arrangements within which they operate (i.e., the building blocks). We focus primarily on the former, and provide sector4P figures (a term we introduced in Chapter 1) to summarize the key features of the sectors, and secondarily on governance, financial and delivery arrangements.

Before describing these sectors, however, some orientation is warranted. On the one hand, each of these sectors appears quite distinct and conjures up classic images about what happens within them. Home and community care includes the nurse who comes to a client's home to change the dressings on a wound after the client has had surgery, and the agency that a client visits when in need of a range of support services to cope with an addiction. Primary care includes the family physician who is a patient's first point of contact with the health system when ill, diagnoses and treats most conditions, refers complex cases to specialists when needed, and ensures continuity of care. Specialty care can mean both a patient's nearest acute-care hospital (which can be called acute care or hospital care) and the specialists (like surgeons) who see patients in their clinics or in the hospital. Specialty care can be called secondary, tertiary or even quaternary care depending on the level of specialization in the care being provided. Rehabilitation care can mean the rehabilitation clinic that clients visit or the rehabilitation hospital where patients stay when recovering from a major accident, as well as the physiotherapist a client visits for help in dealing with back or shoulder pain. Long-term care includes the long-term care homes where adults can live and have access to 24-hour nursing care, personal support services for help with daily activities, and on-call medical (i.e., physician-provided) care. Public health includes the people and laboratories working, often behind the scenes, to protect and promote the health of Ontarians, often using approaches (like water fluoridation) directed at populations, not individuals.

On the other hand, the boundaries between these sectors can (and perhaps should) be quite porous (patients need to move easily between them after all) and the classic images can be out of date or not fully accurate. For example, home and community care are often lumped together despite each having some unique features. Family physicians are increasingly working as part of an interprofessional healthcare team that may be led by a nurse practitioner, involve registered nurses, social workers, dietitians, pharmacists and other registered health professionals, and be more focused on providing patient-centred, comprehensive and coordinated care than ever before. Much specialty care is now provided outside hospitals, in organizations called Independent Health Facilities or Out of Hospital Premises. Rehabilitation care includes many types of health professionals, including the occupational therapist who can help an adult with a disability participate in paid or unpaid work, and the speech-language pathologist who can help a child with a speech delay or disorder. Long-term care is sometimes considered part of home and community care because the residents of long-term care homes are living in their home and community just like everyone else. And public health practitioners are often involved in direct service provision (e.g., sexually transmitted disease clinics) and increasingly are being drawn into closer partnerships with primary-care organizations.

While in the past specialty care (particularly hospitals) and to a lesser extent public health (particularly after the SARS outbreak) have been the focus of a great deal of attention, for the past few years the home and community care sector and the primary-care sector have been the ones garnering the most attention.(1; 2) These two sectors, as well as the public health sector, will be affected in significant ways by the passage of the *Patients First Act, 2016*,(3) which is a sufficiently new development that we have not incorporated it in the sector4P figures in this chapter or the rest of this book. We address the home and community care sector before turning to the others.

Home and community care

The key player in home and community care is the Community Care Access Centre (CCAC) in each of Ontario's 14 regions (described in Chapter 1), although these will be absorbed into Local Health Integration Networks (LHINs) by 2017 as a result of the *Patients First Act, 2016*.(3) Each CCAC receives funds from the Government of Ontario (through the LHIN) and uses these funds to pay their own staff and to pay (some or all of the costs of) the many for-profit, not-for-profit and public organizations that provide home and community care. CCAC staff can: 1) provide information about home and community care (and long-term care) options in the area, regardless of whether they are funded (in whole or in part) by the government; 2) determine eligibility for government-funded services and settings (to an upper limit of visits per week, hours per week or both); 3) arrange for and coordinate the delivery of government-funded professional, personal support and homemaking services for people living in their own homes and for school children with special needs (i.e., home care); and 4) make arrangements for admission to (or for getting on the waiting list for) many day programs and supportive housing programs (i.e., community care), as well as to some chronic-care and rehabilitation beds, and all long-term care homes (which we turn to later in this chapter). Any Ontarian can directly approach a CCAC for these types of support and there is no charge for the support provided by CCAC staff to Ontarians with a valid health card. Ontarians can also directly approach agencies that provide home and community care services to obtain care beyond what the government funds, and then pay for this care themselves.

Policies that govern home and community care

The key policies that govern home and community care (Figure 6.1) are the:

1) *Home Care and Community Services Act, 1994*, which established clients' rights, the basket of covered services, the complaints and appeals process, and (through a regulation) the eligibility criteria for services and the maximum levels of nursing, personal support and homemaking services that can be provided to an individual (and also established what we now know as CCACs, although when they began operation in 1996, there were 43 across the province);

2) *Community Care Access Corporations Act, 2001*, which established the mandate, governance and accountabilities of CCACs; and

3) *Local Health Systems Integration Act, 2006*, which, in 2007, reduced the number of CCACs from 43 to 14, aligned their boundaries with those of the LHINs, and established the LHINs as their funder.

The regulated health professionals working in the sector are governed by the *Regulated Health Professionals Act, 1991*, and we return to these professionals below. The accountabilities of the community support service agencies, mental health and addiction organizations, and diabetes education centres that are funded by government to provide home and community care are established through contracts called multi-sector service agreements (of which there are currently 260 between CCACs and these agencies).(4)

Programs offered through home and community care

From a program perspective, home care – for people living in their own homes and for school children with special needs – includes four types of services:

1) professional services, which include assessing a client's needs, providing care or helping the client to care for herself (and the client's family to

cope), and can range from nursing care, physiotherapy, occupational therapy, respiratory therapy, speech-language therapy and social work to help with healthy eating and home healthcare supplies (e.g., walking aids and wound dressings);

2) personal support services, which include helping clients with daily care or helping clients to safely manage these activities on their own, and can range from help with getting in and out of bed or a chair to bathing, dressing (and undressing), eating, personal hygiene (e.g., mouth and hair care), and toilet hygiene;

3) homemaking services, which include housework (e.g., cleaning, doing laundry), planning and preparing meals, shopping for food or clothing, managing money, and caring for children; and

4) end-of-life care at home, which includes the above as well as in-home visits and respite care by trained volunteers (which we will return to in Chapter 7, where we address end-of-life care).

Personal support workers are involved in the delivery of many personal support services, however, they work under the direction of a registered nurse or registered practical nurse and are not a regulated health profession. There is no charge for the home care approved by a CCAC for Ontarians with a valid health card.

Programs can seem less well defined in community care and can vary from community to community and from population group to population group. Depending on the program area, the reasons may be that: the provincial government may play a less visible role as a funder and steward; many parts of the provincial government may be involved depending on the needs of different population groups (e.g., Ministry of Children and Youth Services, Ministry of Community and Social Services, Ministry of Community Safety and Correctional Services, Ministry of Education, and Ministry of Municipal Affairs and Housing); and municipal governments along with a broad range of for-profit, not-for-profit and public organizations may be involved in complementing provincial government efforts to address the needs of local community residents. Some traditional examples of community care programs include:

1) adult day programs that support social, fitness and other healthy activities among those living at home or who are homeless;

2) supportive housing, which means housing, typically paid for by the client, and access to many personal support, homemaking and other services (either provided by the landlord or by a separate organization),

Figure 6.1: Home and community care

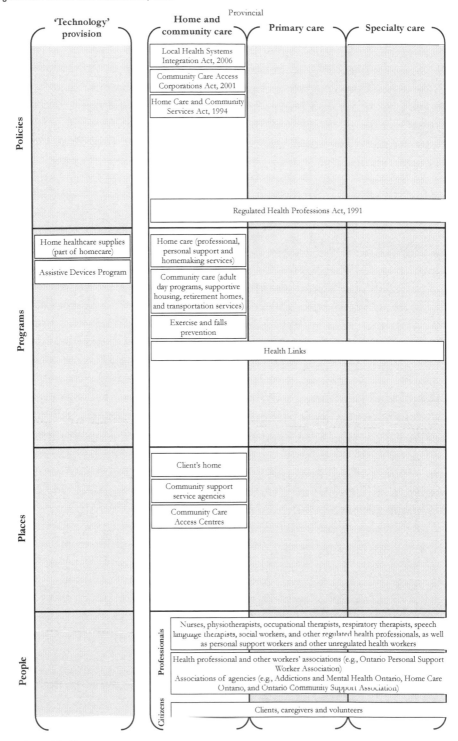

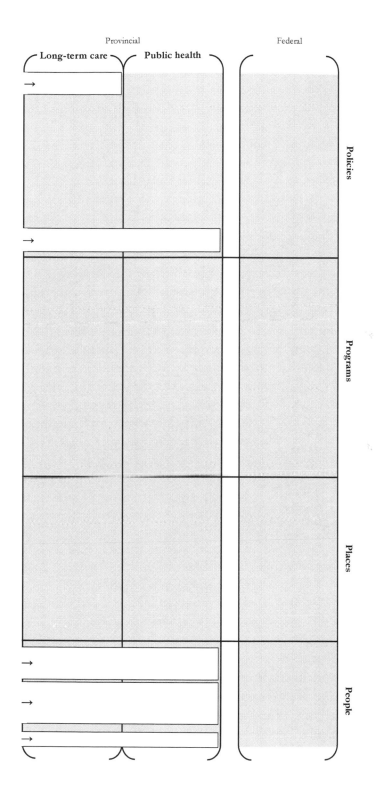

typically at no additional cost (and such 'assisted living services in supportive housing' are often used by the frail elderly and by people with acquired brain injury, HIV/AIDS, mental health issues or physical disabilities);

3) retirement homes, which means housing that includes some personal support (e.g., housework) and homemaking services (e.g., meals), as well as social and recreational opportunities and a 24-hour emergency-response system, all of which is typically paid for fully by the client (and which is often used by elderly Ontarians who no longer can or wish to live at home, but who do not need the more intensive care provided in a long-term care home); and

4) transportation services for those who do not have access to public transportation or need help in using it.

Other examples of community care programs are specific to a population group. For example, those with a terminal illness can access community hospice services (which include counselling and support groups, among other services) and residential hospices (which provide a broad range of palliative care in a home-like setting). We discuss end-of-life care in greater detail in Chapter 7.

Community care programs are also typically considered to include exercise and falls-prevention programs. Through these programs, individuals can participate in classes that help them improve their strength and balance and that are led by fitness instructors, trained peer facilitators or support workers (not physiotherapists). While not formally considered part of the health system, 'elderly persons centres' offer a range of cultural, learning, recreational and social programs for seniors.

Home and community care clients with long-term physical disabilities can also benefit from the Assistive Devices Program, which provides access to a range of personalized assistive devices when prescribed by a physician, including: 1) enteral feeding supplies; 2) insulin pumps and supplies for diabetic children; 3) monitors and test strips for insulin-dependent diabetics (through an agreement with the Canadian Diabetes Association); 4) oxygen and oxygen delivery equipment; 5) respiratory equipment; 6) hearing aids; 7) visual and communication aids; 8) orthoses (braces, garments and pumps); 9) prostheses; and 10) wheelchairs/mobility aids and specialized seating systems.

Health Links is a program designed to meet the needs of clients with complex needs (often multiple, complex conditions that require frequent interactions with professionals in many sectors). CCACs can be the lead organization for Health Links, while community support service agencies and mental health and addiction organizations are its key service providers. Each of the (currently 82) Health Links in the province strives to ensure that those involved in a client's care (nurses, personal support workers, family physician and others) work as a team to develop an individualized coordinated care plan and ensure the plan is followed. They also ensure that clients are taking the right medications and have someone to call who knows them and their situation.

Places and people involved in home and community care

The places where home and community care are provided range from the client's home (for home care and for assisted living services in supportive housing or in retirement homes), to community support service agencies and mental health and addictions organizations (for classes, day programs, etc.) and residential hospices, to the CCACs themselves (for information, eligibility determinations and some services).

The people involved in home and community care include the clients themselves, caregivers and volunteers, as well as a broad range of health professionals (including those mentioned above as well as the physicians involved in the clients' medical care, and the personal support workers and other unregulated providers of home and community care services). The health professionals are represented by their respective professional associations (and personal support workers by the Ontario Personal Support Worker Association), however, the agencies for which they work are represented by member associations such as Addictions and Mental Health Ontario (for mental health and addiction organizations), Home Care Ontario (for for-profit community support service agencies), and the Ontario Community Support Association (for not-for-profit community support service agencies). Also, CCACs are represented by the Ontario Association of Community Care Access Centres.

Governance, financial and delivery arrangements in home and community care

Governance, financial and delivery arrangements (i.e., the building blocks) are another lens through which home and community care can be described. Most of the governance arrangements that are salient to home and community care have been addressed under 'policies' above. Three key financial arrangements for this sector include: 1) the greater reliance on out-of-pocket payments as a source of financing compared to hospital-based and physician-provided care; 2) the funding to providers flowing primarily through the LHINs and then to CCACs (although the latter will be absorbed into the LHINs under the terms of the *Patients First Act, 2016*); and 3) the use of a 'commissioning' model according to which CCACs pay for care that meets the performance standards outlined in service agreements (as is done by the Workplace Safety and Insurance Board and Cancer Care Ontario, or CCO, which we return to in Chapter 7). Also, unlike hospital-based and physician-provided care, home care is not covered under an inter-provincial agreement for Ontarians visiting another province. In terms of delivery arrangements, as of 2014, there were over 800 community support service agencies, over 300 mental health and addiction organizations, 245 diabetes education centres, and 14 CCACs (see Table 4.1). Also, in 2015, 16,877 nurses (17% of all nurses in Ontario) worked in home and community care (see Table 5.4).

Primary care

The key player in primary care is increasingly the primary-care team and less the individual family physician or nurse practitioner, even though they are likely to be deemed the 'most responsible' provider on a given team. That said, about three quarters of Ontarians still receive primary care from a family physician working independently and, as we discuss in Chapter 11, access to family physicians remains a significant concern for some Ontarians. The concept of a 'patient's primary-care home' is gaining traction in Ontario, and includes a number of pillars beyond delivering care using teams and providing access to a most responsible care provider.(5) Examples of other pillars include providing patient-centred care (e.g., setting care goals appropriate to a patient's condition and context), ensuring timely access to care (e.g., using advanced access scheduling to provide same-day appointments for those who need them and providing

24/7 coverage for more urgent issues), providing comprehensive and coordinated care (e.g., proactively providing preventive services to those who may benefit), and ensuring continuity of care (e.g., communicating with home and community care providers, specialists, long-term care homes, and public health practitioners, as well as with pharmacies and dental offices, which we discuss in Chapter 8).(5)

A topic newer to the sector is accountability for a geographically defined population, as opposed to accountability for the patients who have chosen to join the roster of a family physician who (or more rarely a primary-care clinic that) receives at least some form of capitation payment, meaning a fixed payment per patient per year (and as opposed to the lack of explicit accountability for the patients who visit a family physician paid on a fee-for-service basis for each visit). Rural and remote communities, particularly in northern Ontario, have been experimenting with local health hubs over the past few years.(6) These health hubs are connected to a designated local hospital (a 'district health campus') and to other health-care providers in the area (e.g., CCACs and community service agencies) as part of an integrated district network, although the primary-care providers involved in these health hubs typically still approach accountability in terms of their patient roster. The Government of Ontario has signalled through the *Patients First Act, 2016* a commitment to establishing geographically defined populations at a 'LHIN sub-region' level, which may range from 40,000 citizens to 350,000 in densely populated urban areas.(1).

Policies that govern primary care

Unlike other sectors, primary care is notable for the lack of policies (or at least acts and regulations) that govern care in the sector (Figure 6.2). Existing policies include:

1) self-regulation regimes established under the *Medicine Act, 1990* and *Regulated Health Professions Act, 1991* for the physicians and later the nurse practitioners, nurses, social workers, dietitians, pharmacists and other health professionals involved in primary care (as well as under the *Health System Improvements Act, 2007*, which regulated kinesiology, naturopathy and homeopathy, and psychotherapy, and the *Regulated Professions Statute Law Amendment Act, 2009*, which increased the scopes of practice of many regulated health professionals);

2) the *Health Insurance Act, 1990* that governs the Ontario Health

Figure 6.2: Primary care

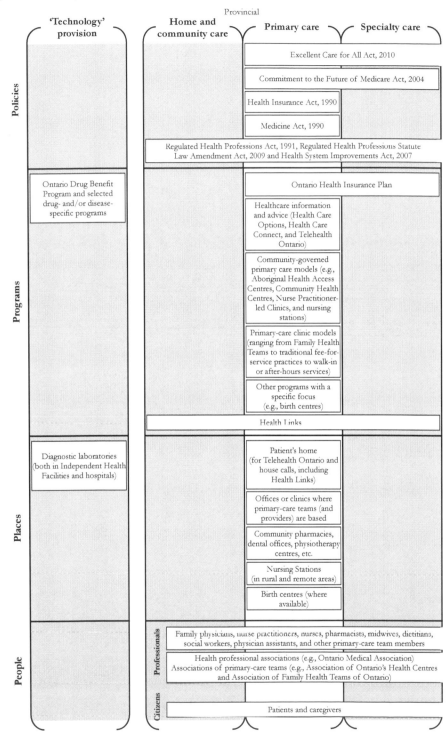

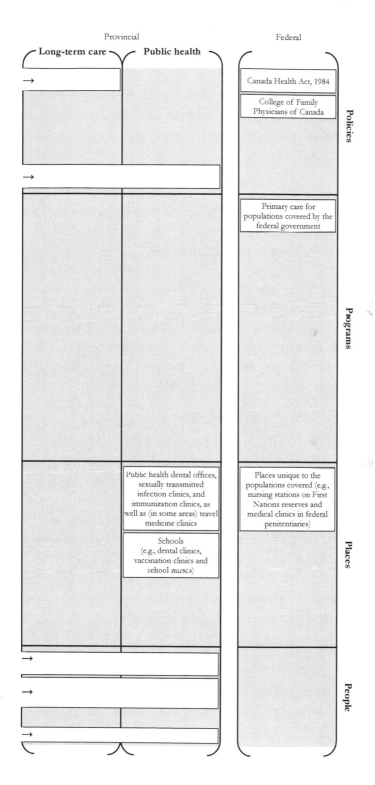

Insurance Plan (OHIP), through which all physicians (not just primary-care physicians) are paid;

3) the *Commitment to the Future of Medicare Act, 2004* that reaffirmed the province's commitment to no user fees for medically necessary physician-provided care (as is also required by the federal government's *Canada Health Act, 2004*) and established an organization (that became what is now known as Health Quality Ontario, or HQO) to publicly report on health-system performance and support continuous quality improvement; and

4) the *Excellent Care for All Act, 2010* that extended HQO's role in supporting evidence-based practice, albeit in ways that are likely not very visible in primary care (except for the interprofessional teams – Family Health Teams, Nurse Practitioner-led Clinics, Community Health Centres, and Aboriginal Health Access Centres – that must now submit an annual Quality Improvement Plan to HQO as an *Excellent Care for All Act*-inspired addition to their contracts with government).

The College of Family Physicians of Canada plays a role in setting the educational and continuing professional development requirements for family physicians, which are then given force of law by the College of Physicians and Surgeons of Ontario (one of the self-regulation regimes).

If one broadens the notion of policies to include contracts (an economic instrument, as we described in Chapter 2), however, then much of primary care is now subject to performance standards. About three quarters of family physicians (those who have chosen to enter into an alternative funding model) and all interprofessional teams now work under a contract with government and can face penalties when these standards are not met (see Table 3.7 in Chapter 3). Contracts offer greater flexibility than acts and regulations, which can be seen as either a pro or a con depending on one's perspective.

The only accountabilities for any of the pillars of a patient's primary-care home are established through contracts. The Government of Ontario and an advisory group reporting to it have floated the idea of making commitments to certain aspects of the patient's primary-care home applicable across all of primary care, supporting access to other aspects of the patient's primary-care home that are now available only to those working in some models (e.g., other health professionals who can participate as part of a team), and (as noted above) establishing accountability for a defined population.(1; 7)

The policies governing primary care, even when contracts are included in their definition, leave most family physicians operating as small business owners who must live within the norms of their profession (like all physicians) and the terms of an insurance plan that, either some or most of the time, pays them a fee for each service they provide (and prohibits them from charging patients for medically necessary primary care). An evolution in the first category of policies governing primary care – self-regulation regimes – has led to a broadening of the health professionals who can prescribe drugs. Initially only physicians and dentists (and veterinarians) could prescribe, but now nurse practitioners can prescribe, pharmacists can play a very limited role in prescribing, and the government has indicated that it plans to introduce nurse prescribing.

Perhaps the murkiest area in the policies governing primary care involves organizations like Medcan and the Cleveland Clinic that target private companies' senior executives and wrap a concierge-type service around a mix of: 1) medically necessary care for which they can bill OHIP; 2) non-necessary care (and the concierge service) itself that they can bill executives or their companies for directly; and 3) referrals to for-profit facilities in the U.S. that can bill executives directly (even though regular follow-up and addressing complications back in Ontario are likely to be considered medically necessary care for which they can again bill OHIP).

Programs constituting primary care

A wide variety of programs – beyond OHIP that pays for most primary-care services – operate in the primary-care sector (Table 6.1):
1) healthcare information and advice, including to assist with finding local healthcare services (Health Care Options), finding a primary-care provider (Health Care Connect) and getting free telephone health advice (Telehealth Ontario);
2) community-governed primary-care models that serve socially disadvantaged and hard-to-serve populations (Community Health Centres), Indigenous peoples (Aboriginal Health Access Centres, which we discuss in Chapter 9), and small rural and First Nations communities (nursing stations, which we also discuss in Chapter 9), and the broader population (Nurse Practitioner-led Clinics);
3) primary-care clinic models that range from organizations that tick many of the boxes for a patient's primary-care home (Family Health

Table 6.1: Primary-care programs and services

Program	Services	Who delivers/funds	Who is covered
Health care information and advice			
Health Care Options	Online healthcare services locator (database searchable by postal code)	• Information updated by Community Care Access Centres (CCACs) and community partners • Website hosted and funded by the Ministry of Health and Long-Term Care (MOHLTC)	Ontarians with a valid health card (formerly called an Ontario Health Insurance Plan card)
Health Care Connect	Links 'unattached' patients to primary-care providers	• Website hosted and funded by the MOHLTC	Ontarians with a valid health card
Telehealth Ontario	Free telephone health advice and healthcare options	• Registered nurses provide teletriage services • Funded by the MOHLTC	Anyone
Community-governed primary-care models			
Community Health Centres (CHCs)	Primary-care services, health-promotion and illness-prevention services, and outreach for socially disadvantaged and hard-to-serve populations	• 105 CHCs comprising almost 400 physicians, 300 nurse practitioners, 1,700 other clinical, health promotion and community development professionals, and 800 administrative personnel[1] • Funded by Local Health Integration Networks (LHINs) (with funds from the MOHLTC)[2]	Ontarians with a valid health card and newcomers with a temporary card
Aboriginal Health Access Centres (AHACs)	Combination of traditional healing, primary care, cultural programs, health promotion, community development, and social-support services provided to First Nations, Inuit and Métis peoples and communities	• 10 AHACs across Ontario provide access to physicians, nurse practitioners, traditional healers, dictitians, social workers, and mental health and addiction support services • Funded by LHINs (with funds from the MOHLTC)[3] • Revenue for additional programs obtained from other government branches, community partners, donations, etc.	Indigenous Ontarians
Nurse Practitioner-led Clinics (NPLCs)	Basic primary care, including annual physicals, immunizations, episodic illness care, chronic disease management, health promotion, etc.	• 26 NPLCs in 27 communities across Ontario • Salaries and operational costs funded through transfer payment agreements between LHINs (with funds from the MOHLTC) and the boards of directors[4]	Ontarians with a valid health card who are enrolled with the NPLC

Continued on next page

Program	Services	Who delivers/funds	Who is covered
Community-governed primary-care models – continued			
Nursing stations	Provide front-line primary healthcare and assess for urgent or non-urgent care in small, rural communities, and First Nations communities	• 43 stations in small and rural communities funded by LHINs (with funds from the MOHLTC) • 29 federally funded stations in First Nations communities (four community-operated, 25 Health Canada nurse-run)	Anyone (those without a health card are asked to make a $100 donation)
Primary-care clinic models			
Family Health Teams (FHTs)	Primary care, health promotion and disease prevention, patient system navigation support, facilitation of community-based chronic disease management and self-care, and linking to other healthcare organizations	• 184 FHTs, comprised of at least 2,400 physicians and a range of non-physician providers (nurses, nurse practitioners, social workers, dietitians, pharmacists, and other providers) • Mostly physician-led but with some governed by mixed provider/community boards • Funded by the MOHLTC	Ontarians with a valid health card who are enrolled with the FHT
Family Health Groups (FHGs)	Physician delivered primary care (with patient rostering voluntary)	• 237 FHGs, with a minimum practice size of three physicians • Funded by the MOHLTC	Ontarians with a valid health card
Family Health Networks (FHNs)	Comprehensive primary-care services facilitated through provider networks; includes extended hours and nurse after-hours telephone health advice	• 21 FHNs, with a minimum practice size of three physicians • FHNs require participating physicians to sign governance and FHN agreements to join with the MOHLTC; may also apply to become FHTs	Ontarians with a valid health card who are enrolled with the FHN
Family Health Organizations (FHOs)[5]	Primarily physician-delivered primary care; includes extended hours, and nurse after-hours telephone health advice	• 475 FHOs with a minimum physician group size of three • Funded by the MOHLTC	Ontarians with a valid health card who are enrolled with the FHO
Traditional fee-for-service practices	Family medicine; includes diagnosis and treatment of diseases, physical disorders and injuries, as well as referral	• Solo-physician practices (no defined practice criteria) • Fee-for-service remuneration for OHIP-insured services	Ontarians with a valid health card

Continued on next page

Program	Services	Who delivers/funds	Who is covered

Primary-care clinic models – continued

Program	Services	Who delivers/funds	Who is covered
Walk-in or after-hours services	Non-emergency care for people who do not have a prima-ry-care provider or are unable to reach their own	• Non-hospital based walk-in clinics • Funded by the MOHLTC	Ontarians with a valid health card
Midwifery clinics	24-hour primary midwife care and support throughout pregnancy, labour, birth and thereafter for six weeks	• Over 400 registered midwives provide care in 103 midwifery clinics • Funded by the MOHLTC	Ontarians with a valid health card
Birth centres	A home-like set-ting for birth and delivery, and other support and services such as prenatal classes, birth and postpartum care	• Currently there are three midwife-led birth centres • Birth centres are not-for-profit Independent Health Facilities and funded by the MOHLTC through service agreements	Ontarians with a valid health card

Other programs and services

Program	Services	Who delivers/funds	Who is covered
Diabetes Education Programs (DEPs)	Guidance on healthy eating, weight man-agement, exercise, blood glucose mon-itoring and other self-management skills	• DEPs usually include nurses and dietitians, and may also include other allied health providers as needed, with some programs requiring referral from a primary-care provider • Funded by LHINs (with funds from the MOHLTC)	Ontarians with a valid health card
Centres for Complex Diabetes Care (CCDCs)	Short-term mul-tidisciplinary, coordinated care to stabilize patients with complex diabe-tes and one or more other associated health needs	• CCDCs have been established in six LHIN regions, chosen based on the prevalence of diabetes and the com-plexity and availability of services in the communities • Funded by LHINs (with funds from the MOHLTC)	18 years of age or older, with Type 1 or Type 2 diabetes
Northern Health Travel Program	Partial reimburse-ment of medical travel-related costs to those who must travel at least 100 km one way to the closest medical spe-cialists or designated healthcare facility	• Approved travel grants are paid at 41 cents per kilometre based on return road distance travel between the area of residence and nearest medical specialist, or approved healthcare facility, with a deductible of 100 kilometres • Funded by the MOHLTC	Eligible north-ern Ontario residents, with a valid health card

Continued on next page

Program	Services	Who delivers/funds	Who is covered
Other programs and services – continued			
Underserviced Area Program (UAP)	A series of incentive programs aimed at recruiting healthcare providers to and retaining them in designated underserviced communities[6]	• Northern Health Programs of the UAP are administered by the Primary Health Care Branch • Funded by the MOHLTC	Physicians, nurses and rehabilitation professionals

Sources: 37-53

Notes

[1] New capital projects announced by the MOHLTC in April 2014 included an additional 12 CHCs and 4 AHACs (54).

[2] In the 2013-14 fiscal year, government funding was $369.9 million. Supplemental revenue for additional programming is obtained through other sources, such as other government branches, charitable donations, etc.(44)

[3] In the 2013-14 fiscal year, government funding was $23.7 million for AHACs.(37)

[4] Salaries for up to four full-time nurse practitioners, four interprofessional staff, an administrative lead and clerical staff, and operational costs (which include medical supplies, facilities, professional development, program supplies, information technology, etc.).(38)

[5] FHOs were created through the harmonization of Health Service Organizations, which were introduced in 1978, and Primary Care Networks, which were introduced in 1999.(40)

[6] Northern Health Programs include the Northern and Rural Recruitment and Retention Initiative, the Northern Physician Retention Initiative, the Rehabilitation Professionals Incentive Grant, Tuition Support Program for Nurses, Community Assessment Visit Program, Nursing Community Assessment Visit Program, and the Physician Outreach Program for General/Family Practitioners Guidelines. Programs offer a range of taxable incentives, incentive grants, tuition support, and travel reimbursement programs to primary-care providers in underserved communities (43)

Teams) to traditional fee-for-service practices (and hybrids between the two, including Family Health Groups, Family Health Networks and Family Health Organizations), to walk-in or after-hours services; and

4) a mix of 'other' programs that have a specific focus, including pregnancy and childbirth (midwifery clinics and birth centres), diabetes (diabetes education programs and centres for complex diabetes care), and care in the north (Northern Health Travel Program that supports patients' travel to receive care) or in underserved areas (Underserviced Area Program that supports the recruitment of primary-care professionals).

The primary-care clinic models (category 3 above) are where 'wide variety' turns into 'bewildering array' and where (as noted above) action is being considered. Also, while not specific to primary care (just as it was not specific to the home and community care organizations discussed in the previous section), interprofessional primary-care teams can be the lead organization for, and be key service providers for, Health Links, a program designed to meet the needs of patients with complex needs.

Primary-care patients can also benefit from the Ontario Drug Benefit (ODB) Program and selected drug- and/or disease-specific programs, which we discuss in Chapter 8, as well as from federal government-supported programs for populations covered by that level of government (i.e., First Nations and Inuit, whom we discuss in Chapter 9, Canadian Forces, eligible veterans, Royal Canadian Mounted Police, inmates of federal penitentiaries, and some refugee claimants).

Places and people involved in primary care

The places where primary care is provided range from the client's home (for the telephone advice provided through Telehealth Ontario, the house calls provided by a small number of family physicians, sometimes as part of Health Links, and the visits by primary-care providers to long-term care homes), to the offices or clinics where primary-care teams (and providers) are based (and where most Ontarians receive primary care), to the far less numerous nursing stations and birth centres. Most of these offices and clinics are rented on the private market, although some may be owned by physicians themselves or be part of a First Nations reserve (e.g., a nursing station or birth centre). Primary care is also provided in community pharmacies (e.g., advice about prescription and over-the-counter drugs, prescriptions of buproprion or varenicline for smoking cessation, and flu shots), dental offices (e.g., regular preventive check-ups and fillings for dental cavities, which we address in Chapter 8), and physiotherapy clinics, among other settings.

The people involved in primary care include the patients themselves and the physicians, nurse practitioners and increasingly other health professionals involved in their care (nurses, dietitians, and social workers on primary-care teams, as well as chiropractors among others typically practising separately). The health professionals are represented by their respective professional associations, with the Ontario Medical Association (OMA) playing a particularly prominent role given its privileged access to authority through the Physician Services Committee (although as noted in Chapter 1, the OMA has been playing a much less visible role while it is in a contract dispute with the provincial government). Physician assistants, who work under the supervision of a physician and are not a regulated health profession, are represented by a national group – Canadian Association of Physician Assistants – not a provincial group. Primary-care teams are represented by member associations such as the Association of Ontario's Health Centres (for Aboriginal Health Access Centres, community-governed Family Health Teams, Community Health Centres, and Nurse

Practitioner-led Clinics) and the Association of Family Health Teams of Ontario (for Family Health Teams, Nurse Practitioner-led Clinics, and other interprofessional primary-care organizations).

Governance, financial and delivery arrangements in primary care

Looking at primary care through the lens of governance, financial and delivery arrangements (i.e., the building blocks) provides a complementary perspective. Most of the governance arrangements that are particularly salient to primary care have been addressed under 'policies' above, although it is worth noting here two additional points. First, at the level of primary-care organizations (and as noted in Chapter 2), community-governed interprofessional teams (a subset of Family Health Teams and all Community Health Centres) are governed by boards of directors comprising community members in addition to or instead of owners (unlike physician practices, which may operate as a single medicine professional corporation or under group agreements, but not with community members on a board of directors). Second, at the level of health professions involved in primary care, the provincial government has taken preliminary steps toward pharmacist prescribing and committed to introducing nurse prescribing, both of which are examples of potential changes to professional authority.

Key financial arrangements for this sector include full public payment for medically necessary primary care delivered by family physicians, but using a complex array of funding and remuneration mechanisms (see Table 3.6) that do not flow through LHINs (with the exception of funding for Community Health Centres and other community-governed primary-care models) as they do for most other providers. That said, the *Patients First Act, 2016* designated interprofessional teams, but not physician practices, as 'health service providers' that are funded by and accountable to LHINs. Public health expenditures tend to be reported for midwifery services but not for other primary-care providers (see Table 3.4).

Turning to delivery arrangements, as of 2014 there were 4,012 pharmacies (most of which are in community settings), 1,206 primary-care practices designated as one of Family Health Organizations/Groups/Teams/Networks or Comprehensive Care Models, 105 Community Health Centres, 103 midwifery clinics, 26 Nurse Practitioner-led Clinics, 10

Aboriginal Health Access Centres, and three birthing centres (see Table 4.1). As of 2013, there were 13,973 family physicians (who are more often male than female, Canada-trained than foreign-trained, and working in urban than rural settings), and as of 2013, there were 608 midwives (see Table 5.2 and 5.5), but most other counts of health professionals do not distinguish those working in the primary-care sector from those working in other sectors. The density of family physicians (in 2013) was one per 1,000 population (or 103 per 100,000 population) (see Table 5.3).

Specialty care

The key player in acute specialty care remains the acute-care hospital, which is where patients go for emergency care, where they are admitted because of the severity of their illness or the nature or complexity of the care they require, and where they may go to see their specialist if the specialist runs a clinic or keeps an office in the hospital. As hospitals have responded to financial incentives for greater volumes of procedures and shorter lengths of stay, and faced a limited supply of long-term care homes and other settings to which they can discharge patients who no longer need care in an acute-care hospital, they increasingly provide care to a large pool of very sick patients and a small pool of healthier patients awaiting discharge to other settings (administratively called 'alternative-level-of-care' patients and sometimes pejoratively called 'bed blockers' because they are taking up a bed that could go to a patient currently waiting on a hospital gurney in the emergency room).

As we point out in previous chapters and return to below, notwithstanding the name of the act that governs them (the *Public Hospitals Act, 1990*), the vast majority of hospitals are private not-for profit hospitals (not public hospitals, which suggests that they are government-owned and -operated). Some larger communities have one 'general' hospital and one 'Catholic' hospital meeting the criteria, with 'Catholic' hospitals typically not providing abortions and in future possibly not permitting medical assistance in dying. Four Ontario cities (Hamilton, London, Ottawa and Toronto) have a dedicated children's hospital. The only public (i.e., government-owned and -operated) hospitals in Ontario – the large psychiatric hospitals – have now become private not-for-profit hospitals as well (e.g., Centre for Addictions and Mental Health in Toronto and Waypoint Centre for

Mental Health Care in Penetanguishene). A small number of hospitals were 'grandfathered' when hospital-care insurance was introduced and continue to operate as private for-profit corporations (e.g., Shouldice Hospital in Toronto, which specializes in hernia repair). Hospitals are funded by the provincial government through the LHIN in their region, and neither not-for-profit nor for-profit hospitals can charge patients for medically necessary hospital care. They can and do charge patients for 'extras' like a private room and parking (although in response to growing frustration with parking fees, hospitals now face limits on these fees). Many hospitals, in particular teaching hospitals, house large hospital research institutes, although these more commonly pursue investigator-driven research than address the evidence needs of the hospital (with some exceptions, including the Centre for Practice-Changing Research at the Ottawa Hospital Research Institute).

While hospitals have been the key player in specialty care – both for acute care and for many other forms of specialty care – for many decades, this is changing, both organically and as a result of the provincial government's commitment to "moving procedures into the community."(8, p.12) Community-based specialty clinics increasingly provide – or could provide – lower risk diagnostic procedures (e.g., echocardiograms and colonoscopies) and therapeutic procedures (e.g., cataract procedures, hysterectomies, knee arthroscopies, and prostate surgery), at least in larger population centres. These clinics include hospitals that only provide such procedures (e.g., Hotel Dieu Hospital in Kingston), free-standing clinics operated by hospitals (e.g., Stoney Creek Campus, St. Joseph's Healthcare Hamilton), organizations called Independent Health Facilities (e.g., Kensington Eye Institute in Toronto), and organizations called Out of Hospital Premises. Independent Health Facilities currently provide many diagnostic procedures (e.g., computed tomography, magnetic resonance imaging, and positron emission tomography, also known as CT, MRI and PET scans) and therapeutic procedures (e.g., abortion, dialysis, and many types of surgery). These facilities are typically privately owned and, in the case of many Independent Health Facilities providing diagnostic tests, such as diagnostic imaging, nuclear medicine tests, pulmonary function tests, and sleep-study tests, they are often owned by large for-profit companies. The facilities receive from OHIP both a facility fee for the use of the facility and a professional fee for the specialist (with the exception of the 10 providing diagnostic procedures, which are globally funded). Out of Hospital Premises, which are also privately owned, currently provide cosmetic surgery, endoscopy and interventional pain management under the administration of a variety of types of anesthesia, but the organization does not receive a facility fee from OHIP (just the physician fee). Neither Independent Health Facilities nor Out of Hospital Premises allow overnight stays. Just as with care in hospitals, medically necessary care in Independent Health Facilities and Out of Hospital Premises is free to patients at the point of use.

There is an interdependence between specialists and hospitals, and perhaps there should be one between community-based specialty clinics and hospitals. Many specialists rely on hospitals for access to operating suites, equipment and staff, among other things. Hospitals, in turn, rely on these specialists to provide inpatient coverage and/or consultation, emergency-room coverage and/or consultation, and education (when the hospital is an academic teaching centre), parts of which are sometimes referred to as 'clinical governance.' Specialty clinics, on the other hand, may rely on hospitals for access to diagnostic services and do rely on them to accommodate referrals of high-risk patients and emergency transfers (whether or not they do so under the terms of a formal arrangement). Hospitals may see such specialty clinics as 'poaching' healthier patients – effectively a source of revenue from their LHIN – who need a procedure, test or assessment that the hospital could have provided.

Policies that govern specialty care

Unlike primary-care clinics, specialty-care settings are directly regulated, but as a patchwork, with many of the policies that govern specialty care depending on what (e.g., anesthesia) or where (hospitals or Independent Health Facilities) care is provided (Figure 6.3):

- private not-for-profit hospitals (including those operating their own free-standing specialty clinics and those effectively operating as specialty clinics) are governed under the terms of the (inaccurately named) *Public Hospitals Act, 1990*;
- private for-profit hospitals are governed by the *Private Hospitals Act, 1990*;
- Independent Health Facilities are governed by the *Independent Health Facilities Act, 1990* and policies from the College of Physicians and Surgeons of Ontario;
- Out of Hospital Premises are governed under the terms of regulation

114/94 of the *Medicine Act, 1991* and related policies from the College of Physicians and Surgeons of Ontario; and

- hospitals and specialty clinics that use radiation are governed by the *Healing Arts Radiation Protection Act, 1990*.

Specialty clinics providing endoscopy, mammography and pathology services are also governed from a quality management and public reporting perspective under the terms of an agreement between CCO and the College of Physicians and Surgeons of Ontario. Hospitals and now specialty clinics can voluntarily subject themselves to accreditation by Accreditation Canada. Specialists, like all physicians, are governed by the *Medicine Act, 1991* and by the *Regulated Health Professions Act, 1991*. Also, the Royal College of Physicians and Surgeons of Canada plays a role in setting the educational and continuing professional development requirements for specialists, which (like family physicians) are then given force of law by the College of Physicians and Surgeons of Ontario. Specialty physician offices (like primary-care clinics) are not regulated directly, even though the specialists working in them may be providing the same procedures as those being provided in regulated settings.

Other relevant policies governing specialty care include the:

1) *Public Sector Labour Relations Transition Act, 1997*, as an extension of its precursor, the *Labour Relations Act, 1995*, that requires specialty clinics to assume the terms of existing collective agreements and collective-bargaining processes when commitments to provide procedures are transferred from hospitals to specialty clinics (whether or not they had any unionized staff at the time that they began providing the services);

2) *Commitment to the Future of Medicare Act, 2004*, that reaffirmed the province's commitment to no user fees for medically necessary hospital care (as noted in the previous section and as is also required by the federal government's *Canada Health Act, 2004*) and established HQO to publicly report on health-system performance and support continuous quality improvement (including the requirement for hospitals to make available to the public an annual Quality Improvement Plan);

3) *Local Health System Integration Act, 2006* that established the LHIN as the payer for medically necessary hospital care; and

4) *Excellent Care for All Act, 2010* that requires all hospitals to prepare and publicly report against an annual Quality Improvement Plan, as well as to tie a proportion of their chief executive officer's pay to performance.

Figure 6.3: Specialty care

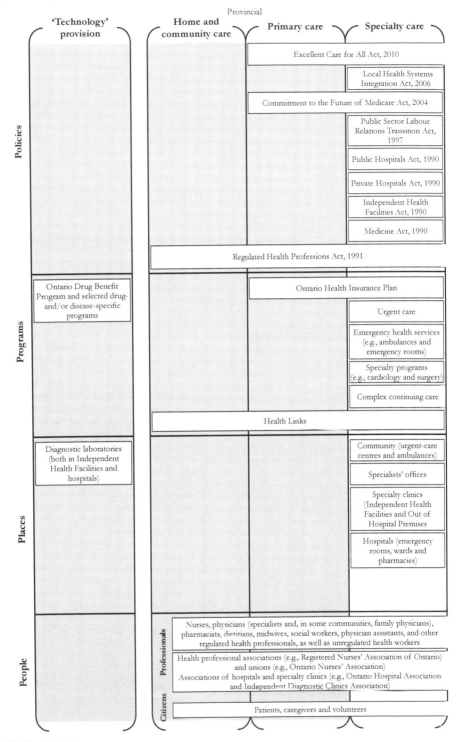

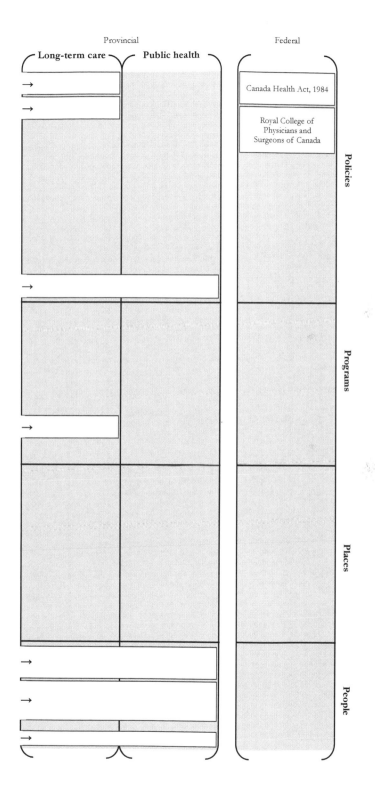

Provincial
Long-term care   Public health

Federal

Canada Health Act, 1984

Royal College of
Physicians and
Surgeons of Canada

Policies

Programs

Places

People

Programs constituting or involving specialty care

A wide variety of programs are available in the acute-care sector or at the intersection between the sector and other sectors:

1) Health Links, a program that is designed to meet the needs of patients with complex needs (ideally without admission to a hospital) and that can be led or contributed to by a hospital;

2) urgent-care centres that fill a gap between primary care and a hospital emergency room;

3) emergency health services that include dispatch centres, land ambulances, air ambulances, base hospitals, and emergency rooms (Table 6.2);

4) specialty programs in over 60 areas (e.g., internal medicine specialties like cardiology and surgical specialties like orthopedics, as well as anesthesia, obstetrics and gynecology, pediatrics, psychiatry, radiology, and laboratory medicine); and

5) complex continuing care for people requiring long-term, medically complex care that cannot be provided at home or in a long-term care home.

Table 6.2: Urgent and emergent specialty care

Program	Services	Who delivers/funds	Who is covered
Ambulatory/outpatient care			
Urgent care	Diagnosis/treatment for urgent, but non-life threatening illnesses or injuries	• Urgent-care centres (day, evening, weekends) • Funded by Local Health Integration Networks (LHINs) (with funds from the Ministry of Health and Long-Term Care or MOHLTC)	All Ontarians with a valid health card
Emergency care			
Dispatch centres	Prioritize 911 requests; deploy, coordinate and direct the movement of all ambulances and emergency response vehicles within a geographic catchment area; and facilitate patient transfers	• 19 Central Ambulance Communications Centres (11 operated by the MOHLTC, five by hospitals, and three by municipalities) and three locally based Ambulance Communications Services • Funded by the MOHLTC	Everyone

Continued on next page

Program	Services	Who delivers/funds	Who is covered
Emergency care – continued			
Land ambulance	Emergency paramedic and patient transfer services	• 42 municipalities and eight other designated delivery agents operate/provide services • Funded by the MOHLTC (50% for municipalities and 100% for First Nations communities and territories without municipal organizations)	All Ontarianss with a valid health card; a portion of the ambulance cost is covered with some exemptions
Air ambulance	Inter-facility patient transfers, on-scene emergency response requiring aero-medical evacuation; transport of organs and surgical recovery teams	• Ornge, a not-for-profit organization responsible for all air transport operations/services, is accountable to the MOHLTC through a performance agreement • Funded by the MOHLTC	All Ontarians with a valid health card; must be requested by a physician
Base hospitals	Provide continuing education, and advice on and monitoring of advanced life support procedures performed by land ambulance paramedics	• Seven regional base hospitals (comprising a group of physicians working out of a hospital) have agreements to provide services with the MOHLTC • Funded by the MOHLTC	Coverage is for emergency health services personnel, not individuals
Emergency rooms (ERs)	Triage, treatment of severe illnesses, and life-threatening injuries	• 126 hospitals provide 90% of Ontario's ER care • Funded by LHINs (with funds from the MOHLTC)	All Ontarians with a valid health card

Sources: 45; 54-60

A key program from the perspective of most specialists is of course OHIP that pays the fees for any medically necessary care they provide. These specialists typically need to have a recent referral from a family physician in order to be eligible for full payment of these fees.

Places and people involved in specialty care

The places where specialty care is provided range from the patient's home in only indirect ways (for Health Links or when calling 911) and community (with urgent-care centres and ambulances) to the far more common specialists' offices, specialty clinics (Independent Health Facilities and Out of Hospital Premises), and hospitals (emergency rooms and wards). Specialty dental services are provided in dental offices, which we address in Chapter 8. Ontarians based in rural and remote communities may need to travel long distances to access a specialist or hospital (and as mentioned in the previous section, the Northern Health Travel Program can provide partial reimbursement for medically necessary travel, and as will be discussed in Chapter 9, another mechanism is available to support travel by Indigenous peoples).

The people involved in specialty care include the patients themselves and the nurses, specialists and many other types of professionals involved in their care. The health professionals are represented by their respective unions (e.g., Ontario Nurses' Association), which engage in collective bargaining on their behalf, and professional associations (e.g., Registered Nurses' Association of Ontario, OMA). Hospitals are represented by the Ontario Hospital Association and many Independent Health Facilities are represented by the Independent Diagnostic Clinics Association.

Governance, financial and delivery arrangements in specialty care

We turn now to the building blocks for specialty care. Most of the complex governance arrangements that are salient to specialty care have been addressed under 'policies' above, and the unevenness of the playing field created by the different acts and regulations governing hospitals, Independent Health Facilities, and Out of Hospital Premises warrants repeating here. Key financial arrangements for this sector include full public payment for medically necessary hospital-based care and specialty physician-provided care, only the former of which flows through LHINs (see Table 3.4). Hospitals remain the single largest recipient of public health expenditures, accounting for 36% of these expenditures in 2013 (see Table 3.3). Funding mechanisms include historically derived 'global' budgets, a funding allocation derived from a (largely) anticipated service-volume model (called the Health-Based Allocation Model), and a set of prospective payments for select episodes of care (called Quality-Based Procedures), as well as philanthropic donations and other private sources (e.g., rent and parking). Turning to delivery arrangements, as of 2014 there were 151 private not-for-profit hospitals (some of which are large, multi-site hospitals), six private for-profit hospitals, and four specialty psychiatric hospitals, as well as 934 Independent Health Facilities and 273 Out of Hospital Premises (see Table 4.1). As of 2013, there were 14,449 specialist physicians (who are even more likely than family physicians to be male rather than female, Canada-trained rather than foreign-trained, and working in urban rather than rural settings) (Table 5.2). The density of specialist physicians (in 2013) is 1.1 per 1,000 population (or 107 per, 100,000 population) (see Table 5.3).

Rehabilitation care

Rehabilitation care is quite different from the other five sectors in several ways: 1) it is less a sector than an element of many other sectors; 2) it lacks an easily identifiable key player that occupies the same pivotal role that CCACs, primary-care teams (or family physicians), hospitals, long-term care homes and local public health agencies play in other sectors; 3) a significant proportion of its focus is 'outside' what is typically understood to be the health system – on children and youth with physical, communication or developmental challenges, on adults with automobile accident-related injuries, and on adults with work-related injuries or diseases (which we discuss in Chapter 7); and 4) it has been more extensively 'privatized' than other sectors, shifting from more public payment to more private payment (i.e., paid for out-of-pocket or with private insurance) and shifting from private not-for-profit delivery to more private for-profit delivery.

To illustrate the first point, rehabilitation care is a key element of:
1) home and community care, given physiotherapy, occupational therapy and speech-language therapy are among the types of professional services included as part of home and community care, and that CCACs can deem eligible for government funding, arrange for and coordinate;
2) primary care, given physiotherapy can be accessed by a referral from a primary-care team member or accessed directly without a referral;
3) specialty care, given there are both dedicated rehabilitation and complex continuing care hospitals (e.g., Toronto Rehabilitation Institute and Holland Bloorview Kids Rehabilitation Hospital) as well as dedicated 'rehabilitation beds' in acute-care hospitals, and given that physiatrists are a type of specialist that focuses specifically on physical medicine and rehabilitation; and
4) long-term care, given physiotherapy is among the types of funded professional services available in a long-term care home, both for long-term care home residents and for individuals receiving temporary convalescent care or respite care in a long-term care home.

As background to the fourth point, before the early 1990s physiotherapy could be accessed only by referral from a physician and typically was available in OHIP-funded physiotherapy clinics and in hospital outpatient clinics. With no increase in the number of, or budget for, OHIP-funded clinics, restrictions on eligibility for government-funded services, and competing pressures on hospitals that caused them to close their outpatient clinics (as well as a number of concurrent changes in the automobile insurance and workers' compensation systems), physiotherapy was largely removed from the basket of covered primary-care services. Payment for physiotherapy now depends on factors such as whether citizens are deemed eligible for government-funded care by the CCAC (for care in their own home) or by the Ontario Disability Support Program; are enrolled with a Family Health Team or obtain care from a Community Health Centre that includes a physiotherapist as a member of the team; have access to a Community Physiotherapy Centre and meet the requirements related to age (under 19 or 65 and older) or recent discharge from hospital; are a hospital inpatient or long-term care home resident; were injured in an automobile accident; or have a work-related injury or disease. Otherwise, citizens (which we mean in the broad sense of the term, including permanent residents and refugees) may pay out-of-pocket or draw on their private-insurance coverage if they have it.

Policies, programs and places for, and people in, rehabilitation care

As an element of other sectors, rehabilitation care has few dedicated policies and few dedicated government-funded programs per se (Figure 6.4 and Table 6.3). The relevant policies and programs in each sector apply to the rehabilitation care provided in that sector. For example, the *Public Hospitals Act, 1990* applies to dedicated adult rehabilitation and complex continuing care hospitals just as it does to other hospitals. And the government pays Community Physiotherapy Centres for eligible rehabilitation care and OHIP pays the physiatrists working in hospitals and specialty clinics for medically necessary rehabilitation care. That said, those elements of rehabilitation care that are 'outside' the aegis of the Ministry of Health and Long-Term Care (e.g., care for children with disabilities or for adults injured in automobile accidents or at work) can be governed by policies in other parts of government, such as the ministries of children and youth services, community and social services, education, finance through the Financial Services Commission of Ontario, and labour through the

Workplace Safety and Insurance Board. Also, rehabilitation care clients with long-term physical disabilities can also benefit from the Assistive Devices Program, which (as described in the home and community care section) provides access to a range of personalized assistive devices when prescribed by a physician.

The places where rehabilitation care is provided range from clients' homes (for home care) and the offices or clinics where physiotherapists are based (for primary care), often alongside other regulated health professionals and unregulated health workers, to hospitals (for specialty care) and long-term care homes.

The people involved in rehabilitation care include the patients or clients themselves and the rehabilitation professionals mentioned above. The health professionals are represented by their respective professional associations (e.g., Ontario Physiotherapy Association) and the clinics they own or work for are represented by member associations such as the Ontario Association of Children's Rehabilitation Services (for Children's Treatment Centres) and Ontario Rehab Alliance (for organizations providing rehabilitation care to those injured in automobile accidents). The sector's work is also supported by a collaborative called the Rehabilitative Care Alliance, the secretariat for which is maintained by the GTA Rehab Network, which itself serves the greater Toronto area.

Governance, financial and delivery arrangements in rehabilitation care

Governance, financial and delivery arrangements (i.e., the building blocks) are another lens through which rehabilitation care can be described. While the most salient governance arrangements have been addressed under 'policies' above, the key point to note is that rehabilitation care is not governed as a sector per se (as are the other five sectors), but as a set of people working, and programs being delivered, in places typically thought of as primarily belonging to other sectors. As with home and community care, rehabilitation care is more often financed from out-of-pocket payments than primary care, specialty care and public health, and is more difficult to track in terms of public expenditures from a sectoral perspective. In terms of delivery arrangements, as of 2014, there were more than 300 Community Physiotherapy Centres and 21 Children's Treatment Centres (see Table 4.1), as well as 55 general rehabilitation hospitals (labelled group

Figure 6.4: Rehabilitation care

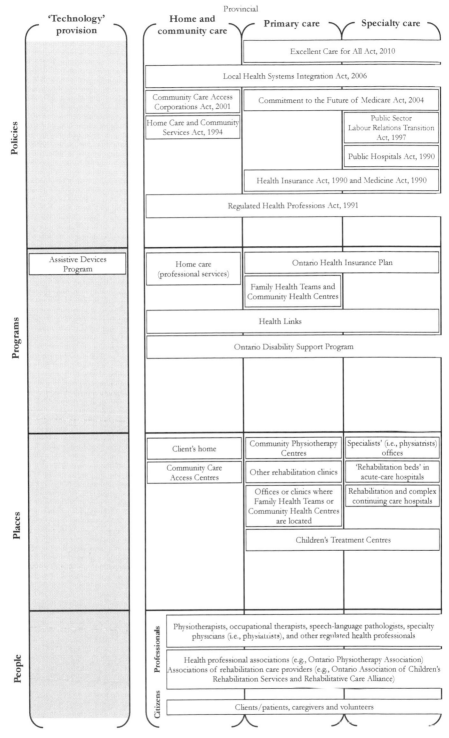

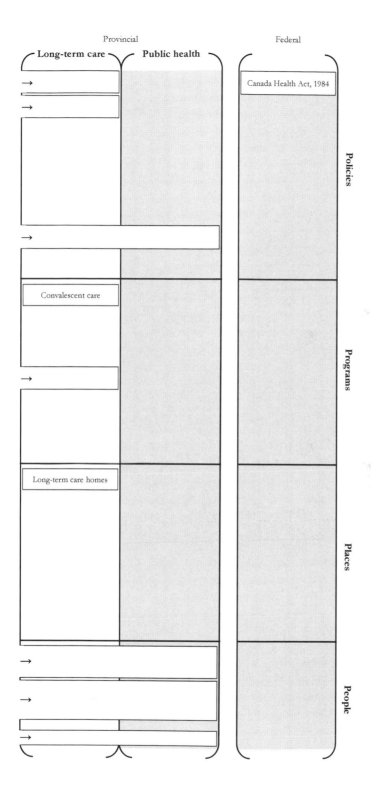

Provincial

Federal

Long-term care   Public health

Canada Health Act, 1984

Convalescent care

Long-term care homes

Policies

Programs

Places

People

Table 6.3: Rehabilitation care

Program	Services	Who delivers/funds	Who is covered
Community-based rehabilitation			
Community Physiotherapy Centres (CPCs)	Physiotherapy services (assessment, diagnosis, treatment) for select patients with injuries, chronic conditions, and disabilities, as well as after certain surgical procedures	• Close to 300 privately owned CPCs (referral from a physician, nurse practitioner or Community Care Access Centre, or CCAC, required) • Funding by Local Health Integration Networks (LHINs) (with funds from the Ministry of Health and Long-Term Care or MOHLTC) with service agreements based on an episode of care model[1]	Under 19 years or 65 years and over; spent at least one night in hospital prior to care; or require therapy at home or in a long-term care home; or income support recipients;[2] as well as a valid health card
Outpatient rehabilitation programs[3]	Physiotherapy, occupational therapy, speech-language pathology, social work, and nursing; may also provide access to adjunct services and specialty clinics	• 113 'health service provider' (HSP) corporations in multiple hospital sites; some programs in Community Health Centres (CHCs) • Funded by LHINs (with funds from the MOHLTC)	All hospital-registered outpatients with a valid health card
Specialized geriatric services (SGS)	Preventive, continuing and restorative care services, including geriatric emergency management[4] for seniors	• SGSs are provided in both community-based and hospital settings (e.g., CHCs, inpatient geriatric rehabilitation units) • Funded by LHINs (with funds from the MOHLTC)	Frail and at-risk and medically complex seniors with a valid health card
Inpatient rehabilitation			
Convalescent care programs (CCP)	Prepare individuals to return home after a stay in hospital, with a focus on recovery of strength and functioning, and can include needed rehabilitation services	• Arranged through CCACs, convalescent care is provided in CCP beds in long-term care homes • Funded by LHINs (with funds from the MOHLTC)	Applicants (from both home and hospital settings) must be 18 years of age or older and have a valid health card
Inpatient rehabilitation	Regular and restorative rehabilitation support including physiotherapy, occupational therapy, speech-language pathology, social work, and nursing	• 154 HSP organizations (includes 55 general rehabilitation and 10 special rehabilitation hospitals, as well as dedicated rehabilitation and complex continuing care beds)[5,6] • Funded by the LHINs (through the MOHLTC)	All hospital rehabilitation inpatients with a valid health card

Continued on next page

Program	Services	Who delivers/funds	Who is covered
Other			
Private rehabilitation services	Private for-profit physiotherapy and other rehabilitation services	• Privately owned and operated clinics/practices, funded through private insurance (e.g., automobile or health) or the Workplace Safety and Insurance Board or paid out-of-pocket	Not covered under the Ontario Health Insurance Plan

Sources: 9; 61-70

Notes:
[1] Under individual funding agreements, the clinic is paid a set price per episode of care (w312 in 2013) to provide physiotherapy services for a total target number of episodes per clinic within the time period of the agreement. The program funds only treatment by a physiotherapist and/or support staff. It does not cover any other services/programs such as group exercise, activation, or falls prevention classes, services to maintain an existing level of function, or services provided concurrently with physiotherapy services already provided or funded by other MOHLTC or health-system programs or through automobile insurance or the insurance plan established under the *Workplace Safety and Insurance Act, 1997*. The costs of any equipment or supplies, including equipment or supplies recommended for individual home use, are not eligible for funding.(9; 66)
[2] Income support programs include Ontario Works and the Ontario Disability Support Program.(66)
[3] These programs include outpatient physiotherapy programs, hand and upper limb clinics, orthopedic rehabilitation (including post-op joint programs), cardiac rehabilitation programs, neurological rehabilitation and stroke programs, outpatient speech-language pathology programs, multidisciplinary outpatient rehabilitation programs, outpatient occupational therapy programs, pediatric rehabilitation (including speech therapy programs), prosthetics and amputee rehabilitation programs, pulmonary and respiratory rehabilitation programs, and geriatric rehabilitation.(70)
[4] Geriatric emergency management involves screening and assessing seniors in emergency departments to determine frailty and if at-risk, and linking them to specialized geriatric services in the community. Ninety geriatric nurse clinicians provide geriatric emergency management as part of emergency department care teams.(62; 70)
[5] Group E hospitals are general rehabilitation hospitals and group J hospitals provide special rehabilitation services for disabled persons in a region of Ontario specified by the minister for each hospital.(12; 13)
[6] In 2013, hospitals had just over 2,500 dedicated regular rehabilitation beds; the number of CCC beds for rehab was not available.

E under the *Public Hospitals Act, 1990*), 10 special rehabilitation hospitals (group J), three 'continuing care centres' (group R) that provide 'low intensity, long duration' rehabilitation, and 108 chronic-care hospitals (groups F and G) that provide rehabilitation care for some of their 'complex continuing care' patients.'(9-16) Beyond these government-funded centres and hospitals, the infrastructure for rehabilitation care is difficult to characterize. In 2013, there were 6,950 physiotherapists (for a density of 0.005 per 1,000 – or 51 per 100,000 population), 4,892 occupational therapists (for a density of 0.004 per 1,000 – or 36 per 100,000 population), 3,137 respiratory therapists, and 3,014 speech-language pathologists (see Tables 5.2 and 5.3).

Long-term care

The key player in the long-term care sector is long-term care homes (historically called 'nursing homes'), where clients receive 24/7 access to nursing and personal care – generally more than can be safely met through supportive housing or a retirement home, but not so much care that they require admission to a hospital unit. Long-term care homes can also provide two short-stay programs, namely convalescent care and respite care, with a maximum stay of 90 days. As we return to below, they can be private for-profit, private not-for-profit or publicly owned (by municipal governments), and some have been established and maintained by the councils of First Nations bands.

All nursing and personal support services (provided by registered nurses or registered practical nurses and by personal support workers, respectively), as well as medical services (provided by physicians and nurse practitioners), rehabilitation therapy (provided by physiotherapists, occupational therapists, speech-language pathologists, and recreation therapists), restorative and social services (provided by social workers), clinical pharmacy services (provided by pharmacists) and nutritional services (provided by dietitians), provided (or arranged for) by long-term care homes are funded by the government (directly, through the LHIN or – in the case of medical services – through OHIP).(17; 18)

Clients, on the other hand, pay standardized charges for their accommodation. For example, in March 2016, these charges were roughly $1,775 per month for the long-stay basic option (which can be subsidized by the government for those who cannot afford it), $2,150/month for a long-stay semi-private room, and $2,550/month for a long-stay private room, and with a daily rate of $37.77 for short stays.(19) The government sets these accommodation fees for all long-term care homes. Clients also pay for any healthcare goods, services and equipment that are not provided as part of the government-funded care listed above. Long-term care home staff provide residents with information about, and assistance in obtaining, these goods, services and equipment.(20)

Two additional players in the sector intersect with other sectors:
1) complex continuing care facilities (or units within hospitals), which were described in relation to both specialty care and rehabilitation care, and which provide complex continuing care for people requiring long-term, medically complex care that cannot be provided at home or in a long-term care home; and
2) CCACs, which determine eligibility for and make arrangements for admission to (or for getting on the waiting list for) all long-term care homes and some complex continuing care facilities (or units), and which will be absorbed into LHINs under the terms of the *Patients*

First Act, 2016.

The CCACs' 'gatekeeper' role does not apply to First Nations' long-term care homes, which make their own decisions about admissions (or what are commonly called 'placements' in the sector).

Policies that govern long-term care

The key policies that govern long-term care (Figure 6.5) are the:

1) *Local Health Systems Integration Act, 2006* that established the government and LHINs as the funder of all long-term care homes (although municipal homes also receive a direct operating and capital subsidy from municipal governments, which varies by municipality);

2) *Long-Term Care Homes Act, 2007* that defined requirements for licensing and regulation, financing, staff training, services to be provided, and quality monitoring and reporting in long-term care facilities, as well as established residents' right to a safe, secure environment and involvement in care planning; and

3) *Excellent Care for All Act, 2010* that, under the terms of related regulations or policies, included long-term care homes under the mandate of the Patient Ombudsman and requires long-term care homes to submit annual Quality Improvement Plans to HQO.

The regulated health professionals (e.g., registered nurses and physiotherapists) providing care in long-term care homes are governed by the *Regulated Health Professionals Act, 1991*. Additional unregulated health workers (e.g., personal support workers) are also heavily involved in care. We return to these groups below.

Programs constituting or involving long-term care

In the long-term care sector, there are not programs in the same way as there are in other sectors, however, the nursing and personal care provided to residents and the social and recreational activities organized for residents can be thought of as programs. Also, residents can access programs available more broadly in the health system. For example, residents needing prescription drugs can obtain them through the ODB Program and residents with long-term physical disabilities can benefit from the Assistive Devices Program, just as home and community care clients and primary-care patients can.

Figure 6.5: Long-term care

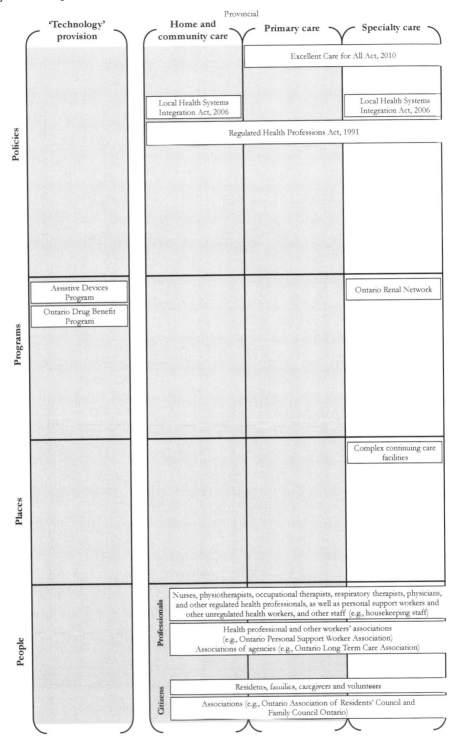

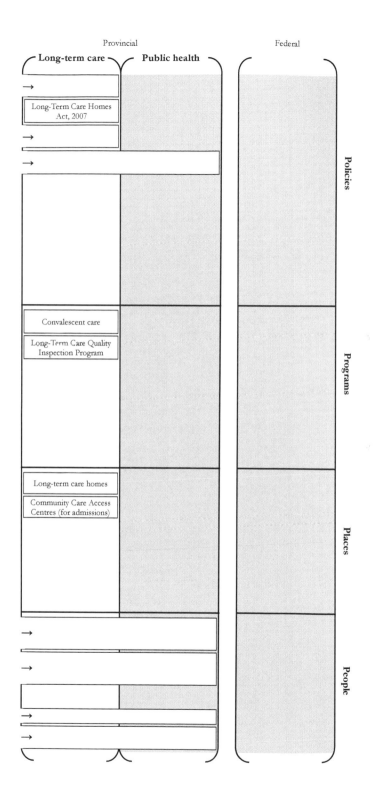

Provincial   Federal

Long-term care   Public health

→

Long-Term Care Homes
Act, 2007

→

→

Policies

Convalescent care

Long-Term Care Quality
Inspection Program

Programs

Long-term care homes

Community Care Access
Centres (for admissions)

Places

→

→

→

→

People

Also, some beds or units are funded programmatically (and separately from other parts of a long-term care home). For example, short-stay convalescent care is a separately funded program, with clients having to take the first available convalescent care bed (and not having the choice of their preferred long-term care home as is the case for long-term stays).(17) As well, there are other types of program-funded units or beds in long-term care homes, including (at the time of writing) four designated units for behaviour supports and one designated unit for peritoneal dialysis (which have their own CCAC-administered wait lists), and many beds for residents receiving peritoneal dialysis (in 28 long-term care homes that receive funding from the Ontario Renal Network), with residents having to accept the long-term care home where the program-funded unit or bed is located (and again not having an unrestricted choice of their preferred long-term care home).(18; 21)

Finally, the Long-Term Care Quality Inspection Program,(22) operated by the Ministry of Health and Long-Term Care under the terms of regulations established through the *Long-Term Care Homes Act, 2007*,(23) provides a level of continuous government oversight that is virtually unknown in other parts of the health system. The ministry is mandated to conduct unannounced inspections of every long-term care home at least annually (to identify any instances of non-compliance with the *Long-Term Care Homes Act, 2007* and its regulations) and to publicly report on all inspections (annual, complaint, critical incident or 'other') through the ministry's website. The ministry has announced plans to transition to a risk-based framework that would enable it to focus its intensive inspections on high-risk long-term care homes.(24)

Places and people involved in long-term care

The places and people involved in this sector are more straightforward than other sectors. There is only one key 'place' – long-term care homes – although CCACs act as a gatekeeper to these homes, and complex continuing care facilities (or units within hospitals) complement them for those requiring long-term, medically complex care. The people include the long-term care home residents themselves, their families and caregivers, and volunteers, as well as health professionals (including those mentioned above), a variety of unregulated health workers (e.g., personal support workers and activity/recreation staff), and other staff (e.g., dietary and housekeeping). Residents and their families play a particularly important role through each long-term care home's Residents' Council and Family Council, which are mandated under the *Long-Term Care Homes Act, 2007*, to independently advise residents about their rights and responsibilities. They also advise long-term care homes about their operations and review key financial and inspection reports. These councils are represented by the Ontario Association of Residents' Councils and by Family Councils Ontario. The health professionals are represented by their respective professional associations, unionized staff are represented by their unions, and long-term care homes are represented by the Ontario Long Term Care Association.

Governance, financial and delivery arrangements in long-term care

The governance arrangements specific to long-term care are addressed under 'policies above,' but the unique organizational/commercial authority operating in the sector warrants some elaboration (Table 4.9). The Ministry of Health and Long-Term Care has the exclusive authority to issue licences or approvals for long-term care homes to long-term care home operators (and each licence or approval is for a specific number of beds). Licences can be granted to for-profit operators (individuals, partnerships or corporations) and to not-for-profit operators (not-for-profit corporations without share capital, which can include charities and hospitals). Approvals (instead of licences) are granted to municipal governments (which in turn are operating under the *Municipal Act, 2001*, or in the case of Toronto the *City of Toronto Act, 2006*).(25; 26) Long-term care home operators can either manage their long-term care homes on their own or contract with another operator (typically a for-profit operator) to manage their homes, although the ministry must approve the contractor. The buying, selling and relocation of licences is strictly controlled by the ministry (e.g., not-for-profit operators cannot sell their licences to for-profit operators unless the former is bankrupt). Municipal governments are prohibited from selling their approved beds to either for-profit or not-for-profit operators.

Turning to financial arrangements, approved long-term care home operators can only receive funding from the government and LHIN for a long-term care home if they have a signed a Direct Funding Agreement or a Long-Term Care Service Accountability Agreement with the ministry or LHIN, respectively.(27) These agreements are specific to a long-term care home so operators with multiple homes have multiple agreements. Long-term care homes can also receive funding from other government sources, including provincial social assistance plans, other provincial government departments, and (as noted above) municipal governments (Table 4.9).

The key infrastructure in the sector includes the 636 long-term care homes and the 117 hospital-based complex continuing care facilities (see Table 4.1),(28) which collectively housed 143,727 residents in 2014-15.(29) Of the licensed/approved long-term care homes, 51% are private for-profit, 22% are not-for-profit, and 27% are public (see Table 4.9).(30; 31) In 2015, 7,923 nurses worked in the sector (Table 5.4). In 2014, the majority of staff in long-term care homes were personal support workers (73% of staff) working in care teams under the leadership of registered nurses (9% of staff) and registered practical nurses (18% of staff).(30)

Public health

The key player in public health is the local public health agency (officially called a board of health), of which there are 36 in the province: 22 organizationally independent of municipal government, seven that are part of a regional administration governing multiple municipalities (Durham, Halton, Niagara, Oxford, Peel, Waterloo and York), three that are part of a single-tier administration created from the merger of a regional administration and its constituent municipalities (Haldimand-Norfolk, Hamilton and Ottawa), and four that are part of a municipal administration (Chatham-Kent, Huron, Lambton and Toronto). A local public health agency is either an autonomous corporation or a department within a larger municipal corporation. Each agency is governed by a board of health (hence the official name) and administered by a medical officer of health (i.e., a physician with specialty training in public health and preventive medicine or other recognized public health training) or by a chief executive officer (advised by a medical officer of health). The agency provides (primarily) prevention, education, health assessment and disease surveillance, enforcement of some public health legislation, and limited clinical services, with the goal of promoting health and preventing disease among the citizens of a defined geographic area (called a public health unit). Each governing board of health is largely comprised of elected representatives from local municipal councils. The medical offer of health or chief executive officer reports to the board of health and oversees unit staff. The provincial government and municipal governments share responsibility for funding local public health agencies. A LHIN may contain from one to seven local public health agencies and a single local public health agency may span multiple LHINs – five in the case of Toronto Public Health. Complicating matters further, the local public health agencies are grouped into six regions (south west, central west, central east, eastern, north east, and north west) (Figure 6.6). The Government of Ontario is taking steps toward establishing a tighter connection between local public health agencies and both LHINs and primary care.(1)

Other important players in public health are the Ministry of Health and Long-Term Care's Population and Public Health Division, the province's chief medical officer of health, and Public Health Ontario, as well as the Ministry of Children and Youth Services and the Ministry of the Environment and Climate Change. The division and/or the chief medical officer of health deal with public health issues at the provincial level, communicate directly with the public about public health issues, and (in the case of the chief medical officer of health) report annually to the legislature on the state of public health. Indeed, the chief medical officer of health is one of only three such officers in Canada who can independently issue public reports without political 'interference,' with the other two being the B.C. and federal governments. Public Health Ontario provides scientific and technical advice and support in six areas (health promotion, infection prevention and control, chronic disease and injury prevention, environmental and occupational health, surveillance and epidemiology, and emergency preparedness and incident response) and operates 11 public health laboratories around the province. Legally, Public Health Ontario is known as the Ontario Agency for Health Protection and Promotion. The latter name derives from its founding legislation (*Ontario Agency for Health Protection and Promotion Act, 2007*). In 2011 it adopted the operating name of Public Health Ontario. Its main clients are government, local public health agencies, and health professionals and organizations.

Policies that govern public health

While the delegation of public health responsibilities to local boards of health goes back to the mid-1880s, the salient policies that govern or

Figure 6.6: Public health unit boundaries[1]

Source: Adapted from 71

Note:
[1] The part of the province shown within the oval has been magnified to show an appropriate level of detail.

organize public health today (Figure 6.7) include the:

1) *Health Protection and Promotion Act, 1990* that established boards of health for all local public health agencies and the authorities of the medical officers of health serving each board;

2) *Health System Improvements Act, 2007,* which was an omnibus act that included the *Ontario Agency for Health Protection and Promotion Act, 2007* that created what is now called Public Health Ontario; and

3) *Health Protection and Promotion Amendment Act, 2011* that established the authority of the provincial chief medical officer of health to direct boards of health and their medical officers of health in cases of a pandemic, public health event or emergency with health impacts (although this is one of many acts amending the *Health Protection and Promotion Act, 1990,* albeit a particularly visible one).

The *Smoke-Free Ontario Act, 1994* is an example of legislation that seeks to achieve a public-health goal, although there are many others, examples of which include: *Immunization of School Pupils Act, R.S.O. 1990*; *Safe Drinking Water Act, 2002*; *Mandatory Blood Testing Act, 2006*; *Skin Cancer Prevention Act, 2013*; and *Child Care and Early Years Act, 2014*.(32-36)

The health professionals working in public health (primarily nurses but also physicians, dietitians and dental hygienists, among others) are governed by the *Regulated Health Professions Act, 1990*, the *Regulated Health Professions Statue Law Amendment Act, 2009,* and their respective regulatory colleges. Public health inspectors, on the other hand, are governed under the *Health Protection and Promotion Act, 1990* and its regulations. Nationally, the *Public Health Agency of Canada Act, 2006* created the Public Health Agency of Canada, which seeks to strengthen intergovernmental collaboration on public health and facilitate national approaches to public health policy and planning. It also funds many small-scale public health projects in Ontario.

While not acts or regulations (i.e., legal instruments), local public health agencies are also governed by:

1) Ontario Public Health Standards and associated protocols, which were published in 2008, came into effect in 2009, and are being thoroughly reviewed in 2016;

2) Ontario Public Health Organizational Standards; and

3) accountability agreements between the provincial government and boards of health, which include accountabilities related to the

Figure 6.7: Public health

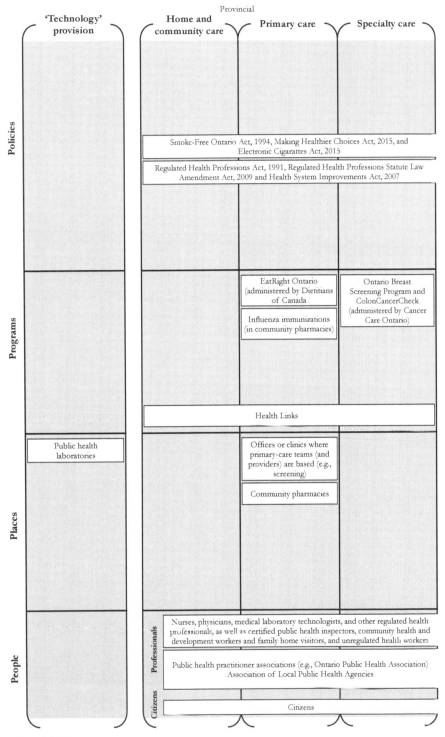

Long-term care   **Public health**

Policies

Health Protection and Promotion Amendment Act, 2011

Public Health Agency of Canada Act, 2006

Ontario Agency for Health Protection and Promotion Act, 2007

Health Protection and Promotion Act, 1990

→

→

Ontario Public Health Standards, 2008

Ontario Public Health Organizational Standards, 2011

Programs

Family health

National Collaborating Centres' evidence programs

Infectious diseases prevention and control

Canadian Institutes of Health Research Institute of Population and Public Health

Chronic disease and injuries

Environmental health

Emergency preparedness

Places

Clients' home (e.g., visits by public health nurses)

Schools (e.g., screening and immunizations)

Private sector businesses (e.g., inspections)

Community (e.g., supervised injection services)

Outdoor environment (e.g., contaminated sites)

Local public health agencies and satellite offices

People

→

→

→

implementation of the above standards.

The two sets of standards can be considered to be voluntary instruments according to the taxonomy of policy instruments described in Chapter 2 (although significant elements of the standards are typically seen to be mandatory), while the accountability agreements (effectively a contract) can be considered an economic instrument.

Programs delivered by or related to public health

The many programs delivered by local public health agencies can be grouped according to how they are described in the Ontario Public Health Standards:

1) family health (part of what Public Health Ontario includes in health promotion);
2) infectious diseases prevention and control (what Public Health Ontario calls infection prevention and control);
3) chronic disease and injuries (what Public Health Ontario calls chronic disease and injury prevention, and what is partly included in health promotion);
4) environmental health (part of what Public Health Ontario calls environmental and occupational health, with elements of the latter also addressed in the workers' compensation system); and
5) emergency preparedness (which Public Health Ontario calls emergency preparedness and incident response).

Assessment and surveillance is an example of a foundational standard that applies across programs. While public health is typically considered to be focused on population-based strategies, not individually focused treatment, some of these programs, particularly the Family Health Program, offer clinical services (e.g., dental care to eligible children whose parents cannot afford it, and the diagnosis and treatment of sexually transmitted infections).

Some public health programs (Table 6.4) do not involve local public health agencies directly, such as:

1) EatRight Ontario, a website maintained by Dietitians of Canada;
2) Universal Influenza Immunization Program, through which influenza immunizations are provided in primary-care settings and community pharmacies, in addition to local public health agency clinics; and
3) breast and colon cancer screening programs delivered by CCO.

Also, some national public health infrastructure (e.g., Public Health Agency of Canada and the National Collaborating Centres for Public Health that it funds) supports public health practitioners in Ontario.

Places and people involved in public health

Public health programs can be delivered in many places, and many public health 'places' are not open to the public. Public health 'places' range from homes (e.g., home visits by a public health nurse or family home visitor), schools (e.g., dental screenings), restaurants (e.g., inspections)

Table 6.4: Public health programs

Programs[1]	Services[2]	Who delivers/funds	Who is covered
Chronic disease and injuries			
Chronic-disease prevention programs[3]	Focus on healthy eating[4] and healthy weights; tobacco control; physical activity; alcohol use; exposure to UV radiation; food affordability; and work stress	Local public health agencies[5] funded by the Ministry of Health and Long-Term Care (MOHLTC) and municipalities	Any eligible person in the local public health unit (a geographic area)
Injury and substance misuse prevention programs	Focus on alcohol and other substances (e.g. harm-reduction programs); falls across the lifespan; on- and off-road safety; and other areas for injury prevention based on local epidemiology	Local public health agencies funded through the MOHLTC and municipalities	Any eligible person in the local public health unit
Family health			
Reproductive health	Focus on services related to preconception health; healthy pregnancies (e.g. prenatal care and services); reproductive health outcomes; and preparation for parenting	Local public health agencies funded through the MOHLTC and municipalities	Any eligible person in the public health unit
Children's health	Focus on positive parenting and healthy family dynamics; breastfeeding; healthy eating and healthy weight; physical activity, growth and development; and child oral health	Local public health agencies funded through the MOHLTC and municipalities	Eligible children and families in the public health unit
Elementary school dental screenings	Visual screening lasting 30-60 seconds	Local public health agencies funded through the MOHLTC and municipalities	All children in elementary schools
Healthy Smiles Ontario	Preventive care and basic and urgent treatments (e.g., check-ups, cleaning, fillings, X-rays, and scaling) for children in low-income households without access to any form of dental coverage	Local public health agencies funded through the MOHLTC and municipalities	Children 17 years and younger meeting eligibility requirements

Continued on next page

Programs[1]	Services[2]	Who delivers/funds	Who is covered
Family health – continued			
Healthy Babies, Healthy Children Program	Provides a mix of services including new-born screening, assessment, referrals and other support services (e.g., public health nurse or family home visitors)	Local public health agencies funded by the MOHLTC and municipalities; Ministry of Children and Youth Services	Pregnant women, and families with young children up to the age of six in the local public health agency
Infectious diseases prevention and control			
Infection prevention and control	Infection prevention and control practices in settings associated with a risk of infec-tious diseases (e.g., hospitals, long-term care homes, and licensed day nurseries)	Local public health agencies funded by the MOHLTC and municipalities	Any eligible person or setting in the local public health unit
Infectious diseases	Follow-up of reportable infectious diseases to prevent further spread; and collecting and reporting on surveillance data on these infectious diseases	Local public health agencies funded by the MOHLTC and municipalities	Any eligible person in the public health unit
Rabies prevention and control	Assessment/surveillance; knowledge-aware-ness promotion; regional prevention/control strategies; and the development of local rabies contingency plans	Local public health agencies funded by the MOHLTC and municipalities	Any eligible person in the public health unit
Sexual health, sexually-transmitted infections and blood-borne infections	Assessment/surveillance; clinical services for priority populations addressing contracep-tion, pregnancy and infection; provision of (or ensuring access to) medications for treat-ment; and provision and/or distribution of harm-reduction materials/equipment (e.g. sterile drug using equipment, condoms)	Local public health agencies funded by the MOHLTC and municipalities	Any eligible person in the public health unit
Tuberculosis prevention and control	Assessment/surveillance of persons with active and latent TB infections; health promotion; disease prevention/protection for identified priority populations and those working with them; and provision of (or ensuring access to) medications for treatment	Local public health agencies funded by the MOHLTC and municipalities	Any eligible person and priority populations in the public health unit
Vaccine-preventable deaths	Assessment/surveillance of children's immu-nization status; provision of immunization programs in public health clinics, school- and community-based clinics, and outreach clinics to priority populations; distribution of publicly funded vaccines to primary-care clinics, pharmacies, and local public health agency clinics; conducting cold-chain inspections in these settings and broader vaccine-safety measures; and education	Local public health agencies funded by the MOHLTC and municipalities	Any eligible person in the public health unit

Continued on next page

Programs[1]	Services[2]	Who delivers/funds	Who is covered
Environmental health			
Food safety	Food safety communication strategies; safe food-handling training programs; inspection of food premises; and provision of Food Safety Program	Local public health agencies funded by the MOHLTC and municipalities	Any eligible person in the public health unit
Safe water	Identification of water contaminants and illnesses, associated risk factors, and emerging trends; education and training for owners/operators of, and inspections of, drinking-water systems and recreational water facilities	Local public health agencies funded by the MOHLTC and municipalities	Any eligible person in the public health unit
Laboratory testing	Clinical and environmental testing (e.g., water, food-borne illness tests); clinical consultation, education and training programs for laboratory professionals; and evaluation of new laboratory technologies	Public Health Ontario-operated laboratories funded by the MOHLTC	Public Health Ontario
Health-hazard prevention and management	Identification and management of exposures of health concern and public health risks; and public awareness program associated with indoor/outdoor air quality, extreme weather, climate change, radiation exposure, and other emergent issues	Local public health agencies funded by the MOHLTC and municipalities	Any eligible person in the public health unit
Emergency preparedness			
Public health emergency preparedness	Identification and assessment of hazards and risks to public health; development of plans to sustain time-critical public health services; raising public awareness; and staff education and training	Local public health agencies funded by the MOHLTC and municipalities	Internal to public health agencies
Other provincial programs			
EatRight Ontario	Website providing advice and articles on food, nutrition, healthy eating, and phone/email feedback from registered dietitians	Maintained and delivered by Dietitians of Canada and funded by MOHLTC	Anyone in Ontario can use the website or call for advice
Universal Influenza Immunization Program	Influenza immunization at local participating primary-care clinics, pharmacies, and local public health agency clinics	Ontario pharmacies, immunizations funded through the MOHLTC	Anyone over 4 years of age with a valid health card
ColonCancer Check	Organized colon cancer at-home screening program for colorectal cancer for those at average risk for colorectal cancer	Cancer Care Ontario (CCO) funded by MOHLTC	Ontarians aged 50 and over with a valid health card

Continued on next page

Programs[1]	Services[2]	Who delivers/funds	Who is covered
Other provincial programs – continued			
Ontario Breast Screening Program	Organized breast screening program providing mammography and breast magnetic resonance imaging (MRI) (depending on level of risk) services to women at risk for breast cancer	CCO funded by the MOHLTC	Women aged 50 to 74 (average risk) and aged 30 to 69 years (identified high risk), valid health card

Sources: 65; 72-77

Notes:

[1] The Ontario Public Health Standards (OPHS) and Protocols outlines those programs and services that all boards of health in Ontario are required to provide, including assessment and surveillance, health promotion and policy development, disease and injury prevention, and health protection. Program standards and protocols are grouped under five program areas: chronic disease and injuries (three protocols), family health (five protocols), infectious diseases (11 protocols), environmental health (five protocols), and emergency preparedness (one protocol). The assessment, planning, delivery, and management of public health programs and services under these standards and protocols are the responsibility of each local board of health.(78)

[2] Given that the specific programs and services encompassed within assessment and surveillance, health promotion and policy development, disease and injury prevention, and health protection can vary in design based on local needs and epidemiology, we have described the focus of the services in each of the five program areas in general terms.

[3] Chronic diseases of public health importance include cardiovascular diseases, cancer, respiratory diseases, and Type 2 diabetes.(78)

[4] For example, the Northern Fruit and Vegetable Program provides two servings of fruits and vegetables a week to elementary and intermediate school-aged children in 191 northern Ontario schools. It is delivered by the Algoma, Porcupine and Sudbury public health units and the Ontario Fruit and Vegetable Growers' Association, and funded through the MOHLTC.(79)

[5] The work of local public health agencies may include working with municipalities and/or community partners (including, but not limited to, non-governmental organizations; governmental bodies such as the ministries of agriculture and food, children and youth services, education, environment, or transportation; school boards and/or staff, school councils, and students of elementary, secondary, and post-secondary educational institutions; parents; employers and employees in workplaces; and other relevant stakeholders.(78)

and community (e.g., immunization campaigns) to the offices or clinics where nurses, physicians, dentists and other health professionals work and to long-term care homes. Public health laboratories are an example of a public health 'place' that is not open to the public.

The people involved in public health include all citizens (given public health touches all of our lives, whether we know it or not), regulated health professionals (public health nurses, physicians and others), public health inspectors, and a variety of unregulated health workers (e.g., community health and development workers and family home visitors). The health professionals are represented by their respective professional associations or practitioner groups (e.g., Ontario Public Health Association), unionized staff are represented by their unions, and local public health agencies are represented by the Association of Local Public Health Agencies.

Governance, financial and delivery arrangements in public health

Governance, financial and delivery arrangements look quite different for public health compared to other sectors. Governance arrangements are unique in their connections to municipal government (where this holds true) and their lack of connection to LHINs (although the latter is expected to change), and more detail has already been provided about these arrangements under 'policies' above. Financial arrangements are unique in the near 100% public financing of local public health agencies (which in 2013 represented 8% of health expenditures by government) and the cost-sharing between provincial and local governments. In the absence of a needs-based funding formula as is used in many other sectors, each board of health determines its agency budget and municipal governments are then expected to contribute 25% of the cost of most programs, and the provincial government matches up to 75% of the cost. Some programs are up to 100% funded by the provincial government. Infrastructure in the sector comprises the 36 local public health agencies, 105 satellite offices of these local public health agencies, and 11 public health laboratories (Table 4.1), but the health professionals working in the sector tend not to be identified as such in the high-level health-workforce descriptions we provide in Chapter 5.

Conclusion

The division of labour among the six sectors comprising Ontario's health system can be seen as integral to a well-functioning system or a reflection of an unhelpful siloing of care in the system, depending on your perspective. And the historical legacies of Ontario's hospital and medical (physician) insurance system have meant that the specialty sector tends to be dominated by hospitals and specialists, and primary care is thought of as synonymous with family physicians. Only in the past decade has significant attention been given to primary care and, more recently, to home and community care and to efforts (through Health Links) to provide continuity of care across home and community, primary and specialty care. The *Patients First Act, 2016* will integrate CCAC functions into the LHINs, connect primary care to the LHINs (in the context of LHIN sub-regions), and encourage local public health agencies to connect to the LHINs and to primary care, all of which could help to keep the benefits of a division of labour while avoiding unnecessary siloing

References

1. Ministry of Health and Long-Term Care. Patients first. A proposal to strengthen patient-centred health care in Ontario. Toronto: Queen's Printer for Ontario; 2015. http://www.health.gov.on.ca/en/news/bulletin/2015/docs/discussion_paper_20151217.pdf (accessed 25 August 2016).

2. Ministry of Health and Long-Term Care. Patients first: A roadmap to strengthen home and community care. Toronto: Queen's Printer for Ontario; 2015. http://www.health.gov.on.ca/en/public/programs/ccac/roadmap.pdf (accessed 17 October 2016).

3. Legislative Assembly of Ontario. Bill 41, Patients First Act, 2016. Toronto: Queen's Printer for Ontario; 2016. http://www.ontla.on.ca/web/bills/bills_detail.do?locale=en&Intranet=&BillID=4215 (accessed 7 October 2016).

4. Ministry of Health and Long-Term Care. Bringing care home. Report of the Expert Group on Home and Community Care. Toronto Queen's Printer for Ontario; 2015.

5. Wilson MG, Reid RJ, Lavis JN, Moat KA, Guta A. Evidence brief: Building a primary-care 'home' for every Ontarian. Hamilton: McMaster Health Forum; 2016.

6. Multi-Sector Rural Health Hub Advisory Committee. Rural health hubs framework for Ontario. Toronto: Ontario Hospital Association; 2015. https://www.oha.com/AboutUs/Membership/BecomeaMember/Documents/Rural Health Hub Framework_Ontario_FNL.pdf (accessed 24 August 2016).

7. Price D, Baker E, Golden B, Hannam R. Patient care groups: A new model of population based primary health care for Ontario. A report on behalf of the Primary Health Care Expert Advisory Committee. Toronto: Ministry of Health and Long-Term Care; 2015.

8. Ministry of Health and Long-Term Care. Patients first: Action plan for health care. Toronto: Queen's Printer for Ontario; 2015. http://www.health.gov.on.ca/en/ms/ecfa/healthy_change/docs/rep_patientsfirst.pdf (accessed 25 August 2016).

9. Ministry of Health and Long-Term Care. Community physiotherapy clinic services: Selection of transfer payment recipients. Toronto: Queen's Printer for Ontario; 2013. http://www.health.gov.on.ca/en/pro/programs/physio/docs/physio_application_guidelines_pro_en.pdf (accessed 25 August 2016).

10. Ministry of Health and Long-Term Care. Publicly-funded physiotherapy: Clinic locations. Toronto: Queen's Printer for Ontario; 2015. http://www.health.gov.on.ca/en/public/programs/physio/pub_clinics.aspx (accessed 25 August 2016).

11. Ontario Association of Children's Rehabilitation Services. The voice of children's rehabilitation centres. Toronto: OACRS; 2016. http://www.oacrs.com/en/about (accessed 24 August 2016).

12. Ministry of Health and Long-Term Care. Classification of hospitals. Group E hospitals: General rehabilitation hospitals. Toronto: Queen's Printer for Ontario; 2015. http://www.health.gov.on.ca/en/common/system/services/hosp/group_e.aspx (accessed 25 August 2016).

13. Ministry of Health and Long-Term Care. Classification of hospitals. Group J hospitals: Special rehabilitation hospitals. Toronto: Queen's Printer for Ontario; 2015. http://www.health.gov.on.ca/en/common/system/services/hosp/group_j.aspx (accessed 25 August 2016).

14. Ministry of Health and Long-Term Care. Classification of hospitals. Group R hospitals: Continuing care centres. Toronto: Queen's Printer for Ontario; 2015. http://www.health.gov.on.ca/en/common/system/services/hosp/group_r.aspx (accessed 14 October 2016).

15. Ministry of Health and Long-Term Care. Classification of hospitals. Group F hospitals: Chronic > 200 beds. Toronto: Queen's Printer for Ontario; 2015. http://www.health.gov.on.ca/en/common/system/services/hosp/group_f.aspx (accessed 14 October 2016).

16. Ministry of Health and Long-Term Care. Classification of hospitals. Group G hospitals: Chronic < 200 beds. Toronto: Queen's Printer for Ontario; 2015. http://www.health.gov.on.ca/en/common/system/services/hosp/group_g.aspx (accessed 14 October 2016).

17. Ministry of Health and Long-Term Care. A guide to the Long-Term Care Homes Act, 2007 and Regulation 79/10. Toronto: Queen's Printer for Ontario; 2014.

18. Ministry of Health and Long-Term Care. Home, community and residential care services. Toronto: Queen's Printer for Ontario; 2016. http://www.health.gov.on.ca/en/public/programs/ltc/default.aspx (accessed 17 October 2016).

19. Government of Ontario. Find a long-term care home - Costs. Toronto: Queen's Printer for Ontario; 2016. https://www.ontario.ca/page/find-long-term-care-home - section-3 (accessed 17 October 2016).

20. Ontario Association of Non-Profit Homes & Services for Seniors. Tell me more about long term care homes. Toronto: Ontario Association of Non-Profit Homes & Services for Seniors; 2016. https://www.oanhss.org/OANHSS/Consumers/About_Long_Term_Care/OANHSS/Navigation/Consumers/AboutLongTermCare/About_LTC.aspx (accessed 16 October 2016).

21. Porteous A, Donskov M, Luciani T, Orosz Z. Understanding the designation process for specialized units in long-term care homes: A multi-stakeholder toolkit. Ottawa: Bruyere Research Institute; 2016.

22. Ministry of Health and Long-Term Care. Long-Term Care Home Quality Inspection Program (LQIP). Toronto: Queen's Printer for Ontario; 2015. http://www.health.gov.on.ca/en/public/programs/ltc/31_pr_inspections.aspx (accessed 14 October 2016).

23. Legislative Assembly of Ontario. Ontario regulation 79/10 made under the Long-term Care Homes Act, 2007. Toronto: Queen's Printer for Ontario; 2007. http://www.e-Laws.gov.on.ca/html/source/regs/english/2010/claws_src_regs_r10079_e.htm (accessed 25 August 2016).

24. Ministry of Health and Long-Term Care. Ontario ensuring quality care at long-term care homes. Toronto: Queen's Printer for Ontario; 2016. http://www.health.gov.on.ca/en/news/bulletin/2016/hb_20160811.aspx (accessed 13 October 2016).

25. Legislative Assembly of Ontario. Municipal Act, 2001, S.O. 2001, c. 25. Toronto: Queen's Printer for Ontario; 2001. https://www.ontario.ca/laws/statute/01m25 (accessed 13 October 2016).

26. Ministry of Municipal Affairs and Ministry of Housing. City of Toronto Act, 2006. Toronto: Queen's Printer for Ontario; 2015. http://www.mah.gov.on.ca/Page343.aspx (accessed 22 October 2016).

27. Ministry of Health and Long-Term Care. Long-Term Care Home Service Accountability Agreement (L-SAA). Toronto: Queen's Publisher for Ontario; 2016. http://www.health.gov.on.ca/en/public/programs/ltc/lsaa_policies.aspx (accessed 14 October 2016).

28. CIHI. Continuing Care Reporting System, 2014–2015, quick stats. Table 1: Number of facilities and residents in continuing care facilities submitting to CCRS by province/territory, 2014–2015. Ottawa: Canadian Institute for Health Information; 2015. https://www.cihi.ca/en/ccrs_quickstats_14_15_en.xlsx (accessed 27 October 2016).

29. CIHI. Continuing Care Reporting System, 2014–2015, quick stats. Table 2: Selected characteristics of residents in continuing care facilities, 2014–2015. Ottawa: Canadian Institute for Health Information; 2015. https://www.cihi.ca/en/ccrs_quickstats_14_15_en.xlsx (accessed 27 October 2016).

30. Ontario Long Term Care Association. This is long-term care 2015. Toronto: Ontario Long Term Care Association; 2015. http://bluetoad.com/publication/?i=281415 (accessed 18 October 2016).

31. Ontario Long Term Care Association. About long-term care in Ontario: Facts and figures. Toronto: Ontario Long Term Care Association; 2016. http://www.oltca.com/oltca/OLTCA/LongTermCare/OLTCA/Public/LongTermCare/FactsFigures.aspx?hkey=b-4823fa8-b615-49e3-8097-e67fa4224d40 - Ontario%27s%20long-term%20care%20homes%20(2015) (accessed 18 October 2016).

32. Legislative Assembly of Ontario. Child and Family Services Act, R.S.O. 1990, c. C.11. Toronto: Queen's Printer for Ontario; 2016. https://www.ontario.ca/laws/statute/90c11 (accessed 24 August 2016).

33. Legislative Assembly of Ontario. Safe Drinking Water Act, 2002, S.O. 2002, c. 32. Toronto: Queen's Printer for Ontario; 2002. https://www.ontario.ca/laws/statute/02s32?search=Safe+Drinking+Water+Act%2C+2002 (accessed 25 August 2016).

34. Legislative Assembly of Ontario. Mandatory Blood Testing Act, 2006, S.O. 2006, c. 26. Toronto: Queen's Printer for Ontario; 2006. https://www.ontario.ca/laws/statute/06m26?search=Mandatory+Blood+Testing+Act%2C+2006 (accessed 25 August 2016).

35. Legislative Assembly of Ontario. Child Care and Early Years Act, 2014, S.O. 2014, c. 11, Sched. 1. Toronto: Queen's Printer for Ontario; 2014. https://www.ontario.ca/laws/statute/14c11?search=Child+Care+and+Early+Years+Act%2C+2014 (accessed 25 August 2016).

36. Legislative Assembly of Ontario. Skin Cancer Prevention Act (Tanning Beds), 2013, S.O. 2013, c. 5. Toronto: Queen's Printer for Ontario; 2013. https://www.ontario.ca/laws/statute/13s05?search=Skin+Cancer+Prevention+Act%2C+2013 (accessed 25 August 2016).

37. Aboriginal Health Access Centres. Our health, our seventh generation, our future - 2015 Aboriginal Health Access Centres Report. Toronto: Association of Ontario Health Centres. Toronto: Association of Ontario Health Centres; 2015.

38. Dinh T. Improving primary health care through collaboration: Briefing 1 – October 2012. Ottawa: Conference Board of Canada; 2012. http://www.conferenceboard.ca/e-library/abstract.aspx?did=5157 (accessed 25 August 2016).

39. Glazier R, Kopp A, Schultz SE, Kiran T, Henry DA. All the right intentions but few of the desired results: Lessons on access to primary care from Ontario's patient enrolment models. *Healthcare Quarterly* 2012;15(3): 17.

40. Hutchinson B, Glazier R. Ontario's primary care reforms have transformed the local care landscape, but a plan is needed for ongoing improvement. Health Affairs 2013;32(4): 695.

41. Ministry of Health and Long-Term Care. Family health teams. Advancing family health care. Guide to physician compensation. Toronto: Queen's Printer for Ontario; 2009. https://www.rtso.ca/wp-content/uploads/2015/06/MOHLTC-fht_inter_provider-Oct-2013.pdf (accessed 25 August 2016).

42. Ministry of Health and Long-Term Care. Establishing midwife-led birth centres in Ontario. Application guidelines July, 2012. Toronto: Queen's Printer for Ontario; 2012.

43. Ministry of Health and Long-Term Care. Northern Health Programs. Toronto: Queen's Printer for Ontario; 2013. http://www.health.gov.on.ca/en/pro/programs/northernhealth/programs.aspx (accessed 25 August 2016).

44. Ministry of Health and Long-Term Care. Community health centres. Toronto: Queen's Printer for Ontario; 2014. http://www.health.gov.on.ca/en/common/system/services/chc/ (accessed 25 August 2016).

45. Ministry of Health and Long-Term Care. Results-based plan briefing book 2014-2015. Community mental health and addictions. Toronto: Queen's Printer for Ontario; 2015. http://www.health.gov.on.ca/en/common/ministry/publications/plans/rbplan14/ (accessed 25 August 2016).

46. Ministry of Health and Long-Term Care. Midwifery in Ontario. Toronto: Queen's Printer for Ontario; 2015. http://www.health.gov.on.ca/en/public/programs/midwife/ (accessed 25 August 2016).

47. Ministry of Health and Long-Term Care. Stand up to diabetes. Toronto: Queen's Printer for Ontario; 2015. http://www.health.gov.on.ca/en/pro/programs/diabetes/dep.aspx (accessed 25 August 2016).

48. Ministry of Health and Long-Term Care. At work for you and your patients: Centres for Complex Diabetes Care. Toronto: Queen's Printer for Ontario; 2015. http://www.health.gov.on.ca/en/pro/programs/diabetes/ccdc.aspx (accessed 25 August 2016).

49. Moat KA, Lavis JN, Hutchison B. Learning from promising primary care practice models for the USA: A Canadian case study. Hamilton: McMaster Health Forum; 2014.

50. Nurse Practitioners' Association of Ontario. Nurse Practioner-Led Clinics. Toronto: Nurse Practitioners' Association of Ontario; 2014. http://npao.org/nurse-practitioners/clinics/ - .U7v8X7EXtmo (accessed 26 August 2016).

51. Office of the Auditor General of Canada. 2015 spring reports of the Auditor General of Canada. Report 4. Access to health services for remote First Nations communities. Ottawa: Office of the Auditor General of Canada; 2015. http://www.oag-bvg.gc.ca/internet/English/parl_oag_201504_04_e_40350.html - ex1 (accessed 24 August 2016).

52. Ontario Medical Association. Primary care comparison. Fee for service, comprehensive care model, family health groups, family health networks, and family health organizations. Toronto: Ontario Medical Association; 2013.

53. Ministry of Health and Long-Term Care. Primary health care status report - Signed at June 1, 2016. Toronto: Queen's Printer for Ontario; 2016.

54. Ministry of Health and Long-Term Care. Results-based plan briefing book 2014-2015. Toronto: Queen's Printer for Ontario; 2015. http://www.health.gov.on.ca/en/common/ministry/publications/plans/rbplan14/ (accessed 25 August 2016).

55. Office of the Auditor General of Ontario. Special report: Ornge air ambulance and related services. Toronto: Office of the Auditor General of Ontario; 2012.

56. Ornge. Operations control centre. Mississauga: Ornge; 2012. http://www.ornge.ca/Programs/Pages/OperationsControlCentre.aspx (accessed 24 August 2016).

57. Ornge. Air operations. Mississauga: Ornge; 2012. http://www.ornge.ca/Programs/Pages/AirOperations.aspx (accessed 24 August 2016).

58. Ornge. Critical care land program. Mississauga: Ornge; 2012. http://www.ornge.ca/PROGRAMS/Pages/CriticalCareLandProgram.aspx (accessed 24 August 2016).

59. Ornge. What is air ambulance. Toronto: Ornge; 2015. http://www.ornge.ca/AboutOrnge/Pages/WhatisTransportMedicine.aspx (accessed 24 August 2016).

60. Ministry of Health and Long-Term Care. Ontario wait times: ER wait times. Toronto: Queen's Printer for Ontario; 2014. http://www.health.gov.on.ca/en/public/programs/waittimes/edrs/faq.aspx (accessed 25 August 2016).

61. GTA Rehab Network. Rehab definitions initiative: Final report. Toronto: GTA Rehab Network; 2010. http://www.gtarehabnetwork.ca/uploads/File/reports/report-rehab-definitions-intiative.pdf (accessed 25 August 2016).

62. Sunnybrook Hospital. Geriatric emergency management. Toronto: Sunnybrook Hospital; 2015. http://sunnybrook.ca/content/?page=dept-sgs-gem (accessed 24 August 2016).

63. Ministry of Health and Long-Term Care. Long-term care home policy, July 2010. Toronto: Queen's Printer for Ontario; 2010. http://www.health.gov.on.ca/en/public/programs/ltc/docs/short_stay_beds_policy.pdf (accessed 25 August 2016).

64. Ministry of Health and Long-Term Care. Transforming long-term care – Backgrounder. Toronto: Queen's Printer for Ontario; 2013. http://news.ontario.ca/mohltc/en/2013/01/transforming-long-term-care.html (accessed 26 August 2016).

65. Ministry of Health and Long-Term Care. Independent Health Facilities fact sheet. Toronto: Queen's Printer for Ontario; 2014. http://www.health.gov.on.ca/en/public/programs/ihf/docs/ihf_fact.pdf (accessed 25 August 2016).

66 Ministry of Health and Long-Term Care. Physiotherapy clinics: OHIP-funded. Toronto: Queen's Printer for Ontario; 2015. http://www.ontario.ca/page/physiotherapy-clinics-ohip-funded (accessed 24 August 2016).

67. Ministry of Health and Long-Term Care. Classification of hospitals. Group E: Rehabilitation hospitals. Toronto: Queen's Printer for Ontario; 2015. http://www.health.gov.on.ca/en/common/system/services/hosp/group_e.aspx (accessed 25 August 2016).

68. Ministry of Health and Long-Term Care. Classification of hospitals. Group J: Special rehabilitation hospitals. Toronto: Queen's Printer for Ontario; 2015. http://www.health.gov.on.ca/en/common/system/services/hosp/group_j.aspx (accessed 25 August 2016).

69. Office of the Auditor General of Ontario. 2013 annual report of the Office of the Auditor General of Ontario. Chapter 3, section 3.08: Rehabilitation services in hospitals. Toronto: Office of the Auditor General of Ontario; 2013.

70. Rehabilitative Care Alliance 2015. Rehabilitative Care Alliance 2013-105 report: Inspiring new directions in rehabilitative care. Toronto: Local Health Integration Networks; 2015. http://rehabcarealliance.ca/uploads/File/Final_Report_2013-15/RCA_Final_Report_2015__FINAL__v1.pdf (accessed 24 August 2016).

71. King A. Setting the stage - Public health in Ontario. Presentation by the Chief Medical Officer of Health to Best Brains Exchange: Public health within health system reform. March 22nd, 2012.

72. Cancer Care Ontario. About the Ontario Breast Screening Program. Toronto: Cancer Care Ontario; 2015. https://www.cancercare.on.ca/pcs/screening/breastscreening/OBSP (accessed 24 August 2016).

73. Cancer Care Ontario. Colorectal cancer screening. Toronto: Cancer Care Ontario; 2015. https://www.cancercare.on.ca/pcs/screening/coloscreening/ (accessed 24 August 2016).

74. Dietitians of Canada. About EatRight Ontario. Ottawa: Dietitians of Canada; 2015. http://uat.eatrightontario.ca/en/aboutERO.aspx (accessed 23 August 2016).

75. Ministry of Health and Long-Term Care. Public health units. Toronto: Queen's Printer for Ontario; 2014. http://www.health.gov.on.ca/en/common/system/services/phu/default.aspx (accessed 25 August 2016).

76. Ministry of Health and Long-Term Care. Influenza immunization program. Toronto: Queen's Printer for Ontario; 2015. https://www.ontario.ca/page/get-flu-shot/?_ga=1.129617740.1705045639.1415043906 (accessed 24 August 2016).

77. Public Health Ontario. Laboratory services. Toronto: Ontario Agency for Health Protection and Promotion; 2014. http://www.publichealthontario.ca/en/ServicesAndTools/LaboratoryServices/Pages/default.aspx (accessed 24 August 2016).

78. Ministry of Health and Long-Term Care. Ontario Public Health Standards (OPHS) and Protocols. Toronto: Queen's Printer for Ontario; 2014. http://health.gov.on.ca/en/pro/programs/publichealth/oph_standards/default.aspx?/index.html (accessed 26 August 2016).

79. Government of Ontario. Healthy choices. Toronto: Queen's Printer for Ontario; 2016. https://www.ontario.ca/page/healthy-choices (accessed 27 October 2016).

7. Care for select conditions

John N. Lavis and Amanda C. Hammill

Key messages for citizens

- Care for people with mental health or substance use problems is delivered in many types of places (e.g., community mental health and addictions organizations and hospitals specializing in mental health and addictions) and by many types of health professionals (e.g., psychologists and social workers).

- Care for people with work-related injuries and diseases often takes place in familiar healthcare settings (e.g., physician offices and hospital clinics), but is financed by employers (directly or through premiums), with eligibility for funding determined by the Workplace Safety and Insurance Board.

- Cancer care – from diagnosis to treatment and follow-up – occurs primarily in hospital-linked regional cancer centres.

- End-of-life care takes place in a wide variety of places (e.g., home, hospices, hospitals and long-term care homes) and regional palliative care networks are starting to bring more consistency to what patients, families and caregivers can expect with such care.

Key messages for professionals

- A range of programs – from information and advice (e.g., Connex-Ontario) and community services (e.g., counselling and therapy services) to hospital-sponsored programs, and outreach programs – are available to individuals facing mental health or substance use problems.

- Eligible workers with work-related injury and disease have their care paid for by the Workplace Safety and Insurance Board according to its own fee schedule.

- Regional cancer centres act as local hubs for the diagnosis and treatment of cancer while Cancer Care Ontario supports province-wide programs (e.g., breast cancer screening) and linkages to primary care and other parts of the health system.

- The Ontario Palliative Care Network and regional palliative care networks, as well as many resources (e.g., Learning Essential Approaches to Palliative Care) and supports (e.g., specialist palliative care teams), are available to professionals engaged in palliative care.

Key messages for policymakers

- Many government ministries (e.g., health and long-term care, children and youth services, education, and correctional services) and stakeholders are involved in operationalizing and implementing the province's 2011 strategy for transforming mental health and addictions care.

- The Workplace Safety and Insurance Board, which is financed by employers and governed by the Ministry of Labour, coordinates and pays for care for work-related injury and disease.

- Cancer care takes place in an almost fully parallel sub-system to the rest of Ontario's health system, with Cancer Care Ontario, an arm's-length agency, overseeing and funding cancer care in 14 regional cancer programs.

- Key 'pieces' of end-of-life care are in place – nursing and personal support workers providing palliative home care services, primary-care providers delivering palliative care with the support of specialist palliative care teams, and interprofessional palliative care teams providing care in residential hospices, palliative care units, and hospitals – but without any consistency in what can be expected from one community or region to the next.

. . .

In the second of four chapters focused on using the building blocks to provide care, we examine care for select conditions. We consider four conditions or groupings of conditions that are handled in unique ways in the health system, namely mental health and addictions, work-related injuries and diseases, cancer, and end of life. As with care by sector (the focus of the previous chapter), care for select conditions can be described in two ways: 1) by the policies that govern care, the programs and service provided as part of that care, the places where care is provided, and the people who provide the care (i.e., by the 4Ps); and 2) by the governance, financial and delivery arrangements within which care is provided (i.e., the building blocks). We again focus primarily on the former and secondarily on the latter.

Before describing care for these select conditions, however, some background is necessary. First, the assertion that care for these conditions is handled in unique ways requires some justification, if only briefly. Care for people with mental health or substance use problems is delivered in many types of places (e.g., community mental health and addictions organizations and hospitals specializing in mental health and addictions) and by many types of health professionals (e.g., psychologists and social workers), some of which are rarely accessed by those not living with such problems. Care for people with work-related injuries and diseases is typically governed by the Ministry of Labour and funded by the Workplace Safety and Insurance Board (WSIB), not by the Ministry of Health and Long-Term Care. And while there are features shared with care for automobile accident-related injuries, care for people with work-related injuries and diseases has more unique attributes. Cancer care takes place in a sub-system almost fully parallel to the rest of Ontario's health system, with an arm's-length government agency – Cancer Care Ontario (CCO) – playing a unique role in many key governance, financial and delivery arrangements. End-of-life care – or the palliative care of which it is a part – is unique in how it cuts across sectors. As yet, however, end-of-life care lacks the coordination and integration that are the goals for what are arguably the sub-systems of care for those living with mental health or substance use problems, work-related injury and disease, or cancer.

Second, the points of intersection with the six sectors described in the previous chapter need to be acknowledged. People facing challenges related to mental health or addictions, for example, may live in supportive housing (and receive an array of assisted services as part of home and community care), rely on a primary-care team for comprehensive and continuous care, and be admitted to an acute-care hospital for reasons related to their physical and/or mental health. People who are living with a work-related injury or disease or who are no longer receiving cancer care (with the latter's situation sometimes called 'survivorship in the community') do not stop needing care for other conditions. In addition, end-of-life care and palliative care more generally draw significantly on home and community care as well as primary care, may draw on significant specialty input, and may take place in acute specialty care settings plus in long-term care homes.

In the past decade or two, cancer care has been alone in being singled out for significant attention (in no small part because of concerns about wait times and quality in cancer care in the early 2000s), but this is starting to change. Both mental health and addictions and palliative care are increasingly being moved to centre stage. We will address these two groupings of conditions next and last in this chapter, respectively. In Chapter 10 we describe the reforms that led to how care for these four conditions is currently supported, and in Chapter 11 we discuss what has been learned about whether these reforms and our current approach to care are improving the patient experience and population health while keeping the amount spent per person manageable.

Mental health and addictions

The boundaries of the mental health and addictions field can be difficult to define. While children and youth may exhibit concerning behaviours and face significant challenges but not have a formal diagnosis of mental illness, they may still be cared for by mental health and addictions professionals (and as such are considered in scope for this chapter). On the other hand, adults with Alzheimer's disease may share certain signs or symptoms with those experiencing mental illness or addiction, but are often cared for by family physicians, geriatricians or neurologists instead of mental health and addictions professionals (and are considered out of scope for this chapter). Moreover, many behaviours (e.g., gambling) and substances (e.g., alcohol, tobacco and prescription opioids) may be legal, but can lead to impairment and distress (e.g., problem gambling and alcohol, tobacco or substance use disorder) and hence be treated as addictions by mental health and addictions professionals. The full range of substance use problems and addictions are considered in scope for this chapter. We use the phrase 'mental health or substance use problems' to capture challenges that have not necessarily resulted in a formal diagnosis of mental illness or addiction (and, for lack of an inclusive short term, we include in 'substance use problems' challenges such as problem gambling, even though they involve behaviours, not substances).

The key players in care for mental health and addictions have shifted dramatically over the last few decades and depend on whether the focus is adults (18 years of age or older) or children and youth, and whether the focus is the general population and those at risk of mental health and or substance use problems (for whom efforts to reduce stigma or screen for depression or anxiety may be appropriate), those with mild to moderate mental health or substance use problems, or those with severe and persistent mental illness or addiction. For adults with severe and persistent mental illness or addiction, community mental health and addictions organizations (e.g., local branches of the Canadian Mental Health Association – Ontario Division and community agencies represented by Addictions and Mental Health Ontario), and hospitals specializing in mental health and addictions, could be said to be the key players. For children and youth exhibiting concerning behaviours, lead agencies are now available in each region to provide a 'way in' to the children- and youth-focused community mental health organizations (which are represented by Children's Mental Health Ontario) and hospital-based services. It is much more difficult to identify key players for adults with mild to moderate mental health or substance use problems, although we return below to the many places where care for such adults can be accessed.

Policies that govern care for mental health and addictions

The key policies that govern care for mental health and addictions are (Figure 7.1):

1) the *Mental Health Act, 1990,* which established rules for involuntary admissions to psychiatric facilities;

2) the *Homes for Special Care Act, 1990*, which established requirements for the housing and support services provided to people with serious mental illness as a 'non-institutional' (i.e., community living) alternative to care in what were then commonly called psychiatric facilities;

3) the *Substitute Decisions Act, 1992*, which established provisions for the naming of powers of attorney and statutory guardians for those found to be mentally incapable of personal care or managing property;

4) the *Health Care Consent Act, 1996*, which established rules with respect to consent to treatment (and situations of emergency treatment), admission to a care facility (including crisis admissions) and receipt of personal assistance services, rules for when a person lacks the capacity to make decisions about such matters, and rules for such a person to contest a decision made for them to an independent provincial tribunal (Consent and Capacity Board);(1) and

5) *Bill 168, Brian's Law (Mental Health Legislative Reform), 2000,* which modified assessment and committal criteria for seriously mentally ill people to enable earlier intervention by their families and health professionals, and to enable their treatment in the community rather than in a psychiatric facility.

As well, select policies attempt to prevent addictions, such as the *Smoke-Free*

Many policies that govern care in the broader health system also apply to mental health and addictions, such as the:

1) *Regulated Health Professions Act, 1991*, which provided the legislative framework for the self-governance of the many regulated health professions providing care for mental health and addictions (e.g., registered nurses, physicians, psychologists and social workers);

2) *Public Hospitals Act, 1990*, which governs the private not-for-profit hospitals where those with mental illness or addiction may be treated; and

3) *Local Health Systems Integration Act, 2006*, which established Local Health Integration Networks (LHINs) to plan, fund and integrate care, including the care delivered by community mental health and addictions organizations and by hospitals providing care for mental health and addictions (with the funding provided under the terms of multi-sectoral accountability agreements or hospital service accountability agreements, respectively).

The College of Physicians and Surgeons of Ontario, whose role is defined by the first of these three policies, addresses issues such as the appropriate prescribing of opioids.(3)

Policies that govern the broader public sphere – provincially or nationally – can also be highly relevant to mental health and addictions. Examples of provincial policies include the:

1) *Child and Family Services Act, 1990*,(4) which established the terms under which services can be provided to children and youth from birth to 18 years of age (including those exhibiting concerning behaviours and facing significant challenges with or without a formal diagnosis of mental illness);

2) *Ontario Disability Support Program Act, 1997*, which established the terms under which people living with mental illness or addiction may receive social assistance; and

3) *Liquor License Act, 1990*,(5) which established terms for the sale and possession of alcohol.

Examples of federal policies include the:

1) *Criminal Code of Canada, 1985*,(6) which established rules for finding a person to be not criminally responsible or unfit to stand trial for

Figure 7.1: Mental health and addictions care

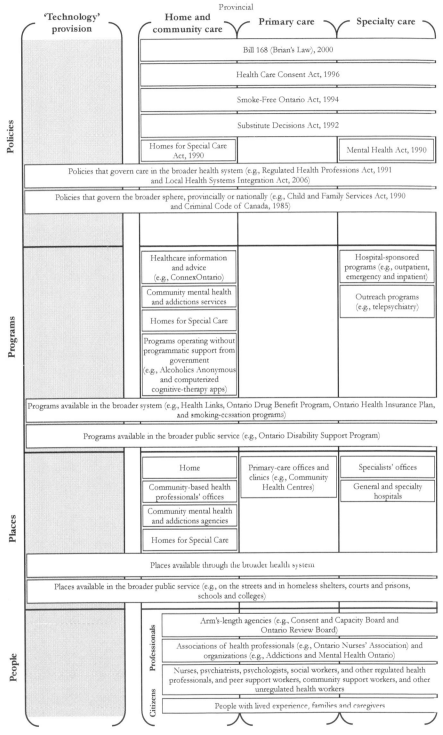

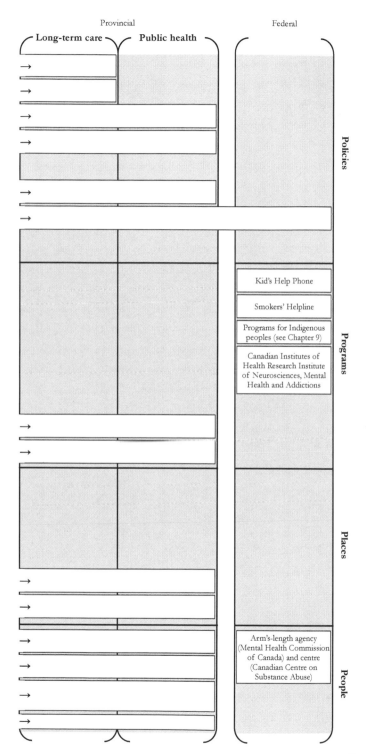

criminal offences on account of a serious mental illness, as well as the independent provincial tribunal (Ontario Review Board) that annually reviews the status of such persons;(7) and

2) *Controlled Drugs and Substances Act, 1996*,(8) and amendments to it (such as Bill C-2, 2015),(9) which make it difficult to offer supervised injection services as a harm-reduction strategy for those living with addiction.

Programs constituting care for mental health and addictions

Care for mental health and addictions – particularly publicly funded programs and how they are accessed – is in a transformative period, with the strategy for going forward articulated in 'Open Minds, Healthy Minds: Ontario's Comprehensive Mental Health and Addictions Strategy' (released in 2011 with an initial focus on children and youth, and expanded in 2014 to include adults).(10) The action plan for care for children and youth is documented in a 2012 report entitled 'Moving on Mental Health: A System that Makes Sense for Children and Youth' (11) and significant progress has already been made in creating and supporting pathways to care, defining core services to be available in communities across the province, establishing (as noted above) a lead agency that can serve as a 'way in' to the full range of available services in each defined geographical area (much like Community Care Access Centres or CCACs do for home and community care and for long-term care), creating a new funding model for these agencies, and building a legal framework for these agencies.(12; 13) Similar work for adults, such as defining core services, is now being undertaken by the Mental Health and Addictions Leadership Advisory Council, which is a time-limited (three-year) body created by the Government of Ontario in 2014 to advise the Minister of Health and Long-Term Care on the implementation of Ontario's mental health and addictions strategy. (14)

A wide range of programs are available in the mental health and addictions sub-system (Figure 7.1):

1) healthcare information and advice, including telephone helplines specific to mental health, drug and alcohol, and problem gambling concerns (ConnexOntario), and for healthcare in general (Telehealth Ontario), and an online tool that can be used to locate healthcare services, including mental health services for children and youth (Health

Care Options);(15; 16)

2) children and youth mental health services, which include targeted prevention, brief services, counselling and therapy services, family/caregiver skill building and support, specialized consultation and assessment, crisis support services, intensive treatment services, and secure treatment;(17)

3) community mental health and addictions services for adults, which can range from mental health promotion (e.g., stigma reduction), mental illness and substance abuse problem prevention (e.g., needle-exchange and other harm-reduction services) and early identification and information/referral (e.g., client-navigation services) to peer support (e.g., people with lived experience as part of team-based care), counselling and therapy services, psycho-social intervention (e.g., case management and family intervention), intensive treatment (e.g., assertive community treatment and intensive case management), and crisis services (e.g., mobile crisis response), as well as social determinants support services (e.g., supportive housing);(14; 18; 19)

4) Homes for Special Care, which provide long-term and permanent residential care for people with severe and persistent mental illness who require supervision or need assistance with activities of daily living;(20)

5) hospital-sponsored programs, which provide care on an outpatient, day treatment, emergency and inpatient basis, consultative and educational support to community-based agencies and providers,(21) and a range of specialized services (including justice-related services, like forensic services) that are typically for adults with severe and persistent mental illness or addiction;(22-25) and

6) outreach programs to provide – at a distance – clinical and support services to adults, children and youth, healthcare providers and organizations in rural, remote and underserved communities (Ontario Psychiatric Outreach Program, which is provided by six university psychiatry programs, and Ontario Child and Youth Tele-Psychiatry Program, which is provided by the Child and Parent Resource Institute and several partners in southwestern Ontario, the Hospital for Sick Children for central Ontario, and the Children's Hospital of Eastern Ontario for southeastern Ontario).(26; 27)

While clarity is currently lacking in what the core services should look like for adults living with different levels of complexity in their mental health or substance use needs, this issue is a current focus for the Mental Health and Addictions Leadership Advisory Council, as are complementary issues like better integration in services, improved transition across services, and more robust performance measurement.(14; 28)

Some programs in the sub-system are volunteer-driven (e.g., Alcoholics Anonymous, Gamblers Anonymous, and Narcotics Anonymous, as well as Al-Anon Family Groups for friends and families of problem drinkers) or more generally operate without programmatic support from government (e.g., self-help support, such as computerized cognitive-therapy apps, and the workplace supports and awareness-raising initiatives funded by many companies). Many programs can be accessed by self-referral and are free of charge. Several system-wide programs also play key roles, including Health Links (which targets clients with complex needs, including mental health or substance use problems), the Ontario Drug Benefit (ODB) Program (which covers the cost of drugs for eligible individuals), the Ontario Health Insurance Plan (OHIP, which remunerates both family physicians and psychiatrists providing care for people at risk of, or living with, mental health or substance use problems), and smoking-cessation programs. Programs are also available in the broader public service that can support those living with mental illness or addiction (e.g., Ontario Disability Support Program).

Programs in the mental health and addictions sub-system are often supported by the capacity building, policy advocacy and other activities of the Mental Health Commission of Canada, which developed and implements Canada's first mental health strategy with provincial partners,(29) and the Canadian Centre on Substance Abuse.(30) For children and youth, the programs are complemented by the Kid's Help Phone,(31) which is operated by an independent national organization. For smokers, the programs are complemented by the Smoker's Helpline, which is operated by the Canadian Cancer Society.(32) For Indigenous peoples, the programs are also complemented by federal government programs (see Chapter 9).

Places and people involved in care for mental health and addictions

The places where care for mental health or substance use problems is provided include a person's home (e.g., where they may access telephone helplines, self-help apps, telepsychiatry, and supportive housing), the offices of community-based health professionals (e.g., psychologists and social workers), community mental health and addictions agencies, Homes for Special Care, primary-care offices and clinics (including Community

Health Centres), specialists' (e.g., psychiatrists and psychologists) offices, and general and specialty hospitals (outpatient clinics, emergency rooms, and inpatient wards), as well as in a variety of other settings where people at risk of, or living with, mental health or substance use problems can be found (e.g., on the streets and in homeless shelters, in courts and prisons, and in schools and colleges) (Figure 7.1).

The people involved in care for mental health and substance use problems include those living with mental health or substance use problems themselves (who are often referred to as people with lived experience) and their families and caregivers (who may be supported by organizations such as the Mood Disorders Association of Ontario, the Schizophrenia Society of Ontario, and Parents for Children's Mental Health, among others), as well as a broad range of regulated health professionals (e.g., nurses, psychiatrists, psychologists and social workers) and unregulated health workers (e.g., peer support workers and community support workers). People with lived experience increasingly play formal roles in the governance and delivery of care for mental health or substance use problems. The health professionals are represented by their respective professional associations (e.g., Ontario Nurses' Association), and the agencies for which they work are represented by member associations such as Addictions and Mental Health Ontario.(24) Some citizens and professionals are members of arm's-length agencies like the Consent and Capacity Board and the Ontario Review Board (both described above),(33) as well as programs like the Ontario Centre of Excellence for Child and Youth Mental Health (at the Children's Hospital of Eastern Ontario), Provincial Systems Support Program (at the Centre for Addictions and Mental Health), and Gambling Research Exchange Ontario (which support evidence-informed practice and policy in their respective areas of focus).(34; 35)

Governance, financial and delivery arrangements in care for mental health and addictions

Governance, financial and delivery arrangements (i.e., the building blocks) are another lens through which mental health and addictions can be described. The governance arrangements that are particularly salient to the sub-system have been addressed under 'policies' above. One key financial arrangement for mental health and addictions care is the funding provided by the Ministry of Children and Youth Services and the Ministry of Education (for children and youth) and the Ministry of Health and Long-Term Care (for adults), with the latter providing funding directly (e.g., for ConnexOntario and Homes for Special Care), through LHINs (e.g., for community mental health and addictions agencies and hospitals) or through system-wide programs (e.g. OHIP and Underserviced Areas Program).(28) Proportionately smaller contributions are made by other government ministries (e.g., advanced education and skills development, attorney general, community and social services, community safety and correctional services, and municipal affairs and housing). The second key financial arrangement is the mix of out-of-pocket payments (e.g., for psychologists and social workers in private practice) and payments by private insurance plans, employee-assistance programs, and other sources, although many services – particularly those for people with severe and persistent mental illness and addiction – have no fees.(28)

In terms of delivery arrangements for adults needing care for mental health or substance use problems, as of 2015 there were more than 300 community-based mental health and addictions agencies (36) and 71 hospitals with a psychiatric-facility designation under the *Mental Health Act, 1990,* of which four – Centre for Addiction and Mental Health (Toronto), Ontario Shores Centre for Mental Health Sciences (Whitby), the Royal Ottawa Mental Health Centre (Ottawa), and the Waypoint Centre for Mental Health (Penetanguishene) – are specialty hospitals.(21) Care for children and youth can be accessed through lead agencies in 31 service areas across the province, and is provided in over 260 mental health and addictions agencies (including 90 accredited children's mental health centres), 17 hospital-based (outpatient) children's mental health programs, and one child and youth mental health facility (Parent Resource Institute, which is located in London).(37)

Work-related injuries and diseases

Care for people with work-related injuries and diseases was deemed by government to be a collective responsibility in 1914 – long before the same was done for other types of care.(38) The idea is that employers, through a compulsory no-fault liability insurance scheme, should bear the costs when an injury or disease was clearly work-related, such as a severed limb or broken back among those working in construction, or mesothelioma (a cancer of the lining of the lungs or abdomen) among those working in an asbestos mine. Workers could reasonably argue that they bear these costs collectively given the costs effectively represent part of their total compensation package. The costs include income replacement (i.e., regular payments to partially offset lost earnings) or survivor benefits (in the case of work-related fatalities) and healthcare, as well as industry-specific health and safety information for employers, help and support for workers to return to work, and regulatory enforcement by the Ministry of Labour. A broadly analogous scheme has been put in place for automobile injuries, although here the costs are assumed by drivers with automobile insurance.

The key player for work-related injuries and diseases is the WSIB, which was called the Workers' Compensation Board until 1998. The WSIB operates under government legislation, is fully financed by employers and earned investment income (although legislation mandates that it will be fully financed only by employers by 2027), and governed by an independent board of directors (representing employers, workers and others).(39) At one time the WSIB played a fairly passive role as the payer of bills submitted by providers (e.g., physicians) and organizations (e.g., hospitals) providing care to eligible workers, but more recently it has played a more active role in commissioning care to achieve better health and return-to-work outcomes (and a network of providers and organizations has evolved to meet this demand).

Four key features of the WSIB sub-system warrant mention as context to what follows: 1) a determination of work-relatedness is key to coverage and hence can be contentious; 2) the historical focus on physical injuries has left a legacy of unevenness in attention to mental health; 3) the long latencies and multifactorial nature of most work-related diseases has left a legacy of unevenness in coverage of such diseases; and 4) incentives for under-reporting work-related injuries and diseases means that many costs can be covered by the publicly funded health system that is the focus of the rest of the book. One other point worth noting is that the URLs for WSIB webpages can be many lines long, so to save space we have opted to provide in the reference list the URL for the WSIB home page rather than for the specific webpage we are referencing.

Policies that govern care for work-related injuries and diseases

The key policies that govern care for work-related injuries and diseases are the:

1) *Occupational Health and Safety Act, 1990*,(40) which established the contemporary standards for making workplaces safe and healthy (thereby preventing work-related injury and disease), including the rights and duties of all parties in the workplace, procedures for dealing with workplace hazards, and enforcement mechanisms; and

2) *Workplace Safety and Insurance Act, 1997*,(41) which set the termsfor the no-fault liability insurance scheme (including the role of the WSIB and the independent agencies – Office of the Employer Advisor, Office of the Worker Advisor, and Workplace Safety and Insurance Appeals Tribunal – that complement the WSIB) and established the industries that are exempt (e.g., banks, insurance companies, law firms, real estate agencies, private schools, and health clubs), the two types of participating employers (i.e., schedule 1 employers that contribute to and are covered under the collective liability scheme and schedule 2 employers that self-insure the benefit-compensation and administration costs incurred by the WSIB), how benefits are determined, how the experience-rated premiums are calculated for employers, and the WSIB's service-delivery model.

Roughly three quarters of the workforce is covered by the WSIB, either through schedule 1 or schedule 2 employers (Table 7.1).

Programs constituting care for work-related injuries and diseases

Six categories of programs are relevant to care for work-related injuries and diseases (Figure 7.2):

1) WSIB services that form a part of the WSIB's service-delivery model,(42) which aims – first and foremost – to reduce the duration of claims and which includes nurse consultants (who make decisions about healthcare entitlement) and medical consultants (who interact with the worker's physician and conduct case file reviews), as well as a number of:

   a. unregulated workers such as registration clerks (who process the initial form 6 from workers, form 7 from employers, and form 8 from health professionals), primary adjudicators (who ensure that there is a worker, an employer, proof of accident,

Table 7.1: Workplace Safety and Insurance Board coverage and claims for schedule 1 and 2 employers, 2004, 2010 and 2014

Coverage and claims	2004[1]	2010	2014	10-year percentage change
Schedule 1				
Number of employers	217,693	250,536	299,339	38%
% workforce covered	64%	61%	64%	1%
Workplace Safety and Insurance Board (WSIB)-covered employees	4,022,010	4,009,201	4,431,674	10%
Registered claims	308,865	198,617	195,495	-37%
Lost time claims by gender				
Female	26,012	17,967	15,321	-41%
Male	49,466	28,137	25,237	-49%
Schedule 2				
Number of employers	630	611	600	-5%
% workforce covered	9%	11%	10%	10%
WSIB-covered employees	577,816	702,383	690,942	20%
Registered claims	42,479	39,781	38,150	-10%
Lost time claims by gender				
Female	6,577	7,015	6,648	1%
Male	8,577	7,019	6,454	-25%

Source: Adapted from: 87; 88

Note:
[1] Data for the baseline year of 2000 used elsewhere in the book were unavailable.

personal work-related injury, and compatibility of the diagnosis to the accident or disablement history, and hence an initial entitlement to WSIB benefits), eligibility adjudicators (who adjudicate more complex claims, alone or with the support of a nurse consultant), case managers (who assist with work re-integration, recurrences, etc.), return-to-work specialists (who act as facilitators), work-transition specialists (who provide support when the worker has not returned to suitable, available work), and employer liaison specialists (who share best practices), and

b. dedicated teams (e.g., case-management re-employment team, recurrence and work-disruption team, second-injury and enhancement fund team, mental health team, and appeals team);(43)

2) health professional services and programs, which include physician services paid via the Ministry of Health and Long-Term Care (which

Figure 7.2: Care for work-related injuries and diseases

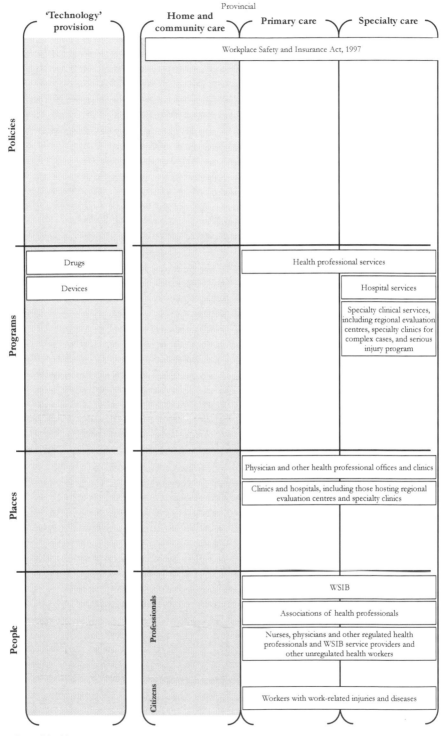

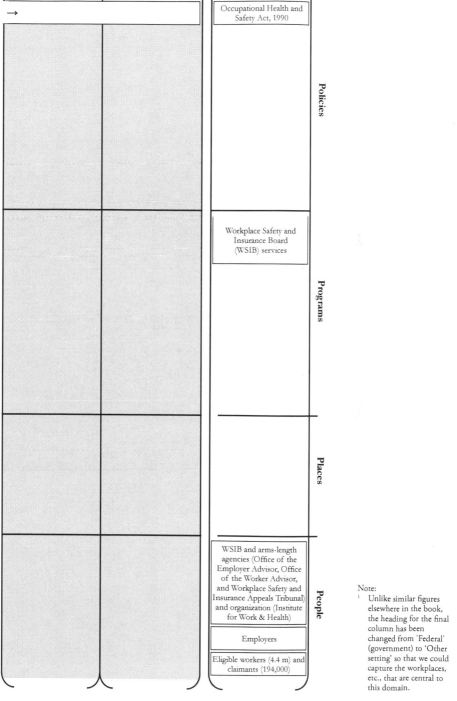

Provincial

Long-term care   Public health   Other setting[2]

Occupational Health and
Safety Act, 1990

Policies

Workplace Safety and
Insurance Board
(WSIB) services

Programs

Places

WSIB and arms-length
agencies (Office of the
Employer Advisor, Office
of the Worker Advisor,
and Workplace Safety and
Insurance Appeals Tribunal)
and organization (Institute
for Work & Health)

Employers

Eligible workers (4.4 m) and
claimants (194,000)

People

Note:
[1]   Unlike similar figures
      elsewhere in the book,
      the heading for the final
      column has been
      changed from 'Federal'
      (government) to 'Other
      setting' so that we could
      capture the workplaces,
      etc., that are central to
      this domain.

processes the service claims on behalf of the WSIB, which ultimately pays them), services delivered by physiotherapists, chiropractors and other select non-physician providers, and specialized clinical services and programs;

3) hospital services, which include both outpatient and inpatient care;
4) drugs, which includes prescription drugs listed on a drug formulary;
5) devices (e.g., hearing aids and medical devices); and
6) travel, accommodations and other healthcare-related allowances.

Healthcare constitutes the third-largest category of benefit payment, after income replacement for lost earnings and workers' pensions (Table 7.2).

Table 7.2: Workplace Safety and Insurance Board benefit payments by benefit category, 2010 and 2014

Benefit category	2010[1] payments ($ millions)	2014 payments ($ millions)	Four-year percentage change
Schedule 1			
Total benefit payments	3,067	2,420	-21%
Loss of earnings	1,117	863	-23%
Workers' pension	701	596	-15%
Healthcare	497	452	-9%
Future economic loss	292	230	-21%
Survivor benefits	178	184	3%
External providers	151	44	-71%
Non-economic loss	126	48	-62%
Other	5	3	-40%
Schedule 2			
Total benefit payments	300	240	-20%
Loss of earnings	110	86	-22%
Workers' pension	61	52	-15%
Healthcare	65	59	-9%
Future economic loss	20	14	-30%
Survivor benefits	21	18	-14%
External providers	5	2	-60%
Non-economic loss	16	6	-63%
Other	2	3	50%

Source: Adapted from: 87; 88

Note:
[1] Data for the baseline year of 2000 used elsewhere in the book were unavailable.

Specialized clinical services, which are the largest expenditure category of healthcare benefit payments (Table 7.3), include an array of purportedly

Table 7.3: Workplace Safety and Insurance Board healthcare benefit payments by healthcare service category, 2012 and 2014

Healthcare service category	2012[1] ($ thousands)	2014 ($ thousands)	Two-year percentage change
Schedule 1			
Total healthcare benefits	457,494	452,246	-1%
Specialized clinical services and programs	83,229	93,025	12%
Drug benefits	71,129	61,883	-13%
Allowances (clothing, independent living, personal care)	30,706	53,951	76%
Hospital in/outpatient	36,587	38,596	5%
Physician services via Ministry of Health and Long-Term Care	39,503	37,285	-6%
Hearing aid devices and services	28,860	37,131	29%
Reports and information	25,084	24,841	1%
Travel and accommodations	24,176	23,700	-2%
Physiotherapy, chiropractic, and other select (non-physician) providers	55,670	21,675	-61%
Medical devices	20,072	20,557	2%
Other	42,478	39,062	-7%
Schedule 2			
Total healthcare benefits	58,488	58,593	0%
Specialized clinical services and programs	13,160	15,243	16%
Physiotherapy, chiropractic, and other select (non-physician) providers	7,091	5,367	-24%
Hearing aid devices and services	3,899	5,083	30%
Drug benefits	5,860	5,015	-14%
Hospital in/outpatient	3,957	4,925	24%
Physician services via Ministry of Health and Long-Term Care	5,072	4,717	-7%
Allowances (clothing, independent living, personal care)	4,749	4,465	-6%
Reports and information	3,892	3,903	0%
Travel and accommodations	3,579	3,403	-5%
Medical devices	2,316	2,558	9%
Other	4,913	3,914	-20%

Source: Adapted from: 87-90

Note:
[1] Data for the baseline year of 2000 used elsewhere in the book were unavailable.

evidence-based 'programs of care' that aim to achieve the best functional outcomes and include specific admission criteria, program duration, treatment interventions, and outcome measures. The programs address: 1) low-back injury; 2) shoulder injury; 3) musculoskeletal injury other than those above; 4) noise-induced hearing loss; and 5) mild traumatic brain injury.(44) Health professionals delivering these programs must register to do so, agree to adhere to the relevant program reference guide, and consent to having their contact details made available through a searchable database on the WSIB website.(45)

Specialized clinical services also include:
1) regional evaluation centres (in 13 locations around the province), which provide assessments (including expedited migrant worker assessments) and make recommendations about early intervention to enhance functional recovery of, and support return to work by, workers with musculoskeletal injuries (to both the WSIB and the worker's primary health professional);(46)
2) specialty clinics for complex cases, which provide access to care through 11 programs – amputee, back and neck, burn, function and pain, lower extremity, mental health, neurology, occupational disease, substance management, surgical, and upper extremity – operating in 15 hospitals, as well as a time-limited demonstration project (early low-back assessment service);(47) and
3) serious injury program, which provides the specialized services and devices needed to maximize the recovery of function and quality of life for workers with a serious or permanent disability or with specific injuries (e.g., paraplegia, blindness, major amputation or burns).(48)

Places and people involved in care for work-related injuries and diseases

Much of the care for work-related injuries and diseases is provided in the same physician (e.g., family physician) offices and other health professional (e.g., physiotherapy) clinics as the care provided to those whose injury or disease is not work related. Even the regional evaluation centres and specialty clinics are typically just dedicated units within clinics and hospitals that provide a much broader range of services. That said, because of the separate programs of care and payment mechanisms, some offices and clinics may focus exclusively on care for work-related injuries and diseases.

The people involved in care include two types of 'clients,' namely employers (for the liability-insurance scheme) and workers (for the income replacement and healthcare benefits), as well as the broad array of regulated health professionals (both those working at the WSIB, like the nurse consultants making decisions about healthcare entitlement, and the medical consultants interacting with the worker's physician and conducting case file reviews, and those working in the offices, clinics and hospitals where care is being provided) and unregulated workers (like those listed above as contributors to the WSIB's service-delivery model). The health professionals are, as usual, represented by their respective professional associations (e.g., Ontario Nurses' Association). Some citizens and professionals are members of the board of the WSIB, the Office of the Employer Advisor (an independent agency of the Ministry of Labour that provides free advice about managing workplace safety and insurance costs), the Office of the Worker Advisor (a second independent agency of the Ministry of Labour, which in this case provides free advice, education and representation in workplace insurance matters and occupational health and safety reprisal issues), and the Workplace Safety and Insurance Appeals Tribunal (a third independent agency of the Ministry of Labour, which provides the final level of appeal to which workers and employers can bring disputes about workplace safety and insurance), as well as independent organizations like the Institute for Work & Health (which support evidence-informed practice and policy in this domain).(49-52)

Governance, financial and delivery arrangements in care for work-related injuries and diseases

The governance arrangements that are particularly salient to care for work-related injuries and diseases have been addressed under 'policies' above. The key financial arrangements for this care are the employer premiums (i.e., the source of financing), the income replacement provided to workers, and the payments made to health professionals, pharmacies and device suppliers. As noted above, most physicians bill the Ministry of Health and Long-Term Care for both providing services and completing reports, according to a fee schedule set and reimbursed by the WSIB. Some physicians and all other health professionals (including pharmacists dispensing drugs) use an electronic-billing system administered by a third party (TELUS Health), but again according to a fee schedule set by the WSIB.(45) Four preferred providers of approved healthcare equipment and supplies bill the WSIB directly.(53) As alluded to above, the WSIB is a fairly unique organization in the health system in its use of a 'commissioning' model that pays for care that meets the performance standards outlined in service agreements (and we return to another key example in the next section). In terms of delivery arrangements for workers needing care for work-related diseases and injures, as noted above, there are the 'usual' components of the system's infrastructure, as well as 13 regional evaluation centres and 15 hospitals hosting specialty clinics.(46; 47)

Cancer

As noted in the introduction, cancer care takes place in a sub-system that operates almost fully in parallel to the rest of Ontario's health system. For adults, some prevention and screening, most aspects of diagnosis, virtually all aspects of treatment, and most aspects of follow-up care are coordinated by those working in the cancer sub-system. The health system's traditional sectors play comparatively smaller roles: the home and community care and long-term care sectors play a role in supporting those receiving treatment while living at home or in long-term care homes; the primary-care sector plays a role in some individually targeted cancer-prevention and screening activities, and more and more often in follow-up care (with the latter occurring as cancer care leaders increasingly recognize that it is no longer sustainable for cancer survivors to be returning indefinitely to their clinics); and the public health sector plays a role in some population-based cancer-prevention activities. For children, diagnosis and follow-up care and most aspects of treatment take place primarily in children's hospitals, although they may receive radiation therapy in a regional cancer centre.

The key player for cancer care for adults is an arm's-length government agency – CCO – that is alone among provincial health agencies in the spectrum of governance, financial and delivery arrangements that it can alter to ensure that care is well planned and coordinated, and continually improved. Established in its current form in 1997, CCO's very existence, the span of control it has been given and the size of the budget it is allocated annually (roughly $1.7 billion, of which roughly $800 million is provided to hospitals and other cancer-care providers) have effectively singled out cancer in a way that has not been done for other conditions.(54) The reforms that created CCO are described in Chapter 10. CCO's executive team is supported by a Provincial Leadership Council (with regional representation), a Clinical Council (with representation from across the agency), and an arm's-length advisory body called the

Cancer Quality Council of Ontario (with 'external' professional, patient/family and expert representation). The Pediatric Oncology Group of Ontario acts as an arm's-length advisory body for cancer care in children.

Periodically the Ministry of Health and Long-Term Care has considered (or key stakeholders have encouraged it to consider) expanding CCO's mandate to include other 'singled out' conditions or groups of conditions, such as chronic kidney disease, diabetes, and mental health and addictions, or other cross-system functions. Currently, it serves such a function only for chronic kidney disease, which it does through the Ontario Renal Network (established in 2009), and for the province's wait-times strategy and its emergency room/alternate-level-of-care strategy, which it does through the Access to Care program.(55-57) The Ontario Renal Network organizes and funds dialysis and other renal services across the province. While it is an 'in-house' analogue to CCO, the closest 'external' analogue would be the Cardiac Care Network, which operates within a narrower span of control to improve access, quality, efficiency and equity in the delivery of cardiac services.(58)

Policies that govern cancer care

The key policies that govern cancer care (Figure 7.3) are the:
1) *Cancer Act, 1990*, which formalized the governance of the precursor to CCO (the Ontario Cancer Treatment and Research Foundation, first established in 1943) and its objectives (e.g., creation and operation of regional treatment centres and of laboratories, coordination of treatment, collection and reporting of data, and education of the public about cancer), but the act does not cover the wide spectrum of activities currently undertaken by CCO (which are dealt with through administrative agreements with it);
2) *Freedom of Information and Privacy Protection Act, 1990*, which provided individuals with the right to access their own personal health information (and to have the privacy and confidentiality of their personal healthcare information respected), but which, through later amendments, established that the head of organizations like CCO can refuse to disclose a record that contains information provided in the context of quality assessment and improvement efforts; and
3) *Personal Health Information Protection Act, 2004*, which enshrined patient confidentiality as an individual right by outlining rules for

Figure 7.3: Cancer care

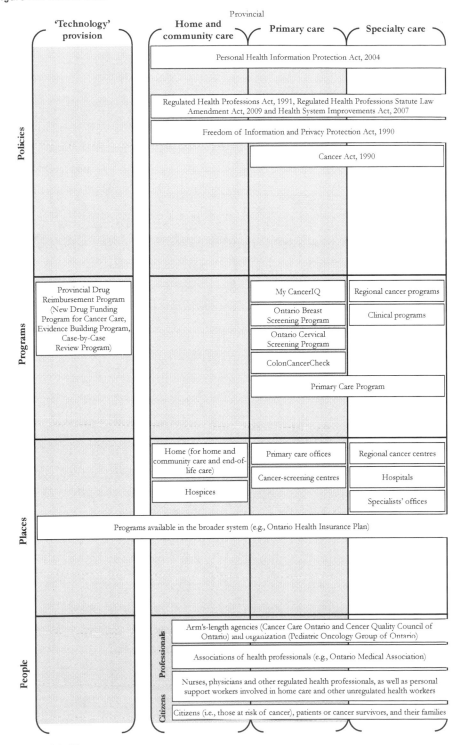

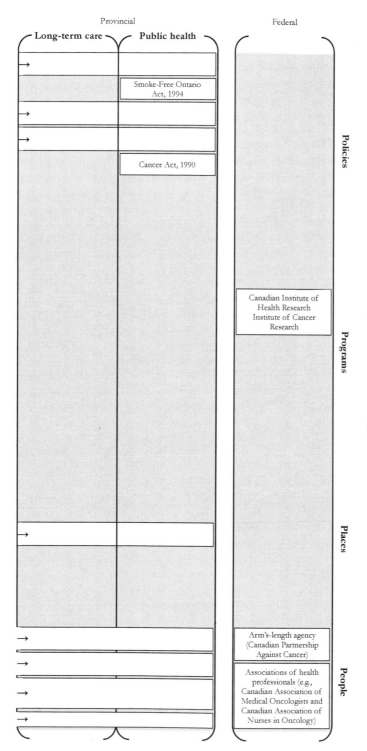

collecting, using and disclosing personal information about individuals that protect confidentiality while also providing effective healthcare, and which reaffirmed the role of an agency like CCO as a custodian for such information (providing it with the 'prescribed registry' status that allows it to, for example, write to Ontarians to notify them about their eligibility for breast, cervical and colorectal cancer screening, and requiring it to be reviewed by the Information and Privacy Commissioner every three years).

As well, select policies govern efforts to prevent specific types of cancer, such as the *Smoke-Free Ontario Act, 1994*. And many policies that govern care in the broader health system also apply to cancer care, such as the *Regulated Health Professions Act, 1991*, which provided the legislative framework for the self-governance of the many regulated health professions providing cancer care (e.g., registered nurses and physicians).

Also, CCO and its regional cancer centres effectively work under many other policies that support safe, high-quality cancer care, including the following examples: 1) an accreditation process for stem-cell transplants, which is overseen by the Foundation for the Accreditation of Cellular Therapy;(59) 2) regulations for the safe delivery of radiation therapy, which have been established by the Canadian Nuclear Safety Commission;(60) and 3) regulations for the use of drugs in clinical trials, which have been established by Health Canada.(61)

Programs constituting cancer care

Two broad categories of programs are highly visible in cancer care, namely prevention and screening programs and diagnosis and treatment programs (Figure 7.3). The prevention and screening programs include:

1) MyCancerIQ (www.mycanceriq.ca) – a website that helps Ontarians understand their risk of developing specific cancers (breast, cervical, colorectal, kidney and lung cancer, as well as melanoma) and what they can do to help lower that risk;

2) the Ontario Breast Screening Program – an organized screening program that reminds eligible women by letter about the need for screening, and that provides, in dedicated locations across the province, either: a) mammograms every two years for women aged 50 to 74 who are at average risk for breast cancer; or b) mammograms and breast magnetic resonance imaging (MRI) every year for women aged 30 to 69 who are

at high risk for breast cancer;(62)

3) the Ontario Cervical Screening Program – a screening program that reminds eligible women by letter about the need for screening and that supports family physicians and nurse practitioners to provide the Pap tests used in screening women (typically those aged 21-70) every three years;(63) and

4) ColonCancerCheck – an organized screening program that reminds eligible men and women by letter about the need for screening, that supports family physicians and nurse practitioners to provide a fecal occult blood test every two years to screen Ontarians aged 50 to 74 who are at average risk of colorectal cancer (although the tests are also available by calling Telehealth Ontario), and that provides, in dedicated locations across the province: a) follow-up colonoscopy for those with abnormal fecal occult blood test results; b) flexible sigmoidoscopy every 10 years for those seeking additional reassurance (which can be provided by a physician or a specially trained registered nurse); and c) colonoscopy every 10 years for those at high risk (i.e., with one or more first-degree relatives with the disease).(64)

Two regions of the province (North West region and Hamilton Niagara Haldimand Brant region) have mobile screening coaches (i.e., buses) to screen eligible women for breast cancer (mammography), cervical cancer (Pap test), and colorectal cancer (fecal occult blood test kits).(65)

The diagnosis and treatment programs can be grouped into two sub-categories:

1) 14 regional cancer programs (one for each LHIN), which were established in 2005, are networks of organizations (e.g., regional cancer centre), professionals and patient/family groups, headed by a regional vice-president (who also leads the regional cancer centre), that implement provincial standards and programs for cancer care, ensure service providers meet the requirements and targets set out in their partnership agreements with CCO, coordinate care across local and regional healthcare providers, respond to local cancer issues, and work to continually improve access to care, wait times, and quality of care;(66) and

2) 10 clinical programs, which are provincial programs that aim to improve the accessibility, quality and safety of the cancer care being provided in the regional cancer programs – across the patient journey from diagnosis (i.e., diagnostic assessment, pathology and laboratory medicine, and cancer imaging programs) to treatment (i.e., systemic

treatment, radiation treatment, and surgical oncology programs), to recovery/survivorship, palliative care, and other points in the patient journey (i.e., patient education, oncology nursing, psycho-social oncology, and specialized services) – and that do so by monitoring quality, developing evidence-based guidance for the system, and working with organizations, professionals and patient/family groups to implement best practices province-wide.(67)

The clinical program portfolio is also responsible for McMaster University's Program in Evidence-Based Care, which develops evidence-based guidance for practice and policy decisions for all disease sites and clinical programs across the cancer-care continuum.(68)

Additionally, CCO performs a number of functions and oversees a number of initiatives that also support cancer care:

1) planning, which includes both long-term planning (as reflected in the four-year Ontario Cancer Plan) (69) and capacity planning;

2) Indigenous programming, which includes the Aboriginal Cancer Strategy, the aboriginal tobacco program, and the aboriginal cancer and prevention team;(70)

3) primary-care provider engagement in cancer prevention, screening, care and support, through the Primary Care Program's engagement strategy (focused initially on screening) and its provincial network (launched in 2008) of primary-care leads in each LHIN;(71)

4) drug-reimbursement programs, for which CCO reviews and processes requests from hospitals and regional cancer centres for reimbursement for new injectable cancer drugs (New Drug Funding Program for Cancer Care), new drugs for which clinical and cost-effectiveness data need to be collected (Evidence Building Program), and drugs for specific patients (Case-by-Case Review Program), although decisions about which drugs to pay for are informed by the pan-Canadian Oncology Drug Review and made by the government's public drug programs, which are described in Chapter 8, and the funds to pay for the drugs come from government (and are then transferred by CCO to the hospitals that dispense them);

5) performance improvement, which involves the use of performance monitoring (e.g., against the 21-day target set for the time from referral from a physician to an initial appointment with a cancer surgeon), performance-based funding (i.e., making some funding conditional upon achieving particular results), and public reporting (i.e., reporting

results to providers and to the public), as well as targeted initiatives with regional vice-presidents and cancer-care providers to address particular problems;(72) and

6) surveillance, monitoring and public reporting on patterns and trends in cancer risk factors, incidence, prevalence, mortality and survival.(73)

CCO also works in partnership with other organizations, such as:

1) the College of Physicians and Surgeons of Ontario, with which it co-leads the Quality Management Partnership that designs and implements provincial quality-management programs for mammography (for breast screening), colonoscopy (for colorectal cancer screening, among other purposes), and pathology (for the diagnosis and staging of cancer, among other purpose);(74) and

2) Canadian Partnership Against Cancer, with which it implements the national strategy for cancer control.(75)

Places and people involved in cancer care

The places where cancer care is provided include, first and foremost, the 14 regional cancer centres and their affiliated hospitals and specialists' offices. But of course cancer care can also be provided in a person's home (e.g., where they may receive home and community care or palliative care), primary-care offices (e.g., where they may access cancer screening or comprehensive primary care, through which they may access care in a regional cancer centre, and to which they may be 'discharged' when their cancer treatment has been completed), and cancer-screening centres (e.g., those providing breast screening or colonoscopies), as well as residential hospices (for palliative care) (Figure 7.3).

The people involved in cancer care include those at risk of cancer, those being treated for or surviving after treatment for cancer (who are often referred to as cancer survivors), and those being provided with palliative care (who are often referred to as patients) and their families, as well as a broad range of regulated health professionals (e.g., nurses and physicians) and unregulated health workers (e.g., personal support workers involved in home care). The health professionals are represented by their respective professional associations (e.g., Ontario Medical Association) or by associations representing their particular area of specialty (e.g., Canadian Association of Nurses in Oncology). Some patients and family members are involved in roles ranging from members of the Cancer Quality Council of Ontario or CCO's Patient and Family Cancer Advisory Council (who are chosen to ensure geographic diversity), to Patient and Family Advisors (who provide input into policies, programs and practices that affect care). Cancer advocacy groups, such as the Canadian Cancer Society and many disease-specific (e.g., breast cancer, prostate cancer) groups, also play important roles, particularly in education, fundraising and supporting patients and families. The Canadian Partnership Against Cancer – an arm's-length agency of the federal government – works in partnership with many of those involved in cancer care.(76)

Governance, financial and delivery arrangements in cancer care

Governance, financial and delivery arrangements (i.e., the building blocks) are another lens through which cancer care can be described. The governance arrangements that are particularly salient to the sub-system have been addressed under 'policies' above. The key financial arrangement for cancer care is the funding provided by the Ministry of Health and Long-Term Care to CCO and, through it (sometimes for the achievement of particular results, as noted above), to the regional cancer centres, hospitals and other providers of cancer care. CCO (and the Ontario Renal Network that operates as a division within it), WSIB (as described earlier in the chapter) and CCACs are fairly unique organizations in the health system in their use of a 'commissioning' model that pays for care that meets the performance standards outlined in service agreements. Other financial arrangements, such as the funding for home and community care (through LHINs and then through CCACs) and for the family physicians and specialty physicians involved in providing care (through OHIP), operate in the same way as they do for the sectors described in Chapter 6. In terms of delivery arrangements, the 14 regional cancer centres and their affiliated hospitals and clinics provide the key infrastructure for cancer care.

End of life

End-of-life is less commonly thought of as a condition in the way that we may think of an addiction, injury or cancer, but there is value in considering it in a way that is analogous to these other conditions. The alternatives for a book organized in the way that we have organized this one would be to consider: 1) end-of-life care as a 'treatment,' as we do in Chapter 8 for prescription and over-the-counter drugs, complementary and alternative therapies, and dental services; or 2) those at the end of life as a 'population,' as we do in Chapter 9 for Indigenous peoples. When considered as a category of 'treatment,' the most appropriate term would be 'palliative care,' which increasingly emphasizes the importance of intervening early in the trajectory of a life-threatening condition (or a potentially life-threatening condition) and much earlier than the 'end-of-life' phase (that in the past was unhelpfully defined as only the remaining hours or days of life). We have adopted here a much broader conception of end of life and we use the broader term 'palliative care.'

Palliative care, like rehabilitation care and to some extent care for mental health and addictions, can involve or take place in four of the six sectors described in Chapter 6 (i.e., home and community care, primary care, specialty care, and long-term care). The Supreme Court decision about medical assistance in dying,(77) and the resulting federal government legislation that responded to this decision, have skewed public attention to just this one potential consideration at the end of life.(78) With the legislation now passed and being implemented, attention will likely return to the state of palliative care in general and how it can be improved.

To the extent that there is a key player in palliative care, it is (or hopefully one day will be) the 14 regional palliative-care networks (sometimes called hospice palliative-care programs) that operate within the boundaries of each of the LHINs and that bring together service providers such as CCACs, home and community care agencies, family and specialty physicians, and hospitals to plan, coordinate and improve the delivery of palliative care in their region. In the March 2016 budget announcement, the government committed to establish the Ontario Palliative Care Network, a partnership among CCO, LHINs, Health Quality Ontario and other partners such as patient, caregiver and clinical representatives, to develop provincial palliative-care standards, and to support the regionally focused networks that already exist.(79) The budget announcement also committed to increasing support for caregivers, and partnering with the Ontario Palliative Care Network to provide training and support to new hospice volunteers each year. From the perspective of patients, however, the key players are likely their caregivers and the health professionals, workers or teams involved in their care.

Policies that govern palliative care

Broadly speaking, no provincial government policies govern palliative care specifically, however, many sector-specific or system-wide policies govern it indirectly (Figure 7.4), such as the:

1) *Local Health Systems Integration Act, 2006*, which established the LHINs that fund: a) the CCACs that act as the gateway to government-funded home and community care and provide information about care that is not funded by government; b) the home and community care agencies that provide nursing, personal support and homemaking services that comprise one element of palliative care; and c) the residential hospices, palliative-care units and hospitals where much palliative care is provided;

2) *Home Care and Community Services Act, 1994*, which established eligibility criteria for home and community care services and the maximum levels of nursing, personal support and homemaking services that can be provided to an individual, including those receiving palliative care;

3) *Health Insurance Act, 1990*, which governs OHIP, through which all physicians are paid, including the family physicians and specialty physicians providing palliative care;

4) *Public Hospitals Act, 1990*, which governs the private not-for-profit hospitals where some palliative care is provided (including care provided in palliative-care units);

5) *Long-Term Care Homes Act, 2007*, which governs the long-term care homes where some palliative care is provided;

6) *Regulated Health Professions Act, 1991*, which governs the health professions who are involved in providing palliative care;

7) *Cancer Act, 1990*, which governs CCO and, through it, the palliative care provided through regional cancer programs;

8) *Substitute Decisions Act, 1992*, which established provisions for the naming of powers of attorney and statutory guardians, for both personal care and property, for those found to be mentally incapable of personal care or managing property, which may include some individuals receiving palliative care; and

9) *Health Care Consent Act, 1996*, which established rules with respect to consent to treatment and receipt of personal assistance services and rules for when an individual lacks the capacity to make decisions about

such matters.

The last of these policies specifies that even when an advance care plan is in place (as would ideally be for all citizens) or a do-not-resuscitate order is in place (as could be for some patients at the end of life), decisions about treatment and services cannot be made without informed consent, which means that health professionals need to discuss care options with patients or their substitute decision-makers.(80) Support for advance care planning is available through www.advancecareplanning.ca.

The aforementioned federal government legislation stipulates that five conditions must be met by a patient for medical assistance in dying: 1) be eligible for health services funded by the federal or provincial government (which excludes visitors to Canada); 2) be at least 18 years old and mentally competent (i.e., capable of making healthcare decisions for oneself); 3) have a 'grievous and irremediable' medical condition (the definition of which includes being at a point where natural death has become reasonably foreseeable); 4) make a request for medical assistance in dying that is not the result of outside pressure or influence; and 5) give informed consent to receive medical assistance in dying.(78) The College of Physicians and Surgeons of Ontario has developed a policy to guide physicians in providing medical assistance in dying.(81)

Programs constituting palliative care

The two provincial programs most directly related to palliative care are: 1) the 14 palliative-care networks that plan, coordinate and improve the delivery of palliative care in their region (or will do so as they become as fully functional as the Champlain Hospice Palliative Care Program in Ottawa and the Erie St. Clair Hospice Palliative Care Network in southwestern Ontario); and 2) the 39 residential hospices (with somewhere in the range of 300 beds), of which four are privately funded (and all of which rely in significant part on fundraising), that provide care for patients in the last weeks or months of life who either cannot be cared for or do not wish to be cared for at home (Figure 7.4).(82) In the same budget announcement noted above, the Government of Ontario committed to funding 20 new residential hospices across Ontario and to increase funding for existing residential hospices.(79) As noted above, home and community care agencies, hospitals and long-term care homes, as well as regional cancer programs, also provide palliative care, and many have formal programs.

Figure 7.4: Palliative care

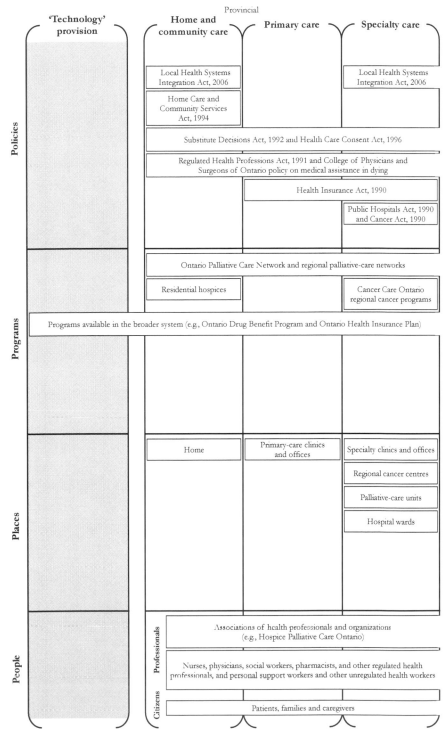

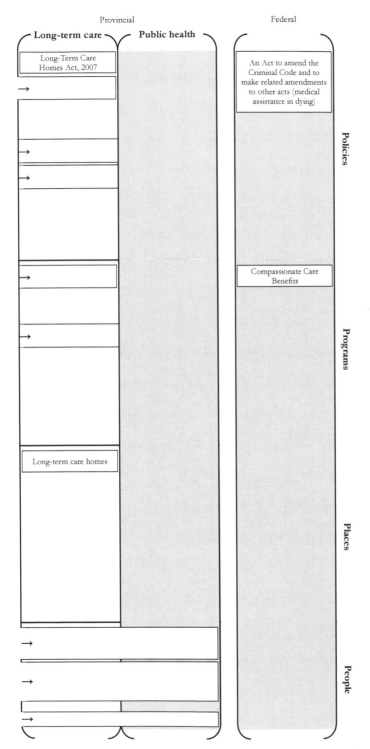

Hospitals may provide such care in a palliative-care unit, on a ward, or on an outpatient basis.

Several system-wide programs also play key roles, including the ODB Program (which covers the cost of drugs for eligible individuals) and OHIP (which remunerates both family physicians and specialists providing palliative care-related telephone and case management, and home, hospital and long-term care home visits).(83) The Palliative Care Facilitated Access program, which is administered by the Ontario Medical Association and funded by the Ministry of Health and Long-Term Care through the ODB Program, allows the ODB Program-eligible patients of registered physicians to access essential palliative care medications (84) more easily than is usually the case under the Exceptional Access Program. Also, the cancer sub-system provides many supports to palliative care for those with cancer.

The federal government administers the Compassionate Care Benefits program that allows eligible Ontarians to receive Employment Insurance benefits if they need to be away from work for up to 26 weeks to provide care or support to a family member who has a significant risk of death within 26 weeks.(85) The benefit can be shared among family members involved in providing care or support.

Places and people involved in palliative care

The places where palliative care may be provided include a person's home (whether that be in a private residence, retirement home, correctional centre, long-term care home or someplace else), offices and clinics (for those who are mobile), residential hospices (typically for patients with less complex needs in the last days or weeks of life), palliative-care units (which may be located in hospitals or complex continuing-care facilities and are for patients with acute or complex needs), and hospitals (typically in a general medical unit if there is no palliative-care unit or if there is no available bed in a palliative-care unit), among others (Figure 7.4). A report by Health Quality Ontario found that, of those receiving palliative care services in 2014-15, less than half (43%) received palliative home care services in their last month of life, about one third (34%) received a home visit from a physician in their last month of life, and nearly two thirds (65%) died in hospital.

The people involved in palliative care include the patients themselves, their families and caregivers, and the regulated health professionals and unregulated health workers providing palliative care. These professionals and workers can draw on many educational supports, including the Learning Essential Approaches to Palliative Care courses and workshops. Some common configurations of these professionals and workers include nurses and personal support workers providing palliative home care services, family physicians providing palliative care alone or with the support of a specialist palliative care team (acting in a consultation and/or shared-care model) and/or nurse-led Palliative Pain and Symptom Management Services, and the interprofessional teams providing palliative care (or consultations about palliative care) in residential hospices, palliative-care units, and hospitals. However, there is little standardization of such models of care and significant unevenness in access to them across the province. Both the health professionals and the organizations where they work may be represented by associations (e.g., Hospice Palliative Care Ontario).

Governance, financial and delivery arrangements in palliative care

The governance arrangements that are salient to palliative care have been addressed under 'policies' above, the financial arrangements operate in the same way as they do for the sectors described in Chapter 6, and the delivery arrangements include the 14 palliative-care networks that plan, coordinate and improve the delivery of palliative care and the many home and community care agencies and offices/clinics, the 39 residential hospices, the 21 palliative-care units, and the many hospitals that provide palliative care.

Conclusion

The unique approaches used in the care of the four conditions or groupings of conditions addressed in this chapter can be seen, in a manner that is somewhat comparable to the division of labour among the six sectors comprising Ontario's health system, as either integral to a well-functioning system that accommodates diversity of care needs, or a reflection of an unhelpful siloing of care in the system, depending on your perspective. As we will return to in the book's concluding chapter, tough questions can (and perhaps should) be asked about why we care for mental health and addictions so separately from 'physical health' (particularly given the numbers of Ontarians living with both mental and physical health challenges),(86) why we care for injuries and diseases so differently when they happen to be work-related (which includes buying preferential access to care), why we only organize cancer care as an almost entirely separate sub-system (and sometimes ask CCO to take on a delivery role for other prioritized conditions or issues), and why we have come so late to the game of standardizing models of palliative care and ensuring equitable access to these models. The answers may either reassure us or lead us to continue the push for integrated care that the LHINs have been empowered to pursue.

References

1. Consent and Capacity Board. About us. Toronto: Queen's Printer for Ontario; 2016. http://www.ccboard.on.ca/scripts/english/aboutus/index.asp (accessed 31 October 2016).

2. Legislative Assembly of Ontario. Smoke-Free Ontario Act, S.O. 1994, c. 10. Toronto: Queen's Printer for Ontario; 1994. https://www.ontario.ca/laws/statute/94t10 (accessed 31 October 2016).

3. College of Physicians and Surgeons of Ontario. Prescribing drugs. Toronto: College of Physicians and Surgeons of Ontario; 2016. http://www.cpso.on.ca/policies-publications/policy/prescribing-drugs#NARCOTICS (accessed 11 November 2016).

4. Legislative Assembly of Ontario. Child and Family Services Act, R.S.O. 1990, c. C.11. Toronto: Queen's Printer for Ontario; 2016. https://www.ontario.ca/laws/statute/90c11 (accessed 24 August 2016).

5. Legislative Assembly of Ontario. Liquor Licence Act, R.S.O. 1990, c. L.19. Toronto: Queen's Printer for Ontario; 2011. https://www.ontario.ca/laws/statute/90l19 (accessed 11 November 2016).

6. Canada Parliament House of Commons. Criminal Code, R.S.C., 1985, c. C-46. Ottawa: Canada Parliament House of Commons; 1985. http://laws-lois.justice.gc.ca/eng/acts/C-46/ (accessed 31 October 2016).

7. Ontario Review Board. About us. Toronto: Queen's Printer for Ontario; 2011. http://www.orb.on.ca/scripts/en/about.asp (accessed 24 August 2016).

8. Canada Parliament House of Commons. Controlled Drugs and Substances Act, S.C. 1996, c. 19. Ottawa: Canada Parliament House of Commons. http://laws-lois.justice.gc.ca/eng/acts/c-38.8/ (accessed 31 October 2016).

9. Canada Parliament House of Commons. Bill C-2, An Act to amend the Controlled Drugs and Substances Act (Respect for Communities Act, S.C. 2015, c. 22). Ottawa: Canada Parliament House of Commons; 2015. http://laws-lois.justice.gc.ca/eng/annualstatutes/2015_22/page-1.html#h-2 (accessed 31 October 2016).

10. Government of Ontario. Open minds, healthy minds: Ontario's comprehensive mental health and addictions strategy. Making healthy change happen. Toronto: Queen's Printer for Ontario; 2014. http://www.health.gov.on.ca/en/public/programs/mental-health/docs/open_minds_healthy_minds.pdf (accessed 25 August 2016).

11. Ministry of Children and Youth Services. Moving on mental health: A system that makes sense for children and youth. Toronto: Queen's Printer for Ontario; 2012. http://www.children.gov.on.ca/htdocs/english/documents/specialneeds/mentalhealth/momh.pdf (accessed 31 October 2016).

12. Ministry of Children and Youth Services. Community-based child and youth mental health program guidelines and requirements. Toronto: Queen's Printer for Ontario; 2015. http://www.children.gov.on.ca/htdocs/English/professionals/specialneeds/momh/pgr.aspx (accessed 31 October 2016).

13. Ministry of Children and Youth Services. Moving on mental health: Service areas and lead agencies for child and youth mental health. Toronto: Queen's Printer for Ontario; 2016. http://www.children.gov.on.ca/htdocs/English/professionals/specialneeds/momh/moving-on-mental-health.aspx (accessed 31 October 2016).

14. Ontario Mental Health and Addictions Leadership Advisory Council. 2015 annual report of the Mental Health and Addictions Leadership Advisory Council. Better mental health means better health. Toronto: Ontario Mental Health and Addictions Leadership Advisory Council; 2015. http://www.health.gov.on.ca/en/common/ministry/publications/reports/bmhmbh/mental_health_adv_council.pdf (accessed 31 October 2016).

15. ConnexOntario. Health services information. Toronto: ConnexOntario; 2016. http://www.connexontario.ca/Home/Services (accessed 25 August 2016).

16. Ministry of Health and Long-Term Care. Telehealth Ontario. Toronto: Queen's Printer for Ontario; 2016. https://www.ontario.ca/page/get-medical-advice-telehealth-ontario?_ga=1.196340716.1705045639.1415043906 (accessed 31 October 2016).

17. Ministry of Children and Youth Services. Child and youth mental health service framework. Toronto: Queen's Printer for Ontario; 2013. http://www.children.gov.on.ca/htdocs/English/documents/topics/specialneeds/mentalhealth/ServiceFramework.pdf (accessed 25 August 2016).

18. Ministry of Health and Long-Term Care. Results-based plan briefing book 2014-2015. Community mental health and addictions. Toronto: Queen's Printer for Ontario; 2015. http://www.health.gov.on.ca/en/common/ministry/publications/plans/rbplan14/ (accessed 25 August 2016).

19. Ministry of Health and Long-Term Care. Mental health and addictions. Toronto: Queen's Printer for Ontario; 2015. http://www.health.gov.on.ca/en/public/programs/mentalhealth/ (accessed 31 October 2016).

20. Ministry of Health and Long-Term Care. Homes for Special Care (HSC) program. Toronto: Queen's Printer for Ontario; 2016. http://www.health.gov.on.ca/en/pro/programs/hsc/ (accessed 31 October 2016).

21. Ministry of Health and Long-Term Care. Designated psychiatric facilities under the Mental Health Act. Toronto: Queen's Printer for Ontario; 2015. http://www.health.gov.on.ca/en/common/system/services/psych/designated.aspx#six (accessed 25 August 2016).

22. Centre for Addiction and Mental Health. Care programs and services. Toronto: Centre for Addiction and Mental Health; 2015. http://www.camh.ca/en/hospital/care_program_and_services/Pages/care_program_and_services.aspx (accessed 25 August 2016).

23. Ontario Shores for Mental Health Sciences. Programs and services. Whitby: Ontario Shores for Mental Health Sciences; 2015. http://ontarioshores.ca/cms/one.aspx?portalId=169&pageId=531 (accessed 26 August 2016).

24. Waypoint Centre for Mental Health. Waypoint programs and services. Penetanguishene: Waypoint Centre for Mental Health; 2015. http://www.waypointcentre.ca/programs___services (accessed 24 August 2016).

25. Royal Ottawa Mental Health Centre. Mental health programs. Ottawa: Royal Ottawa Mental Health Centre; 2016. http://www.theroyal.ca/about-the-royal/ (accessed 31 October 2016).

26. Children's Hospital of Eastern Ontario (CHEO). Ontario Child and Youth Telepsychiatry (OCYT) program. Ottawa: Children's Hospital of Eastern Ontario (CHEO); 2015. http://www.cheo.on.ca/en/ontario-telepsychiatry (accessed 25 August 2016).

27. Ontario Psychiatric Outreach Program. Programs. Toronto: Queen's Printer for Ontario; 2015. http://64.69.79.23/english/View.asp?x=548 (accessed 26 August 2016).

28. Waddell K, Bullock H, Lavis JN. Defining the mental health and addictions 'basket of core services' to be publicly funded in Ontario. Hamilton: McMaster Health Forum; 2016.

29. Mental Health Commission of Canada. Changing directions, changing lives: The mental health strategy for Canada. Ottawa: Mental Health Commission of Canada; 2012. http://www.mentalhealthcommission.ca/English/node/721 (accessed 24 August 2016).

30. Canadian Centre on Substance Abuse. National framework. Ottawa: Canadian Centre on Substance Abuse; 2016. http://www.ccsa.ca/Eng/focus/national/Pages/default.aspx (accessed 11 November 2016).

31. Kids Help Phone. About us. Toronto: Kids Help Phone; 2016. http://org.kidshelpphone.ca/about-us/ (accessed 11 November 2016).

32. Canadian Cancer Society. Smokers' helpline. Toronto: Canadian Cancer Society; 2016. http://www.smokershelpline.ca/ (accessed 31 October 2016).

33. Ontario Mental Health Foundation. Research overview and key priorities. Toronto: Ontario Mental Health Foundation; 2016. https://www.omhf.on.ca/Funding/FundingSupport-Principles (accessed 31 October 2016).

34. Gambling Research Exchange Ontario. What we do. Guelph: Gambling Research Exchange Ontario; 2016. http://greo.ca/about-us/what-we-do (accessed 31 October 2016).

35. Ontario Centre of Excellence for Child and Youth Mental Health. Resource hub. Ottawa: Ontario Centre of Excellence for Child and Youth Mental Health; 2016. http://www.excellenceforchildandyouth.ca/resource-hub (accessed 31 October 2016).

36. ConnexOntario. Number of distinct programs in the ConnexOntario database funded by the Ministry of Health and Long-Term Care - Community Mental Health and Addictions Branch by type of program and Local Health Integration Network (LHIN). Toronto: ConnexOntario; 2015.

37. Ministry of Children and Youth Services. A shared responsibility: Ontario's policy framework for child and youth mental health. Toronto: Queen's Printer for Ontario; 2010. http://www.children.gov.on.ca/htdocs/English/documents/topics/specialneeds/mentalhealth/framework.pdf (accessed 25 August 2016).

38. WSIB Ontario. Overview of workers' compensation in Ontario 1980 to present. Toronto: Workplace Safety and Insurance Board; 2011.

39. WSIB Ontario. WSIB 2015 economic statement. Toronto: Workplace Safety and Insurance Board; 2015.

40. Legislative Assembly of Ontario. Occupational Health and Safety Act, R.S.O. 1990, c. O.1. Toronto: Queen's Printer for Ontario; 1990. https://www.ontario.ca/laws/statute/90o01 (accessed 31 October 2016).

41. Legislative Assembly of Ontario. Workplace Safety and Insurance Act, 1997, S.O. 1997, c. 16, Sched. A. Toronto: Queen's Printer for Ontario; 1997. https://www.ontario.ca/laws/statute/97w16 (accessed 31 October 2016).

42. WSIB Ontario. Service delivery model. Toronto: Workplace Safety and Insurance Board; 2016. http://www.wsib.on.ca (accessed 31 August 2016).

43. Office of the Employer Advisor. The employer's guide to workplace safety and insurance. Toronto: Queen's Printer for Ontario; 2013. http://www.employeradviser.ca/docs/en/documents/report/2016_nonconstruction_em_guide.pdf (accessed 25 August 2016).

44. WSIB Ontario. Programs of care. Toronto: Workplace Safety and Insurance Board; 2016. http://www.wsib.on.ca (accessed 31 October 2016).

45. WSIB Ontario. Instructions for delivering programs of care. Toronto: Workplace Safety and Insurance Board; 2016. http://www.wsib.on.ca (accessed 31 October 2016).

46. WSIB Ontario. Regional evaluation centres. Toronto: Workplace Safety and Insurance Board; 2016. http://www.wsib.on.ca (accessed 31 October 2016).

47. WSIB Ontario. Specialty programs. Toronto: Workplace Safety and Insurance Board; 2016. http://www.wsib.on.ca (accessed 31 October 2016).

48. WSIB Ontario. Serious injury program. Toronto: Workplace Safety and Insurance Board; 2016. http://www.wsib.on.ca (accessed 31 October 2016).

49. Office of the Employer Advisor. OEA Office of the Employer Advisor. Toronto: Queen's Printer for Ontario; 2016. http://www.employeradviser.ca/en/ (accessed 31 October 2016).

50. Office of the Worker Advisor. About the OWA. Toronto: Queen's Printer for Ontario; 2015. http://www.owa.gov.on.ca/en/about/pages/contactus.aspx (accessed 31 October 2016).

51. Workplace Safety and Insurance Appeals Tribunal. About WSIAT. Toronto: Queen's Printer for Ontario; 2016. http://www.wsiat.on.ca/english/about/index.htm (accessed 31 October 2016).

52. Institute for Work & Health. About IWH. Toronto: Institute for Work & Health; 2016. http://www.iwh.on.ca/about (accessed 31 October 2016).

53. WSIB Ontario. Health care equipment and supplies. Toronto: Workplace Safety and Insurance Board; 2016. http://www.wsib.on.ca (accessed 24 August 2016).

54. Cancer Care Ontario. 2014/15 annual report. Toronto: Cancer Care Ontario; 2015. https://www.cancercare.on.ca/common/pages/UserFile.aspx?fileId=350569 (accessed 24 August 2016).

55. Cancer Care Ontario. Wait times. Toronto: Cancer Care Ontario; 2016. https://www.cancercare.on.ca/ocs/wait-times/ (accessed 31 October 2016).

56. Cancer Care Ontario. Alternate level of care. Toronto: Cancer Care Ontario; 2016. https://www.cancercare.on.ca/ocs/alc/ (accessed 31 October 2016).

57. Cancer Care Ontario. Ontario Renal Network. Toronto: Cancer Care Ontario; 2016. https://www.cancercare.on.ca/cms/one.aspx?objectId=75499&contextId=1377 (accessed 31 October 2016).

58. Cardiac Care Network. About the Cardiac Care Network of Ontario. Toronto: Cardiac Care Network of Ontario; 2016. http://www.ccn.on.ca/ccn_public/FormsAboutCCN/about.aspx (accessed 31 October 2016).

59. Foundation for the Accreditation of Cellular Therapy. Why you should become a FACT accredited organization. Omaha: Foundation for the Accreditation of Cellular Therapy; 2016. http://www.factwebsite.org/Accreditation/ (accessed 11 November 2016).

60. Canadian Nuclear Safety Commission. RD/GD-120: Licence application guide radiotherapy. Ottawa: Government of Canada; 2016. http://nuclearsafety.gc.ca/eng/acts-and-regulations/regulatory-documents/published/html/gd120/ (accessed 11 November 2016).

61. Health Canada. Drugs and health products. Ottawa: Health Canada; 2016. http://www.hc-sc.gc.ca/dhp-mps/prodpharma/applic-demande/guide-ld/clini/cta_background-eng.php (accessed 11 November 2016).

62. Cancer Care Ontario. Breast cancer screening. Toronto: Cancer Care Ontario; 2016. https://www.cancercare.on.ca/cms/One.aspx?portalId=1377&pageId=9430 (accessed 31 October 2016).

63. Cancer Care Ontario. Cervical cancer screening. Toronto: Cancer Care Ontario; 2016. https://www.cancercare.on.ca/cms/One.aspx?portalId=1377&pageId=9528 (accessed 31 October 2016).

64. Cancer Care Ontario. Colorectal cancer screening. Toronto: Cancer Care Ontario; 2016. https://www.cancercare.on.ca/cms/One.aspx?portalId=1377&pageId=9851 (accessed 31 October 2016).

65. Cancer Care Ontario. Mobile screening. Toronto: Cancer Care Ontario; 2016. https://www.cancercare.on.ca/cms/one.aspx?objectId=324152&contextId=1377 (accessed 31 October 2016).

66. Cancer Care Ontario. Cancer system overview. Toronto: Cancer Care Ontario; 2015. https://www.cancercare.on.ca/ocs/csoverview/ (accessed 24 August 2016).

67. Cancer Care Ontario. Clinical programs. Toronto: Cancer Care Ontario; 2015. https://www.cancercare.on.ca/cms/One.aspx?portalId=1377&pageId=8665 (accessed 24 August 2016).

68. Cancer Care Ontario. Program in Evidence-Based Care. Toronto: Cancer Care Ontario; 2016. https://www.cancercare.on.ca/cms/one.aspx?portalId=1377&pageId=7582 (accessed 31 October 2016).

69. Cancer Care Ontario. Ontario Cancer Plan IV 2015-2019. Toronto: Cancer Care Ontario; 2015. http://ocp.cancercare.on.ca/ (accessed 26 August 2016).

70. Cancer Care Ontario. Aboriginal Cancer Strategy 2015-2019. Toronto: Cancer Care Ontario; 2015. https://www.cancercare.on.ca/cms/one.aspx?objectId=9315&contextId=1377 (accessed 24 August 2016).

71. Cancer Care Ontario. Primary care program. Toronto: Cancer Care Ontario; 2015. https://www.cancercare.on.ca/cms/One.aspx?portalId=1377&pageId=8679 (accessed 24 August 2016).

72. Cancer Care Ontario. Quality and performance improvement. Toronto: Cancer Care Ontario; 2016. https://www.cancercare.on.ca/cms/One.aspx?portalId=1377&pageId=8799 (accessed 31 October 2016).

73. Cancer Care Ontario. Cancer surveillance. Toronto: Cancer Care Ontario; 2016. https://www.cancercare.on.ca/cms/One.aspx?portalId=1377&pageId=35493 (accessed 31 October 2016).

74. Cancer Quality Council of Ontario. About CQCO. Toronto: Cancer Quality Council of Ontario; 2016. http://www.cqco.ca/about (accessed 25 August 2016).

75. Canadian Partnership Against Cancer. The Canadian Strategy for Cancer Control 2017-2022. Toronto: Canadian Partnership Against Cancer; 2016.

76. Canadian Partnership Against Cancer. Partnership history. Ottawa: Canadian Partnership Against Cancer; 2016. http://www.partnershipagainstcancer.ca/who-we-are/partnership-overview (accessed 11 November 2016).

77. Supreme Court of Canada. Carter v. Canada (Attorney General), 2015 SCC 5, [2015] 1 S.C.R. 331. Ottawa: Supreme Court of Canada; 2015. http://scc-csc.lexum.com/scc-csc/scc-csc/en/item/14637/index.do (accessed 11 May 2016).

78. Canada Parliament House of Commons. An Act to amend the Criminal Code and to make related amendments to other Acts (medical assistance in dying) S.C. 2016, c. 3. Ottawa: Canada Parliament House of Commons; 2016. http://laws-lois.justice.gc.ca/eng/AnnualStatutes/2016_3/FullText.html (accessed 28 October 2016).

79. Ministry of Health and Long-Term Care. Province strengthens end-of-life care with $75 million investment. Toronto: Queen's Printer for Ontario; 2016. https://news.ontario.ca/mohltc/en/2016/3/province-strengthens-end-of-life-care-with-75-million-investment.html (accessed 25 August 2016).

80. Gauvin FP, Lavis JN. Evidence brief: Improving end-of-life communication, decision-making and care in Ontario. Hamilton: McMaster Health Forum; 2013.

81. College of Physicians and Surgeons of Ontario. Medical assistance in dying. Toronto: College of Physicians and Surgeons of Ontario; 2016. http://www.cpso.on.ca/Policies-Publications/Policy/Medical-Assistance-in-Dying (accessed 28 October 2016).

82. Office of the Auditor General of Ontario. 2014 annual report of the Office of the Auditor General of Ontario. Chapter 3, section 3.08: Palliative care. Toronto: Office of the Auditor General of Ontario; 2014.

83. Ministry of Health and Long-Term Care. OHIP schedule of benefits and fees. Toronto: Queen's Printer for Ontario; 2016. http://www.health.gov.on.ca/en/pro/programs/ohip/sob/ (accessed 11 November 2016).

84. Ontario Medical Association. Palliative care facilitated access. Physician declaration form. Toronto: Ontario Medical Association; 2016. https://www.cancercare.on.ca/common/pages/UserFile.aspx?fileId=320097 (accessed 11 November 2016).

85. Government of Canada. Compassionate care benefits. Ottawa: Government of Canada; 2016. http://www.servicecanada.gc.ca/eng/ei/faq/faq_compassionate_care_individuals.shtml (accessed 31 October 2016).

86. Naylor C, Das P, Ross S, Honeyman M, Thompson J, Gilburt H. Bringing together physical and mental health. A new frontier for integrated care. London: The King's Fund; 2016. http://www.kingsfund.org.uk/publications/physical-and-mental-health (accessed 24 August 2016).

87. WSIB Ontario. By the numbers: 2014 WSIB statistical report - Schedule 1. Toronto: Workplace Safety and Insurance Board; 2015.

88. WSIB Ontario. By the numbers: 2014 WSIB statistical report - Schedule 2. Toronto: Workplace Safety and Insurance Board; 2015.

89. WSIB Ontario. By the numbers: 2013 WSIB statistical report - Schedule 2. Toronto: Workplace Safety and Insurance Board; 2013.

90. WSIB Ontario. By the numbers: 2013 WSIB statistical report - Schedule 1. Toronto: Workplace Safety and Insurance Board; 2013.

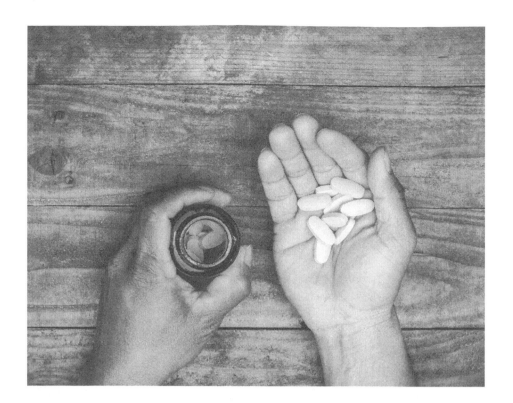

8. Care using select treatments

Cristina A. Mattison and John N. Lavis

Key messages for citizens

- The majority of prescription and over-the-counter drugs, complementary and alternative therapies, and dental services are paid for by private insurers or out-of-pocket, with government funding concentrated in two areas:

  - drugs provided in hospital or covered through programs funded by the provincial government (Ontario Drug Benefit Program and selected drug and/or disease-specific programs); and

  - dental surgery performed in hospital and dental services covered through programs funded by provincial and municipal governments.

- Chiropractors, homeopaths, massage therapists, naturopaths and traditional Chinese medicine practitioners are regulated health professionals who provide complementary and alternative therapies.

Key messages for health professionals

- In the past decade, the scope of practice of pharmacists has been expanded to include: 1) prescription renewal and some alterations; 2) certain smoking-cessation prescriptions; 3) administration of flu vaccines to those aged five years and older; 4) using medication to demonstrate its use to newly diagnosed patients (e.g., asthma inhalers); 5) select below-the-dermis procedures (e.g., blood glucose testing); and 6) provision of the naloxone kit (for opioid overdoses).

- Complementary and alternative therapies are delivered by practitioners who work in private practice and do not receive funding from the government.

- Aside from the dental services offered in hospitals and through select programs, dental services are also delivered in private practice and without funding from government.

Key messages for policymakers

- From 2000-01 to 2013-14, public prescription drug costs have steadily increased, with prescription drug costs to the government and to recipients increasing, in both cases, by 93%, drug costs at formulary prices increasing by 81%, drug mark-up increasing by 47%, and dispensing and compounding fees increasing by 170%.

- From 2000-01 to 2013-14, Ontario Drug Benefit Program beneficiaries and costs have also increased, with the number of beneficiaries increasing by 39% and claims increasing by 200%.

- While the use of complementary and alternative therapies is growing, they are almost exclusively paid for privately, either out-of-pocket or through private insurance plans.

- Only 1% of dental service expenditures were publicly financed in 2010, and while most dental services are paid for privately, there are a number of dental programs that support children, people with disabilities, and those in need of significant jaw reconstruction (offered in hospitals).

. . .

In this chapter we profile care that involves three broad categories of treatments: prescription and over-the-counter drugs, complementary and alternative therapies, and dental services. To begin, we focus on prescription and over-the-counter drugs. As covered in Chapter 1, when public and private spending are combined, drugs are the second largest category of health-system expenditure, which places them behind hospitals but before physicians. Complementary and alternative therapies are discussed as they are increasingly being used by many Ontarians either alongside or instead of the types of treatments covered in Chapters 6 and 7, even though their delivery operates entirely outside of the publicly funded health system. Dental services are also discussed, as they are an often taken-for-granted category of treatments that are also delivered largely outside the publicly funded health system.

Prescription and over-the-counter drugs

Understanding the role of drugs in health systems is important for three reasons: 1) prescription and over-the-counter drugs are the most commonly used therapeutic intervention; 2) such drugs can have major benefits, but they can also cause harm; and 3) drugs are the second most costly component of healthcare in Ontario (see Figure 1.2). For example, the Canadian Health Measures Survey identified that between 2007 and 2011, 41% of the household population (aged six to 79 years) reported using prescription drugs, and use increased with age – from 12% among six-to-14-year-olds to 83% among those aged 65 to 79 years.(1)

Three key features of how prescription and over-the-counter drugs are governed, financed and delivered warrant singling out, and we return to these features in more detail below. First, the provincial government funds a number of programs to subsidize the cost of drugs for eligible Ontarians (Table 8.1), however, private sources of funds – both private insurance and out-of-pocket payments – are relied on by many Ontarians (Table 8.2). Second, pharmacists play a central role in the delivery of prescription and over-the-counter drugs, and their scope of practice has increased significantly over the past decade. Third, the federal government plays a key role in the approval and regulation of drugs and a national body informs provincial government decisions about which drugs to fund through its programs. Where relevant in the sub-sections below, we begin by describing the context in Ontario and then provide any key relevant federal or national details.

Table 8.1: Publicly funded drug programs[1]

Program	Benefit
Ontario Drug Benefit (ODB) Program	Covers most of the cost of prescription drugs, some nutrition products and some diabetic testing agents as listed in the ODB Program formulary (which includes approximately 4,400 products), with set fees for patients[2]
Exceptional Access Program	Covers most of the cost of prescription drugs not on the approved ODB formulary and requested by a physician (e.g., when the drugs on the ODB formulary have been tried but have not worked or an alternative drug is not available on the formulary)
	Each request is reviewed according to Exceptional Access Program criteria, which have been developed by the Committee to Evaluate Drugs (i.e., the Ministry of Health and Long-Term Care's expert advisory committee on drug-related issues)
Trillium Drug Program	Covers most of the cost of prescription drugs for those who have high prescription drug costs relative to their household income[3]

Continued on next page

Program	Benefit
New Drug Funding Program	Full coverage of approved new and expensive intravenous cancer drugs administered in regional cancer centres and hospitals
	The majority of intravenous cancer drugs are funded through this program, with the exception of older and less expensive drugs, which are covered under the Systemic Treatment Quality-Based Program
Special Drugs Program	Full coverage of disease-specific drugs when prescribed to outpatients by a designated centre/physician (e.g., drugs for cystic fibrosis, Gaucher's disease, schizophrenia, thalassemia, and children with growth failure)
Inherited Metabolic Diseases Program	Full coverage of certain outpatient metabolic disorder treatment-related drugs, supplements, and specialty foods (e.g., infant feeds, low protein foods, and modified l-amino acid mixtures)
Respiratory Syncytial Virus Prophylaxis Program	Full coverage of palivizumab, which is used to prevent serious lower respiratory tract infections caused by respiratory syncytial virus in infants less than two years of age (at the start of respiratory syncytial virus season)
Visudyne (Verteporfin) Program	Full coverage of verteporfin, which is used to slow the progression of age-related macular degeneration (an eye-related condition leading to blindness)

Sources: 16; 17; 78-81

Notes:
[1] Called the Ontario Public Drug Programs
[2] A fee (called a co-payment) of up to $6.11 applies to all prescriptions. Higher income seniors also pay a $100 deductible before the cost of prescription drugs is covered. Lower income seniors can apply for the Seniors Co-Payment Program, which caps the co-payment at up to $2 per prescription (the same co-payment paid by social assistance recipients).
[3] An income-based deductible of approximately 4% of total household net income, and subsequent co-payment of up to $2 may apply.

Table 8.2: Drug coverage and costs by source (public and private), 2013

	2013[1]	Percentage of population
Population covered by public and private insurance (thousands)		
Private insurers	7,631	54%
Ontario Public Drug Programs	3,831	27%
Uninsured (entirely out-of-pocket)	2,461	17%
Other public programs[2]	235	2%
Costs by public and private sources ($ millions)		
Ontario Public Drug Programs	4,400	39%
Private insurers	4,000	36%
Out-of-pocket	2,600	23%
Other public programs[2]	200	2%
Total costs	11,200	

Source: 82

Notes:
[1] These data are forecasts from the Canadian Institute for Health Information. We have made an exception to our 'no forecasts' rule (which we explain in Chapter 1) because actual data from earlier years are not publicly available.
[2] Other public programs include the Non-Insured Health Benefits program and other federal government programs.

Policies that govern prescription and over-the-counter drugs

The main policies that govern prescription and over-the-counter drugs at the provincial level are listed in Figure 8.1 and include the:

1) Ontario Drug Benefit Act, 1990, which established the current administration of public drug programs in Ontario and the requirements for the formulary;

2) *Drug and Pharmacies Regulation Act, 1990*, which established the regulations governing pharmacies;

3) *Pharmacy Act, 1991*, which established the scope of practice of pharmacists;

4) *Drug Interchangeability and Dispensing Fee Act, 1993*, which established rules for interchanging one prescribed drug with another (containing the same active ingredients and dosage);

5) *Transparent Drug System for Patients Act, 2006*, which formalized the Ontario Public Drug Programs and includes commitments to consumer/patient engagement, transparency, and using clinical and economic evidence in drug-funding decisions;

6) *Regulated Health Professions Statute Law Amendment Act, 2009*, which expanded the scope of practice for pharmacists, among a number of other health professions; and

7) *Narcotics Safety and Awareness Act, 2010*, which established a monitoring system for the prescribing and dispensing of narcotics and other monitored drugs, in order to reduce the misuse and abuse of these types of drugs.

At the federal level, two key policies govern prescription and over-the-counter drugs:

1) the *Food and Drugs Act, 1985*, which requires drug manufacturers to provide scientific evidence on the safety, efficacy and quality of the product under review in order to obtain authorization to market a drug in Canada and which, through amendments made by Bill C-17, requires a robust drug-surveillance system, procedures to recall unsafe therapeutic products, and clearer labelling for children 12 and under;(2; 3) and

2) the *Patent Act, 1985*, which established the Patented Medicine Prices Review Board and which, through amendments made by regulation SOR/93-133, established the conditions under which generic drugs can be marketed.(4; 5)

Under the terms of the *Food and Drugs Act, 1985*, the Therapeutic Products Directorate of Health Canada's Health Products and Food Branch regulates which prescription and over-the-counter drugs, as well as medical devices, can be offered for sale in Canada.(6) Expedited reviews can be conducted under special circumstances. For example, the Priority Review Process provides faster review of promising drugs for life-threatening conditions, and the Special Access Program allows physicians to prescribe drugs that are not currently offered in Canada, albeit under very restricted circumstances (e.g., when standard treatments have failed or are not appropriate in specific circumstances).(2) On the other hand, some drugs undergo a very lengthy review process. The issue of approving medications for abortion in Canada, for example, was prolonged, and the review of Mifegymiso – the combination of mifepristone and misoprostil that can be used to terminate pregnancies – began in November of 2012, but was not approved until July 2015, and its use is restricted to patients who can access an ultrasound and a physician who is registered and trained to prescribe the drug.(7; 8)

Health Canada sets specific guidelines for the marketing of prescription and over-the-counter drugs. Most notably, direct-to-consumer advertising of pharmaceutical products (whether using print, broadcast or internet media) is prohibited in Canada, with the exception of: 1) public health vaccination campaigns that do not promote a specific product; 2) reminder advertisements (which include only the brand name and not the drug's indications); and 3) disease-oriented or help-seeking advertisements (which describe the disease or condition but do not include a brand name).(9; 10) That said, Ontarians are exposed to a significant amount of pharmaceutical advertising through media from the U.S. Further complicating the issue is that while direct-to-consumer advertising is not allowed, direct-to-consumer information campaigns are allowed, and properly distinguishing between the two requires resources.(11) To ensure compliance with Health Canada's guidelines, the Pharmaceutical Advertising Advisory Board reviews materials for health products directed at health professionals, and it works with Advertising Standards Canada to review (voluntarily submitted) prescription drug and educational materials on medical conditions and diseases aimed at consumers.(12)

Under the terms of the *Patent Act, 1985*, the Patented Medicine Prices Review Board regulates the 'factory gate' ceiling price of patented drugs (not the wholesale price or the retail price charged by pharmacies) and

Figure 8.1: Prescription and over-the-counter drugs

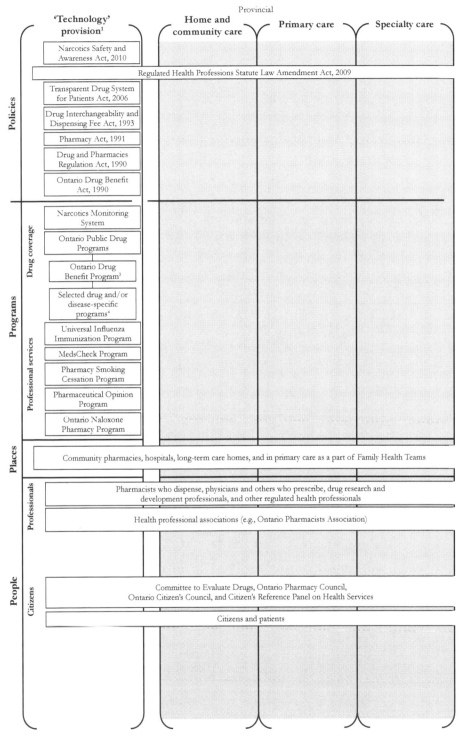

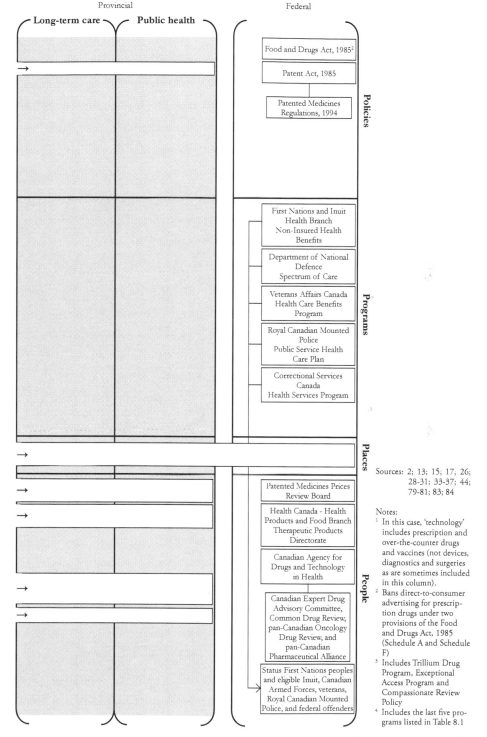

Provincial

Long-term care   Public health

Federal

Policies

Food and Drugs Act, 1985[2]

Patent Act, 1985

Patented Medicines
Regulations, 1994

Programs

First Nations and Inuit
Health Branch
Non-Insured Health
Benefits

Department of National
Defence
Spectrum of Care

Veterans Affairs Canada
Health Care Benefits
Program

Royal Canadian Mounted
Police
Public Service Health
Care Plan

Correctional Services
Canada
Health Services Program

Places

People

Patented Medicines Prices
Review Board

Health Canada - Health
Products and Food Branch
Therapeutic Products
Directorate

Canadian Agency for
Drugs and Technology
in Health

Canadian Expert Drug
Advisory Committee,
Common Drug Review,
pan-Canadian Oncology
Drug Review, and
pan-Canadian
Pharmaceutical Alliance

Status First Nations peoples
and eligible Inuit, Canadian
Armed Forces, veterans,
Royal Canadian Mounted
Police, and federal offenders

Sources: 2; 13; 15; 17; 26;
28-31; 33-37; 44;
79-81; 83; 84

Notes:
[1] In this case, 'technology'
includes prescription and
over-the-counter drugs
and vaccines (not devices,
diagnostics and surgeries
as are sometimes included
in this column).
[2] Bans direct-to-consumer
advertising for prescrip-
tion drugs under two
provisions of the Food
and Drugs Act, 1985
(Schedule A and Schedule
F)
[3] Includes Trillium Drug
Program, Exceptional
Access Program and
Compassionate Review
Policy
[4] Includes the last five programs listed in Table 8.1

Care using select treatments 323

reports on prescription drug-price trends and on research and development spending by pharmaceutical companies.(13) The board began operation in 1987 and is part of the federal government's 'Health Portfolio,' although it operates at arm's-length from the minister of health and independently from Health Canada, which is the federal government's health department.(13) The Patented Medicine Prices Review Board has jurisdiction over 'factory-gate' prices (i.e., product price at the factory) for patented prescription and over-the-counter drugs, and does not extend to wholesaler or retailer pricing.(14)

While also formally part of governance arrangements, we address below – in the sub-section on 'places and people' – the scope of practice of pharmacists and the few health professions who can prescribe drugs.

Drug programs

Publicly funded drug programs (Figure 8.1) are administered as part of the Ontario Public Drug Programs, which were re-designed to their current form in 2007 through the *Transparent Drug System for Patients Act, 2006*.(15) The majority of the drugs offered through the Ontario Public Drug Programs are listed on the Ontario Drug Benefit (ODB) Program formulary, with the exception of those covered through the Exceptional Access Program and its associated Compassionate Review Policy. There are around 4,400 drug products listed on the ODB Program formulary.(16) The Exceptional Access Program provides access to over 850 drugs that are not covered by the formulary, but are approved for sale in Canada.(15) In 2013-14, approximately 64,200 Exceptional Access Program requests were made and 52,000 were approved (81%).(17)

The Ontario Public Drug Programs (Table 8.1) include the:
1) ODB Program for those aged 65 and older, recipients of home care, residents of Homes for Special Care and long-term care homes, and recipients of social assistance through either Ontario Works or the Ontario Disability Support Program;
2) Exceptional Access Program for those meeting the eligibility criteria for the ODB Program and, as noted above, needing drugs that are not covered on the formulary but were requested by a physician (and that are usually expensive drugs and only cost-effective in a small group of patients);

3) Trillium Drug Program for those with very high drug costs relative to household income (those who do not qualify for the ODB Program can apply for the Trillium Drug Program);
4) New Drug Funding Program for select intravenous cancer drugs, which are often very expensive (see Chapter 7);
5) Special Drugs Program for a range of serious conditions (e.g., full outpatient drug coverage for cystic fibrosis and thalassemia, among others, and including clozapine for schizophrenia);
6) Inherited Metabolic Diseases Program for those with metabolic disorders (full outpatient drug coverage, as well as coverage of supplements and specialty foods);
7) Respiratory Syncytial Virus Prophylaxis Program for high-risk infants (full coverage of palivizumab, which is used to prevent serious lower respiratory tract infections); and
8) Visudyne (Verteporfin) for those with age-related macular degeneration.(18; 19)

The Ministry of Health and Long-Term Care's Drugs for Rare Disease framework was created in 2007 by a panel of clinical and health technology assessment experts as a response to the lack of a national strategy.(20) A draft of the framework is used to assess funding requests for drugs for rare diseases. Five drugs have been evaluated using the framework, three of which are available through the Exceptional Access Program.(20; 21)

The Ontario Public Drug Programs are responsible for: 1) determining which products should be eligible for public reimbursement, which is done based on recommendations from the Committee to Evaluate Drugs; 2) making funding decisions; and; 3) negotiating agreements with drug manufacturers as appropriate.(15)

In making its recommendations, the Committee to Evaluate Drugs, which is comprised of 16 members (physicians with additional expertise in drugs or critical appraisal, pharmacists, health economists, and two patient representatives), considers recommendations about patented drugs from the Canadian Drug Expert Committee (or, in the case of cancer drugs, from the pan-Canadian Oncology Drug Review's Expert Review Committee) and extensive drug reviews provided through the broader Common Drug Review.(22) Up until 2003, provinces and territories conducted drug reviews independently. The Common Drug Review is the result of a 2002 intergovernmental agreement to ensure that publicly funded drugs are cost-effective, while eliminating duplication of efforts across jurisdictions.(23; 24) The Common Drug Review is coordinated by the Canadian Agency for Drugs and Technologies in Health, an independent, not-for-profit organization that was created in 1989 by federal, provincial and territorial governments in an effort to centralize the review of health technologies and drugs, and the provision of recommendations.(25)

The Ontario Public Drug Programs' executive officer has the final decision as to whether a drug should be listed on the formulary or made available through the Exceptional Access Program.(15) Through the Compassionate Review Policy, the executive officer, with the assistance of expert clinical reviewers, can consider funding requests on a case-by-case basis in instances where a quick decision is needed (e.g., due to life-, limb- or organ-threatening conditions).(15)

The federal government manages public drug plans for select populations:
1) status First Nations peoples and eligible Inuit through the First Nations and Inuit Health Branch's Non-Insured Health Benefits program, which will likely be extended to non-status First Nations and Métis in light of the 2016 Supreme Court decision (see Chapter 9 for more details on Indigenous health);(26)
2) members of the Canadian Forces (and their dependents) through the Department of National Defence's Spectrum of Care program, which includes the Canadian Armed Forces Drug Benefit List;(27; 28)
3) qualified veterans through Veterans Affairs Canada's Programs of Choice, which includes the Health Care Benefits Program;(29)
4) Royal Canadian Mounted Police through the Public Service Health Care Plan;(30) and
5) federal offenders through Correctional Service Canada's Health Services Program.(31)

Places and people involved in prescription and over-the-counter drugs

Prescription and over-the-counter drugs are available through pharmacies, with private for-profit community pharmacies located in abundance in most non-remote communities. In 2015 there were 4,012 community pharmacies in Ontario, of which:
- 49% (1,967) are independently owned;
- 26% (1,051) are franchises (e.g., Shoppers Drug Mart) or banner

retailers (e.g., Guardian);
- 22% (872) are large chains (greater than 15 stores) (e.g., Rexall); and
- 3% (122) are small chains (from three to 15 stores).(32)

Pharmacy departments are important components of hospitals, providing prescription and clinical pharmacy assistance to patients and prescribers.

Most pharmacists work in pharmacies, but some can be found in home and community care organizations, as members of Family Health Teams, and in long-term care homes.(33) As part of the *Regulated Health Professions Statute Law Amendment Act, 2009*, the government expanded the role of pharmacists.(34) Pharmacists' scope of practice and/or publicly funded practice has grown to include:

1) one 30-minute annual review of prescriptions for those taking a minimum of three medications for a chronic condition, which was expanded in 2010 to include residents of long-term care homes, people living with diabetes, and people who are home-bound (through MedsCheck);
2) influenza vaccine administration in those aged five and up, through the Universal Influenza Immunization Program;
3) prescription of certain smoking-cessation drugs, through the Pharmacy Smoking Cessation Program
4) renewal and adaptation (e.g., dosage amounts) of some prescription medications, through the Pharmaceutical Opinion Program;
5) injections or inhalations to patients for education or demonstration purposes;
6) procedures on tissue below the dermis for the limited purposes of patient self-care education and chronic-disease monitoring (e.g., blood glucose monitoring); and
7) naloxone kit provision without a prescription and at no cost, which involves training from the pharmacist on how to properly administer the drug to treat opioid overdose (intramuscular injection), through the Ontario Naloxone Pharmacy Program.(20; 34-37)

Under the terms of the *Narcotics Safety and Awareness Act, 2010*, pharmacists also contribute data about the dispensing of narcotics and other controlled substances to the Narcotics Monitoring System, and receive warning messages about potential misuse.(17) Pharmacists are represented by the Ontario Pharmacists Association.

Only physicians, dentists, nurse practitioners, midwives and (as noted, in limited ways) pharmacists are allowed to prescribe drugs to humans (and veterinarians can prescribe drugs to animals). In its 2014 election platform, the Liberal Party signalled the Government of Ontario's intent to further expand nurses' and pharmacists' ability to prescribe.(38; 39) The Health Professions Regulatory Advisory Council recently reviewed three models for registered nurse prescribing (independent prescribing, supplementary prescribing, and use of protocols) and made recommendations to the Minister of Health and Long-Term Care on prescribing by registered nurses in Ontario.(40)

National-level associations represent the brand-name pharmaceutical industry (Innovative Medicines Canada, which was formerly called Rx&D), generic-drug industry (Canadian Generic Pharmaceutical Association), and homeopathic product manufacturers and distributors (Canadian Homeopathic Pharmaceutical Association).(41-43) A national initiative (the pan-Canadian Pharmaceutical Alliance) has been created to achieve greater value for brand-name and generic drugs for publicly funded drug programs, with Ontario leading the brand-name-drugs initiative and Nova Scotia and Saskatchewan co-leading the generic-drug initiative.(44) Other national (non-governmental) initiatives, such as the Canadian Deprescribing Network and Choosing Wisely Canada, have been created to reduce the use of potentially inappropriate prescription and over-the-counter drugs.(45)

Governance, financial and delivery arrangements for prescription and over-the-counter drugs

The governance arrangements for prescription and over-the-counter drugs have been established through the provincial and federal government policies described above. In terms of financial arrangements, just over half (54%) of Ontarians are covered by private insurers, 27% are covered by Ontario Public Drug Programs, 17% are uninsured (i.e., requiring out-of-pocket payments for all drugs), and the remaining 2% are covered by federal government programs (Table 8.2, noting that in this table we have made an exception to our 'no forecasts' rule because actual data from earlier years are not publicly available). The number of ODB Program claims have increased significantly over time, increasing by 200% between 2000-01 and 2013-14 in 2002 dollars (Table 8.3). Most notably, among ODB Program beneficiaries, those covered through the Trillium Drug Program

Table 8.3: Ontario Drug Benefit Program beneficiaries and costs, 2000-01 to 2013-14

Indicators	Beneficiaries and costs[1,2]			
	2000-01	2010-11	2013-14	13-year percentage change[2]
All beneficiaries and claims (thousands)				
Beneficiaries	2,080	2,600	2,900	39%
Claims	49,000	124,000	147,000	200%
Beneficiaries by ministry (thousands)				
Health and long-term care	—	1,970	2,180	—
Community and social services	—	670	700	—
Beneficiaries by type (thousands)				
Core senior[3]	884	1,383	1,609	82%
Ontario Disability Support Program[4]	250	351	392	57%
Ontario Works[4]	368	344	332	-10%
Lower income senior[5]	411	300	283	-31%
Trillium Drug Program	52	189	190	265%
Long-term care[6]	41	102	103	82%
Home care[7]	68	85	92	57%
Beneficiaries by age or program (thousands)				
≥65	1,405	1,746	1,961	40%
<65	593	690	716	21%
Trillium Drug Program	61	179	190	211%
Cost per beneficiary				
Long-term care	$1,469	$3,227	$3,134	113%
Home care	$1,927	$2,018	$2,267	18%
Ontario Disability Support Program	$1,402	$2,087	$2,230	59%
Trillium Drug Program	$1,654	$1,652	$2,001	21%
Lower income senior	$1,339	$1,969	$1,920	43%
Core senior	$1,104	$1,997	$1,223	11%
Ontario Works	$230	$429	$499	117%

Sources: 82; 85-88.

Notes:
[1] Inflation adjusted to 2002, according to Statistics Canada's Consumer Price Index (healthcare), CANSIM 326-0020: value x (CPI 2002/CPIi) = value (2002) where i = year
[2] Data not available for the specific reference period are denoted by —.
[3] Refers to the majority of seniors eligible for the Ontario Drug Benefit (ODB) Program, for whom the regular ODB Program deductible (the first $100 of the prescription cost) and co-payment ($6.11 for each approved prescription filled) apply
[4] Offered through the Ministry of Community and Social Services and includes health benefits for those requiring financial assistance
[5] Refers to ODB Program-eligible seniors who meet one of the seniors co-payment income thresholds (e.g., pay up to $2 per prescription if they are a single senior with a yearly net income of less than $19,300 or a senior couple with a combined yearly income of less than $32,300)
[6] Long-term care included Homes for Special Care in 2000-01
[7] Home care included Homes for Special Care in 2010-11 and 2013-14

have increased by 265% over the same time period. Similarly, publicly funded prescription-drug costs have increased significantly between 2000-01 and 2013-14: measured in 2002 dollars, drug costs have increased by 81%, mark-up by 47%, and dispensing and compounding fees by 170% (Table 8.4). Delivery arrangements for prescription and over-the-counter drugs in Ontario include: 4,012 pharmacies as of 2015, mostly in community settings; 12,630 pharmacists as of 2013; and 93 pharmacists per 100,000 population as of 2013 (see Tables 5.2 and 5.3).

Table 8.4: Publicly funded prescription-drug costs, 2000-01 to 2013-14

Indicator	Costs[1,2] ($ millions)			3-year percentage change	13-year percentage change
	2000-01[2]	2010-11	2013-14		
Prescription cost breakdown					
Drug cost[3]	$1,727	$2,916	$3,129	7%	81%
Mark-up[4]	$163	$222	$239	8%	47%
Dispensing and compounding fees	$328	$695	$887	28%	170%
Cost to payer					
Government cost	$1,956	$3,404	$3,768	11%	93%
Ministry of Health and Long-Term Care	—	$2,666	$2,891	8%	—
Ministry of Community and Social Services	—	$738	$877	19%	—
Recipient cost[5]	$262	$435	$505	16%	93%
Cost by type of drug					
Brand name	—	$2,523	$2,696	7%	—
Generic	—	$1,317	$1,597	21%	—
Exceptional Access Program	—	$263	$419	59%	—
Cancer drugs costs					
Ontario Drug Benefit Program	—	$183	$230	26%	—
New Drugs Funding Program[6]	—	$186	$223	20%	—
Special Drugs Program	—	$112	$91	-19%	—

Sources: adapted from 85-89

Notes:
[1] Inflation adjusted to 2002, according to Statistics Canada's Consumer Price Index (healthcare), CANSIM 326-0020: value x (CPI 2002/CPIi) – value (2002) where i = year
[2] Data not available for the specific reference period are denoted by —.
[3] Cost of a drug at formulary prices
[4] Total mark-up paid per eligible claim (maximum 8%)
[5] Co-payment and deductible
[6] Administered by Cancer Care Ontario

Complementary and alternative therapies

Regulated complementary and alternative therapies include:

1) chiropractic, which involves the diagnosis and treatment of health issues of the muscular, nervous and skeletal system, with a particular focus on the spine;
2) homeopathy, which involves giving very small doses of natural substances that are purported to cause the body to produce an immunological and therapeutic benefit (where large doses could cause symptoms of the disease itself);
3) massage therapy, which involves working and acting on the body with pressure;
4) naturopathy, which involves the use of acupuncture, herbal medicine and homeopathy, as well as diet and lifestyle counselling; and
5) traditional Chinese medicine, which involves the use of acupuncture, cupping, herbal medicine and massage, among other approaches.

The health professionals providing such therapies have only become formally regulated in the last one to two-and-a-half decades. There are many other unregulated health workers providing complementary and alternative therapies, such as herbalists, osteopaths and Reiki practitioners. And while such therapies are increasingly being used by Ontarians, they are almost exclusively paid for privately, either out-of-pocket or through private-insurance plans (which tend to have relatively limited coverage). Moreover, there is relatively little integration of such therapies in the care provided in any of the sectors described in Chapter 6, or for any of the conditions described in Chapter 7.

Policies that govern complementary and alternative therapies

The major policies that govern complementary and alternative therapies are the *Regulated Health Professions Act, 1991*, and the acts specific to complementary and alternative therapy-providing professions:

1) *Chiropractic Act, 1991*;
2) *Massage Therapy Act, 1991;*
3) *Traditional Chinese Medicine Act, 2006*;
4) *Homeopathy Act, 2007*; and
5) *Naturopathy Act, 2007*.

These acts establish what these professions can do, and provide for the establishment of the regulatory colleges that govern them (College of Chiropractors of Ontario, College of Massage Therapists of Ontario, College of Traditional Chinese Medicine Practitioners and Acupuncturists of Ontario, College of Homeopaths of Ontario, and College of Naturopaths of Ontario). More detail about such regulatory colleges is provided in Chapter 5.

At the federal government level, the Natural Health Products Regulations (SOR/2003-196) accompanying the *Food and Drugs Act, 1985*, stipulates that natural health products that are classified as a drug must follow the drug-review process, which includes clinical trials to prove safety and efficacy, and must have a Drug Identification Number to be sold.(46) Also, the amendments made by Bill C-17 to the *Food and Drugs Act* (which were mentioned earlier in this chapter), mean that Health Canada will no longer approve any health claims for homeopathic cough, cold and flu products for children 12 and under unless they are backed by scientific evidence. Natural health products that are classified as food are limited in the claims they can make and do not have to provide as much safety information in their labelling.(46)

Programs that involve complementary and alternative therapies

There are no publicly funded programs available to Ontarians, however, the Workplace Safety and Insurance Board (which, as described in Chapter 7, is funded by employer premiums) pays for some chiropractic care and massage therapy for workers who require treatment for musculoskeletal injuries.(47) Also, the Ontario Disability Support Program offered through the Ministry of Community and Social Services provides financial support to help with travel costs for therapies or treatments provided by any of the 28 health professions regulated under the *Regulated Health Professions Act, 1991*, which includes the five professions being discussed here.(48)

Places and people involved in complementary and alternative therapies

Complementary and alternative therapies are primarily provided in private clinics and offices, although they can be provided in a client's home (e.g., massage therapy), in some primary-care offices and clinics (e.g., chiropractic), and in some hospitals, rehabilitation centres, and long-term care homes (e.g., massage therapy). With the exception of traditional Chinese medicine practitioners, the regulated health professions providing complementary and alternative therapy are represented by their respective associations, namely the Ontario Association of Naturopathic Doctors, Ontario Chiropractic Association, Ontario Homeopathic Association, and Registered Massage Therapists' Association of Ontario.

Governance, financial and delivery arrangements for complementary and alternative therapies

The governance arrangements that are the most relevant to complementary and alternative therapies have been covered in the 'policies' section above and pertain to the regulation of the five health professions. The key financial arrangement for this type of care is the complete reliance on out-of-pocket payment or coverage through private insurers. In terms of delivery arrangements, there are 12,660 registered massage therapists as of 2014, 4,515 chiropractors as of 2013 (see Table 5.2), 2,952 registered traditional Chinese medicine practitioners as of 2015, 1,425 registered naturopaths as of 2015, and 396 registered homeopaths as of 2016.(49-52) Naturopaths can be trained in only one school in Canada (Canadian College of Naturopathic Medicine), and chiropractors can be trained in only one school in Ontario (Canadian Memorial Chiropractor College) and one in the rest of Canada (which operates in French in Quebec), whereas registered massage therapists, traditional Chinese medicine practitioners and registered homeopaths can obtain their training through a number of colleges.

Dental services

Dental services include:
1) preventive services (e.g., regular check-ups that may include teeth cleaning, fluoride applications, fissure sealants, and X-rays);
2) curative services, which range from restorative treatments (e.g., dental fillings) to endodontics (e.g., root canals), orthodontics (e.g., braces), periodontics (e.g., gum therapies) and prosthodontics (e.g., dentures), as well as oral surgery (e.g., tooth extractions and dental implants); and
3) cosmetic procedures (e.g., veneers and braces), increases in which reflect a change in focus from oral function to appearance.

Dental visits in Ontario are primarily preventive and curative in nature, although one in five visits are related to dental emergencies.(53)

The health professionals involved in providing dental services include:
1) dental hygienists, who focus primarily on oral disease prevention (e.g., scaling teeth and administering topical fluoride) and who can also work independently or alongside dentists;
2) dentists, who diagnose, prevent, and treat diseases and conditions of the oral cavity and who can be involved in primary care (most dentists) or specialty care (those with a certification in anesthesiology, endodontics, oral and maxillofacial surgery, orthodontics, pediatric dentistry, periodontics, prosthodontics, dental public health, oral pathology and oral radiology);
3) denturists, who design, construct, repair and alter dentures (i.e., removable oral prostheses) and who can work independently or alongside dentists;
4) dental technologists, who design, construct, repair and alter dentures, implants and orthodontic devices and who work alongside dentists and denturists; and
5) dental assistants, who provide clinical and administrative assistance to dentists and dental hygienists but who cannot work independently of such health professionals.

Similar to complementary and alternative therapies, dental services are largely paid for privately, either out-of-pocket or through private insurance plans (which often require significant cost-sharing by patients). In Ontario in 2010, only about 1% of dental-service expenditures were paid for by government,(54; 55) which would place Ontario (if it were a country) very low in a ranking of Organisation for Economic Cooperation and Development (OECD) countries by extent of public financing. Two thirds (68%) of Ontarians reported in 2005 that they have private dental insurance, with the percentage dropping for older adults (36%) and for those with lower income (40%) and education (41%).(53) Even those with private dental insurance can face limits on service units or frequency, significant cost-sharing, and yearly and lifetime maximums on reimbursement.

Policies that govern dental services

The key policies governing the provision of dental services by health professionals (Figure 8.2) include the:

1) *Regulated Health Professionals Act, 1991*, which reaffirmed dentistry and denturism and established dental hygiene and dental technology as regulated health professions that are overseen by the Royal College of Dental Surgeons of Ontario, the College of Dental Hygienists of Ontario, the College of Denturists of Ontario, and the College of Dental Technologists of Ontario, respectively (as well as the *Regulated Health Professions Statute Law Amendment Act, 2009*, which makes changes to scopes of practice for dentists, dental hygienists, and dental technologists);

2) *Dentistry Act, 1991*, which established the self-regulation regime for dentists;

3) *Dental Hygiene Act, 1991*, which established the self-regulation regime for dental hygienists;

4) *Denturism Act, 1991*, which established the self-regulation regime for denturists; and

5) *Dental Technology Act, 1991*, which established the self-regulation regime for dental technologists.

As noted earlier in this chapter, dentists are like physicians, nurse practitioners, midwives, and (in limited ways) pharmacists in being allowed to prescribe drugs to humans, which means that dentists are also governed by policies such as the *Narcotics Safety and Awareness Act, 2010*, which established a monitoring system for the prescribing and dispensing of narcotics and other monitored drugs. Dental assistants are not a regulated health profession and the Ontario Dental Assistants Association acts as the certifying body (and membership association) for them.

Policies governing the provision of dental services in three of the six sectors described in Chapter 6, namely specialty (hospital) care, long-term care and public health, include the:

1) *Health Insurance Act, 1990*, which established the dental services (most notably hospital-based surgical procedures provided by a dental surgeon) covered under the Ontario Health Insurance Plan (OHIP) Schedule of Benefits;

2) *Nursing Homes Act, 1990*, which established that dental services will be arranged for long-term care home residents, albeit at their own expense;

Figure 8.2: Dental services

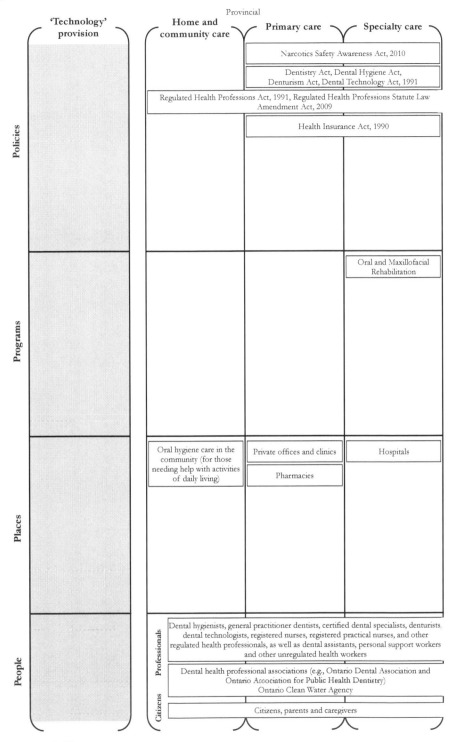

'Technology' provision	Home and community care	Provincial Primary care	Specialty care
Policies		Narcotics Safety Awareness Act, 2010	
		Dentistry Act, Dental Hygiene Act, Denturism Act, Dental Technology Act, 1991	
	Regulated Health Professions Act, 1991, Regulated Health Professions Statute Law Amendment Act, 2009		
		Health Insurance Act, 1990	
Programs			Oral and Maxillofacial Rehabilitation
Places	Oral hygiene care in the community (for those needing help with activities of daily living)	Private offices and clinics	Hospitals
		Pharmacies	
People — Professionals	Dental hygienists, general practitioner dentists, certified dental specialists, denturists, dental technologists, registered nurses, registered practical nurses, and other regulated health professionals, as well as dental assistants, personal support workers and other unregulated health workers		
	Dental health professional associations (e.g., Ontario Dental Association and Ontario Association for Public Health Dentistry) Ontario Clean Water Agency		
People — Citizens	Citizens, parents and caregivers		

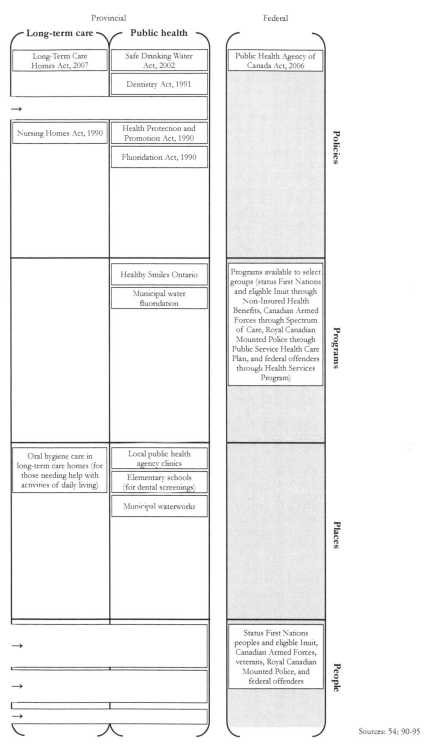

	Provincial		Federal	
	Long-term care	Public health		
Policies	Long-Term Care Homes Act, 2007	Safe Drinking Water Act, 2002	Public Health Agency of Canada Act, 2006	
		Dentistry Act, 1991		
	→			
	Nursing Homes Act, 1990	Health Protection and Promotion Act, 1990		
		Fluoridation Act, 1990		
Programs		Healthy Smiles Ontario	Programs available to select groups (status First Nations and eligible Inuit through Non-Insured Health Benefits, Canadian Armed Forces through Spectrum of Care, Royal Canadian Mounted Police through Public Service Health Care Plan, and federal offenders through Health Services Program)	
		Municipal water fluoridation		
Places	Oral hygiene care in long-term care homes (for those needing help with activities of daily living)	Local public health agency clinics		
		Elementary schools (for dental screenings)		
		Municipal waterworks		
People	→		Status First Nations peoples and eligible Inuit, Canadian Armed Forces, veterans, Royal Canadian Mounted Police, and federal offenders	
	→			
	→			

Sources: 54; 90-95

3) *Long-Term Care Homes Act, 2007*, which established the nature of the oral care provided for residents (e.g., daily mouth care and physical assistance, and an offer of an annual dental assessment, which is subject to payment authorization); and

4) *Health Protection and Promotion Act, 1990*, which established the mandatory health programs and services (which include some dental services) to be provided by boards of health and which we return to below.

Several other policies established specific eligibility criteria for the dental services provided as part of social service and public health programs, including the:

1) *Children and Family Services Act, 1990*, which established the right for 'children in care' to receive dental services;(56)

2) *Ontario Works Act, 1997*, which established the health benefits, including dental services, for Ontarians receiving social assistance payments and their dependents;(57) and

3) *Ontario Disability Support Act, 1997*, which established the health benefits for Ontarians living with a disability and needing help with living expenses.(58)

These policies are not shown in Figure 8.2 because they are outside the formal health system per se. While not acts and regulations (i.e., legal instruments), the Ontario Public Health Standards set the parameters for many of these services (as described in more detail in Chapter 6). Points of intersection with care for select conditions (Chapter 7) include the role of dental professionals in the diagnosis and treatment of some work-related oral injuries, and in screening for oral cancers through routine check-ups.

Policies governing the provision of population-based dental services include the:

1) *Fluoridation Act, 1990*, which established a provision for municipal governments to create, maintain and operate a water-fluoridation system in connection with a municipal waterworks system;(59) and

2) *Safe Drinking Water Act, 2002*, which established the regulation of drinking water systems and drinking water testing, and the subsequent Ontario Drinking Water System Regulation (O.Reg. 170/03), which requires yearly publication of drinking water quality reports by municipalities.(60; 61)

The Public Health Program Standards contain a protocol that outlines the actions needed when fluoride levels fall below the therapeutic range (0.6 - 0.8 ppm) or above the maximum acceptable concentration (1.5 ppm).(62) As of 2007, 76% of Ontarians (9,229,015) have access to fluoridated water.(63) Including fluoride in health products can also be considered a population-based dental service. When such products contain a large concentration of fluoride (e.g., toothpaste and dental rinse) and carry a therapeutic claim, they are considered under the *Food and Drugs Act, 1985* and regulated under the Natural Health Products Regulations.(64)

As may be inferred from the description of these policies, the public stewardship role set for government is relatively limited for dental services compared to many other healthcare services. Moreover, in Ontario there is no chief dental officer, although there is one at the federal level, within the Public Health Agency of Canada. And with the exception of the limited data collection mandated by the Public Health Program Standards, there are no province-level data collected on dental services and dental health (54) and hence no public reporting about access to dental services (e.g., how many people do not seek care or return for recommended treatments because of cost), costs of dental services (e.g., how much do people pay, including out-of-pocket) or outcomes of dental services (e.g., Community Periodontal Index or number of missing teeth).

Programs that involve dental services

Publicly funded dental programs in Ontario are primarily aimed at children through the Healthy Smiles Ontario program, with a small subset focusing on people with disabilities and those in need of significant surgical dental services delivered in hospital (Table 8.5). Covered dental services focus mainly on prevention (e.g., fluoride application) and basic treatment (e.g., fillings, root canals, dentures and extractions), not cosmetics (e.g., whitening, veneers and orthodontics).

Similar to the federal government-funded drug plans for select groups outlined in the prescription and over-the-counter drugs section, the federal government funds dental services for the following groups:
1) status First Nations peoples and eligible Inuit through the First Nations and Inuit Health Branch's Non-Insured Health Benefits program, which will likely be extended to non-status First Nations and Métis

Table 8.5: Dental programs

Program[1]	Services	Who delivers/funds	Who is covered
Children			
Elementary school dental screenings	Visual screening lasting 30-60 seconds	Local public health agencies with funding from the Ministry of Health and Long-Term Care and municipal governments	Children in junior and senior kindergarten and grade 2, and for children in grades 4, 6 and 8 in high-need schools
Healthy Smiles Ontario	Preventive care and basic and urgent treatments (e.g., check-ups, cleaning, scaling, X-rays and fillings) for children in low-income households without access to any form of dental coverage	Ministry of Health and Long-Term Care	Children 17 years and younger who do not have access to any form of dental coverage and whose household income falls below a certain threshold (which varies depending on the number of children in the home)
Children and adults			
Ontario Disability Support Program	Basic dental services as well as additional services if the disability, prescribed medications or treatment affect oral health (available through the Dental Special Care Plan)	Ministry of Community and Social Services	Adults registered in the program as well as spouse (children 17 years and younger are automatically enrolled in the Healthy Smiles Ontario program)
Assistance for Children with Severe Disabilities	Dental services, among other healthcare-related costs, that can be paid for using the $25 to $440 per month provided (with the amount received depending on income and disability severity)	Ministry of Children and Youth Services	Parent(s) or legal guardian whose child is under 18 years, living at home, and has a severe disability (children 17 years and younger are part of the Healthy Smiles Ontario program)
Adults			
Ontario Works	Basic dental services	Ministry of Community and Social Services	Adults registered in the program as well as spouse (children 17 years and younger are automatically enrolled in the Healthy Smiles Ontario program)
Oral and Maxillofacial Rehabilitation Program	Surgical placement of dental implants to attach a prosthetic device	Ministry of Health and Long-Term Care	Adults (18 years and older) who hold a valid health card, and are assessed as a suitable candidate for dental implant surgery

Sources: 54; 90-97

Notes:
[1] With the exception of the programs listed in the table and dental surgery performed in hospital, regular dental services are not publicly covered under the Ontario Health Insurance Plan and residents of Ontario must pay the cost of these services out-of-pocket or through their private insurance plans. Also, in January 2016, six publicly funded dental programs were combined into the new Healthy Smiles Ontario program (dental benefits for children under Ontario Works, Ontario Disability Support Program, Assistance for Children with Severe Disabilities, Children In Need Of Treatment, Healthy Smiles Ontario, and preventive oral health services provided by local public health agencies).(97)

in light of the 2016 Supreme Court decision (see Chapter 9 for more details on Indigenous health);(65)

2) members of the Canadian Forces (and their dependents) through the Department of National Defence;(66)

3) qualified veterans through Veterans Affairs Canada;(67)

4) Royal Canadian Mounted Police through the Public Service Health Care Plan;(30) and

5) federal offenders through Correctional Service Canada.(31)

Places and people involved in dental services

Most primary and specialty dental services are provided in private offices and clinics, and typically not alongside family physicians or other primary-care team members or alongside medical specialists or other specialty team members (Figure 8.2). In select cases, dental services are provided in local public health agency clinics and Community Health Centres, and sometimes alongside other public health practitioners. The maintenance of good oral hygiene is handled by most Ontarians themselves (or in the case of younger children, by their parents), however, those needing help with activities of daily living may receive oral hygiene care in their home or in a school, hospital or long-term care home. Ontarians buy many dental products (e.g., toothpaste, toothbrushes, and interdental cleaning products like dental floss) in pharmacies. Water fluoridation takes place in municipal waterworks.

The people involved in providing dental services include citizens and caregivers as noted above, as well as dental hygienists, dentists, denturists, dental technologists and dental assistants, who are in turn represented by their respective professional associations (e.g., Ontario Dental Association). The Royal College of Dental Surgeons of Ontario (the regulatory college for dentists) offers an online 'find a dentist' service on its website. Registered nurses and registered practical nurses provide assessments of oral health and hygiene practices, and develop care plans for adults requiring help with their activities of daily living (in the home and community sector, hospitals and long-term care homes).(68) Similarly, personal support workers, under the direction of a registered nurse or a registered practical nurse, provide oral hygiene for adults requiring help with their activities of daily living. (69) The Ontario Clean Water Agency provides water services to municipalities, including water fluoridation.

Governance, financial and delivery arrangements for dental services

The key governance arrangements for dental services have been covered in the 'polices' section above, but both financial and delivery arrangements warrant additional comments.

With the exception of the publicly funded dental programs that cover a relatively small proportion of the population and the dental surgery performed in hospital, most dental services are paid for privately (as described in the introduction to this section). These payments are almost always made on a fee-for-service basis, with suggested (usually lower bounds for) fees for dental services set annually by the Ontario Dental Association, (70) and with fixed fees for the small subset of dental services provided in hospitals set in the OHIP Schedule of Benefits.(71) In collaboration with the Canadian Dental Association and other provinces, the Ontario Dental Association developed a national electronic data-interchange network, which allows for dental offices to electronically submit claims to insurance companies.(72) Dental services, excluding cosmetic procedures, are considered eligible medical expenses that can be claimed on tax returns.(73)

There were 13,271 dental hygienists, 9,050 dentists, and 522 dental technologists as of 2013, and 8,500 dental assistants as of 2012.(74; 75) As examples of the limited volume of publicly funded dental services, in 2011-12 local public health agencies provided 27,425 units of scaling, 30,465 topical fluoride applications, and 8,303 fissure sealants.(54) The interval between dental check-ups is typically set by the publicly funded programs and private insurers (and not according to a guideline, as is done in the U.K.).(76) Also, there is typically no risk assessment for the tailored provision of prevention services.

Conclusion

All three of the select treatments profiled in this chapter rely to a significant degree on out-of-pocket payment or private insurance. For conditions without strong evidence of their effectiveness and cost-effectiveness, this may be entirely appropriate. However, for effective and cost-effective treatments, there is a high likelihood of underuse by those with low incomes. Prescription and over-the-counter drugs are a particular source of concern given their high and rising costs. Pharmacare2020 has been launched by pharmaceutical policy advocates and researchers to encourage the creation of a universal pharmacare program that would complement Ontario's existing insurance programs for hospital-based and physician-provided care, and this effort has been supported by the Ontario Liberal government.(38; 77) However, there are no such initiatives for dental services, no talk of alternative remuneration methods for dental professionals that could give greater attention to prevention, and no mention of dental professionals in the *Patients First Act, 2016* despite its focus on interprofessional primary-care teams being accountable for defined populations.

References

1. Statistics Canada. Prescription medication use by Canadians aged 6 to 79. Ottawa: Statistics Canada; 2015. http://www.statcan. gc.ca/pub/82-003-x/2014006/article/14032-eng.htm (accessed 24 August 2016).

2. Health Canada. Drugs and health products. How drugs are reviewed in Canada. Ottawa: Health Canada; 2015. http://www.hc-sc. gc.ca/dhp-mps/prodpharma/activit/fs-fi/reviewfs_examenfd-eng.php (accessed 25 August 2016).

3. Health Canada. Drugs and health products. Protecting Canadians from Unsafe Drugs Act (Vanessa's Law): Questions/answers. Ottawa: Health Canada; 2016. http://www.hc-sc.gc.ca/dhp-mps/legislation/unsafedrugs-droguesdangereuses-faq-eng.php (accessed 27 August 2016).

4. Patented Medicine Prices Review Board. List of act and regulations. Ottawa: Government of Canada; 2014. http://www.pmprb-cepmb.gc.ca/view.asp?ccid=1003 (accessed 24 August 2016).

5. Health Canada. Drug and health products. Guidance document: Patented medicines (notice of compliance) regulations. Ottawa: Health Canada; 2015. http://www.hc-sc.gc.ca/dhp-mps/prodpharma/applic-demande/guide-ld/patmedbrev/pmreg3_mbreg3-eng.php (accessed 26 August 2016).

6. Health Products and Food Branch. Therapeutic Products Directorate. Ottawa: Health Canada; 2014. http://www.hc-sc.gc.ca/ahc-asc/branch-dirgen/hpfb-dgpsa/tpd-dpt/index-eng.php (accessed 25 August 2016).

7. Health Canada. Drugs and health products. Mifegymiso. Ottawa: Health Canada; 2016. http://www.hc-sc.gc.ca/dhp-mps/prod-pharma/sbd-smd/drug-med/sbd-smd-2016-mifegymiso-160063-eng.php (accessed 25 August 2016).

8. Erdman JN, Grenon A, Harrison-Wilson L. Medication abortion in Canada: A right-to-health perspective. *American Journal of Public Health* 2008;98(10): 1764-69.

9. Mintzes B. Direct-to-consumer advertising of prescription drugs in Canada: What are the public health implications? Toronto: Health Council of Canada; 2006.

10. Health Canada. Drug and health products. Interim guidance - Fair balanace in direct-to-consumer advertising of vaccines. Ottawa: Health Canada; 2009. http://www.hc-sc.gc.ca/dhp-mps/advert-publicit/pol/guide-ldir_dtca-pdac_vaccine-vaccins-eng.php (accessed 25 August 2016).

11. Pipon JC, Williams-Jones B. Preparing for the arrival of "pink Viagra": Strengthening Canadian direct-to-consumer information regulations. *Canadian Medical Association Journal* 2016;188(5): 319-20.

12. Health Canada. Drugs and health products. Regulatory requirements for advertising. Ottawa: Health Canada; 2015. http://www.hc-sc.gc.ca/dhp-mps/advert-publicit/index-eng.php (accessed 25 August 2016).

13. Patented Medicine Prices Review Board. Mandate and jurisdiction. Ottawa: Government of Canada; 2015. http://pmprb-cepmb.gc.ca/about-us/mandate-and-jurisdiction (accessed 26 August 2016).

14. Organisation for Economic Co-operation and Development. Gloassary of statistical terms - Factory gate price. Paris: Organisation for Economic Co-operation and Development; 2003. https://stats.oecd.org/glossary/detail.asp?ID=5623 (accessed 24 August 2016).

15. Ministry of Health and Long-Term Care. Tough decisions, made responsibly. Ontario Public Drug Programs annual report 2012-2013. Toronto: Queen's Printer for Ontario; 2013.

16. Ministry of Health and Long-Term Care. Ontario Public Drug Programs. Formulary. Toronto: Queen's Printer for Ontario; 2016. http://www.health.gov.on.ca/en/pro/programs/drugs/odbf_mn.aspx (accessed 27 August 2016).

17. Ministry of Health and Long-Term Care. A focus on continuous improvement. 2013-2014 Ontario Public Drug Programs annual report. Toronto: Queen's Printer for Ontario; 2015.

18. Ministry of Health and Long-Term Care. Working together for change. 2014-2015 Ontario Public Drug Programs annual report. Toronto: Queen's Printer for Ontario; 2015.

19. Ministry of Health and Long-Term Care. Building a better public drug system, together. Ontario Public Drug Programs Toronto: Queen's Printer for Ontario; 2012.

20. Ministry of Health and Long-Term Care. How drugs are considered: Funding decisions. Drugs for rare diseases. Toronto: Queen's Printer for Ontario; 2015. http://www.health.gov.on.ca/en/pro/programs/drugs/how_drugs_approv/review_rare_diseases.aspx (accessed 25 August 2016).

21. Ministry of Health and Long-Term Care. Publicly funded programs. Inherited Metabolic Diseases program. Toronto: Queen's Printer for Ontario; 2015. http://www.health.gov.on.ca/en/pro/programs/drugs/funded_drug/fund_inherited_drug.aspx (accessed 25 August 2016).

22. Ministry of Health and Long-Term Care. How drugs are considered: Funding decisions. The Committee to Evaluate Drugs (CED). Toronto: Queen's Printer for Ontario; 2008. http://www.health.gov.on.ca/en/pro/programs/drugs/how_drugs_approv/funding_ced.aspx (accessed 25 August 2016).

23. Boothe K. Evaluating the cost-effectiveness of pharmaceuticals in Canada. *Health Reform Observer - Observatoire des Réformes de Santé* 2016;4(1).

24. Canadian Agency for Drugs and Technologies in Health CDR. Procedure for the CADTH Common Drug Review. Ottawa: Canadian Agency for Drugs and Technologies in Health; 2014.

25. Canadian Agency for Drugs and Technologies in Health. About CADTH. Ottawa: Canadian Agency for Drugs and Technologies in Health; 2016. https://www.cadth.ca/about-cadth (accessed 24 August 2016).

26. First Nations and Inuit Health Branch. Fact sheet - First Nations and Inuit Health Branch Ottawa: Health Canada; 2008. http://www.hc-sc.gc.ca/ahc-asc/branch-dirgen/fnihb-dgspni/fact-fiche-eng.php (accessed 25 August 2016).

27. National Defence and the Canadian Armed Forces. Spectrum of care: Medical and dental benefits and services Ottawa: Government of Canada; 2015. http://www.forces.gc.ca/en/caf-community-health-services-benefits-drug-coverage/index.page (accessed 25 August 2016).

28. National Defence and the Canadian Armed Forces. Canadian Armed Forces Drug Benefit list. Ottawa: Government of Canada; 2014. http://hrapp.forces.gc.ca/drugbenefitlist-listedemedicaments/index-en.asp (accessed 26 August 2016).

29. Veterans Affairs Canada. Health care benefits (treatment benefits). Ottawa: Veterans Affairs Canada; 2014. http://www.veterans.gc.ca/eng/services/health/treatment-benefits (accessed 24 August 2016).

30. Royal Canadian Mounted Police. Health/dental claims & information. Ottawa: Government of Canada; 2008. http://www.rcmp-grc.gc.ca/fam/health-sante-eng.htm (accessed 24 August 2016).

31. Correctional Service Canada. Health services. Ottawa: Government of Canada; 2014. http://www.csc-scc.gc.ca/health/index-eng.shtml (accessed 25 August 2016).

32. Ontario College of Pharmacists. 2015 annual report. Toronto: Ontario College of Pharmacists; 2016.

33. Ontario Pharmacists Association. Family Health Teams. Toronto: Ontario Pharmacists Association; 2016. https://www.opatoday.com/professional/resources/for-pharmacists/fhts (accessed 24 August 2016).

34. Ontario College of Pharmacists. Expanded scope of practice. Orientation manual. Toronto: Ontario College of Pharmacists; 2012.

35. Ministry of Health and Long-Term Care. Pharmaceutical Opinion Program. Toronto: Queen's Printer for Ontario; 2013. http://www.health.gov.on.ca/en/pro/programs/drugs/pharmaopinion/ (accessed 25 August 2016).

36. Ministry of Health and Long-Term Care. Pharmacy Smoking Cessation Program. Toronto: Queen's Printer for Ontario; 2014. http://www.health.gov.on.ca/en/pro/programs/drugs/smoking/ (accessed 25 August 2016).

37. Ministry of Health and Long-Term Care. Ontario Naloxone Pharmacy Program. Toronto: Queen's Printer for Ontario; 2016. http://www.health.gov.on.ca/en/public/programs/drugs/naloxone.aspx (accessed 27 August 2016).

38. Ontario Liberal Party. Kathleen Wynne's plan for Ontario. Access to the right health care, at the right time, in the right place. Toronto: Ontario Liberal Party; 2014. https://www.aohc.org/sites/default/files/documents/Access-to-the-Right-Health-Care-at-the-Right-Time-in-the-Right-Place.pdf (accessed 24 August 2016).

39. Gauvin FP, Lavis JN, McCarthy L. Evidence brief: Exploring models for pharmacist prescribing in primary and community care settings in Ontario. Hamilton: McMaster Health Forum; 2015.

40. Health Professions Regulatory Advisory Council. Registered nurse (RN) prescribing. Toronto: Queen's Printer for Ontario, 2016. http://www.hprac.org/en/projects/Registered-Nurse-Prescribing.asp (accessed 24 August 2016).

41. Canadian Generic Pharmaceutical Association. About CGPA. Canadian Generic Pharmaceutical Association; 2016. http://www.canadiangenerics.ca/en/about/who_we_are.asp (accessed 25 August 2016).

42. Rx&D. About Canada's research-based pharmaceutical companies. Ottawa: Rx&D; 2015. http://www.rxdserver.ca/en/about-rxd (accessed 24 August 2016).

43. Canadian Homeopathic Pharmaceutical Association. Regulation of homeopathic medicines in Canada. Ottawa: Canadian Homeopathic Pharmaceutical Association; 2013. http://www.chpa-aphc.ca/regulations.html (accessed 22 October 2016).

44. The Council of the Federation. The pan-Canadian Pharmaceutical Alliance. Ottawa: Council of the Federation Secretariat; 2016. http://www.pmprovincesterritoires.ca/en/initiatives/358-pan-canadian-pharmaceutical-alliance (accessed 24 August 2016).

45. Canadian Deprescribing Network. What is deprescribing? 2016. http://deprescribing.org/caden/ (accessed 6 October 2016).

46. Health Canada. Drugs and health products. General questions – Regulation of natural health products. Ottawa: Health Canada; 2016. http://www.hc-sc.gc.ca/dhp-mps/prodnatur/faq/question_general-eng.php (accessed 27 August 2016).

47. WSIB Ontario. Musculoskeletal Program of Care. Toronto: Workplace Safety and Insurance Board; 2016. http://www.wsib.on.ca/WSIBPortal/faces/WSIBArticlePage?fGUID=307702590437000201&_afrLoop=2437072262517525&_afrWindowMode=0&_afrWindowId=null#%40%3F_afrWindowId%3Dnull%26_afrLoop%3D2437072262517525%26_afrWindowMode%3D0%26fGUID%3D307702590437000201%26_adf.ctrl-state%3Dpg5m8n2n6_235 (accessed 27 August 2016).

48. Ministry of Community and Social Services. Ontario Disability Support Program. Toronto: Queen's Printer for Ontario; 2014. http://www.mcss.gov.on.ca/en/mcss/programs/social/odsp/ (accessed 24 August 2016).

49. CIHI. Health personnel database. Canada's healthcare providers, 1997 to 2011 - A reference guide. About chiropractors. Ottawa: Canadian Institute for Health Information; 2011.

50. College of Massage Therapists of Ontario. Emerging transparency at CMTO. 2014 annual report. Toronto: College of Massage Therapists of Ontario; 2015.

51. College of Traditional Chinese Medicine Practioners and Accupuncturists. Continuing the journey: Regulating in the public interest. Annual report 2014-2015. Toronto: College of Traditional Chinese Medicine Practioners and Accupuncturists; 2015.

52. College of Homeopaths. Browse public register of the College of Homeopaths of Ontario. Toronto: College of Homeopaths; 2016. https://app.collegeofhomeopaths.on.ca/en/public/profiles (accessed 27 August 2016).

53. Public Health Ontario. Report on access to dental care and oral health inequalities in Ontario. Toronto: Ontario Agency for Health Protection and Promotion; 2012.

54. Shaw J, Farmer J. An environmental scan of publicly financed dental care in Canada: 2015 update. Ottawa: Public Health Agency of Canada; 2015.

55. Ramraj C, Weitzner E, Figueiredo R, Quinonez C. A macroeconomic review of dentistry in Canada in the 2000s. *Journal - Canadian Dental Association* 2014;80: e55.

56. Legislative Assembly of Ontario. Child and Family Services Act, R.S.O. 1990, c. C.11. Toronto: Queen's Printer for Ontario; 2016. https://www.ontario.ca/laws/statute/90c11 (accessed 24 August 2016).

57. Legislative Assembly of Ontario. Ontario Works Act, 1997, R.S.O. 1997, c. 25, Sched. A. Toronto: Queen's Printer for Ontario; 2016. https://www.ontario.ca/laws/statute/97o25a (accessed 24 August 2016).

58. Legislative Assembly of Ontario. Ontario Disability Support Program Act, 1997, S.O. 1997, c. 25, Sched. B. Toronto: Queen's Printer for Ontario; 2016. https://www.ontario.ca/laws/statute/97o25b (accessed 24 August 2016).

59. Legislative Assembly of Ontario. Fluoridation Act, R.S.O. 1990, c. F.22. Toronto: Queen's Printer for Ontario; 2016. https://www.ontario.ca/laws/statute/90f22 (accessed 24 August 2016).

60. Legislative Assembly of Ontario. O. Reg. 170/03 Drinking water systems. Toronto: Queen's Printer for Ontario; 2016. https://www.ontario.ca/laws/regulation/030170 (accessed 24 August 2016).

61. Legislative Assembly of Ontario. Safe Drinking Water Act, 2002. Toronto: Queen's Printer for Ontario; 2016. https://www.ontario.ca/laws/statute/02s32 (accessed 24 August 2016).

62. Ministry of Health and Long-Term Care. Protocol for the monitoring of community water fluoride levels. Toronto: Queen's Printer for Ontario; 2014.

63. Faculty of Dentistry. Water fluoridation. Toronto: Univeristy of Toronto; 2012.

64. Office of the Auditor General of Canada. The regulation and approval of fluoridation products added to drinking water. Ottawa: Office of the Auditor General of Canada; 2010. http://www.oag-bvg.gc.ca/internet/English/pet_299_e_34270.html (accessed 27 August 2016).

65. First Nations and Inuit Health Branch. Dental benefits. Ottawa: Health Canada; 2016. http://www.hc-sc.gc.ca/fniah-spnia/nihb-ssna/benefit-prestation/dent/index-eng.php (accessed 25 August 2016).

66. Government of Canada. Public Service Health Care Plan. Ottawa: Government of Canada; 2016. http://www.tbs-sct.gc.ca/psm-fpfm/benefits-avantages/health-sante/index-eng.asp (accessed 24 August 2016).

67. Veterans Affairs Canada. Dental services (POC 4). Ottawa: Veterans Affairs Canada; 2016. http://www.veterans.gc.ca/eng/about-us/policy/document/1925 (accessed 24 August 2016).

68. Registered Nurses' Association of Ontario. Oral health: nursing assessment and interventions. Toronto: Registered Nurses' Association of Ontario; 2008.

69. Ontario Personal Support Worker Association. Scope of practice introduction. Ontario Personal Support Worker Association; 2016. http://opswa.webs.com/scope-of-practice (accessed 25 August 2016).

70. Ontario Dental Association. Dental benefits explained. Toronto: Ontario Dental Association; 2016. http://www.oda.on.ca/you-your-dentist/dental-benefits-explained91 (accessed 24 August 2016).

71. Ministry of Health and Long-Term Care. Dental services under the Health Insurance Act. Toronto: Queen's Printer for Ontario; 2012.

72. Ontario Dental Association. History, mission and values. Toronto: Ontario Dental Association; 2016. http://www.oda.on.ca/about-the-oda/history-mission-a-vision (accessed 24 August 2016).

73. Canada Revenue Agency. Lines 330 and 331 – Eligible medical expenses you can claim on your return. Ottawa: Government of Canada; 2016. http://www.cra-arc.gc.ca/medical/ (accessed 25 August 2016).

74. CIHI. Canada's health care providers: Provincial profiles - 2013. Table 7 - Number of providers in selected health professions, Ontario, 2009 to 2013. Ottawa: Canadian Institute for Health Information; 2013.

75. College of Dental Technologists of Ontario. Annual report 2014-2015. Toronto: College of Dental Technologists of Ontario; 2016.

76. National Institute of Health and Care Excellence. Dental checks: Intervals between oral health reviews. NICE guidelines [CG19]. London: National Institute of Health and Care Excellence; 2004.

77. Morgan SG, Martin D, Gagnon MA, Mintzes B, Daw JR, Lexchin J. Pharmacare 2020: The future of drug coverage in Canada. Vancouver: Pharmaceutical Policy Research Collaboration, University of British Columbia; 2015.

78. Cancer Care Ontario. New Drug Funding Program (NDFP). Toronto: Cancer Care Ontario; 2016. https://www.cancercare.on.ca/cms/one.aspx?portalId=1377&pageId=11801 (accessed 24 August 2016).

79. Ministry of Health and Long-Term Care. The New Drug Funding Program (NDFP). Toronto: Queen's Printer for Ontario; 2008. http://health.gov.on.ca/en/public/programs/drugs/programs/ndf.aspx (accessed 26 August 2016).

80. Ministry of Health and Long-Term Care. Inherited Metabolic Diseases (IMD) program list of disorders, covered drugs, supplements and specialty foods. Effective December 9, 2014 (v2). Toronto: Queen's Printer for Ontario; 2014.

81. Ministry of Health and Long-Term Care. The Ontario Drug Benefit (ODB) program. Toronto: Queen's Printer for Ontario; 2015. http://health.gov.on.ca/en/public/programs/drugs/programs/programs.aspx (accessed 25 August 2016).

82. Ministry of Health and Long-Term Care. 2013/14 report card for the Ontario Drug Benefit Program. Toronto: Queen's Printer for Ontario; 2015.

83. Ministry of Health and Long-Term Care. MedsCheck. Toronto: Queen's Printer for Ontario; 2015. http://www.health.gov.on.ca/en/pro/programs/drugs/medscheck/medscheck_original.aspx (accessed 25 August 2016).

84. Ministry of Health and Long-Term Care. Legislation - Ministry statutes. Toronto: Queen's Printer for Ontario; 2016. http://www.health.gov.on.ca/en/common/legislation/statutes/default.aspx (accessed 25 August 2016).

85. Ministry of Health and Long-Term Care. 2001/2002 report card for the Ontario Drug Benefit program. Toronto: Queen's Printer for Ontario; 2003.

86. Ministry of Health and Long-Term Care. 2010/11 report card for the Ontario Drug Benefit program. Toronto: Queen's Printer for Ontario; 2012.

87. Ministry of Health and Long-Term Care. 2011/12 report card for the Ontario Drug Benefit program. Toronto: Queen's Printer for Ontario; 2013.

88. Statistics Canada. Table 326-0020 - Consumer Price Index, monthly (2002=100 unless otherwise noted), CANSIM (database). Ottawa: Statistics Canada; 2016. http://www5.statcan.gc.ca/cansim/a26?id=3260020 (accessed 24 August 2016).

89. Ministry of Health and Long-Term Care. 2012/13 report card for the Ontario Drug Benefit Program. Toronto: Queen's Printer for Ontario; 2014.

90. Government of Ontario. Teeth cleaning, check-ups and dental treatment for kids. Toronto: Queen's Printer for Ontario; 2015. http://www.ontario.ca/health-and-wellness/get-dental-care (accessed 24 August 2016).

91. Ministry of Children and Youth Services. Assistance for children with severe disabilities. Toronto: Queen's Printer for Ontario; 2011. http://www.children.gov.on.ca/htdocs/English/topics/specialneeds/disabilities/index.aspx (accessed 25 August 2016).

92. Ministry of Community and Social Services. How Ontario Works can help you: Health benefits. Toronto: Queen's Printer for Ontario; 2012. http://www.mcss.gov.on.ca/en/mcss/programs/social/ow/help/benefits/health_benefits.aspx (accessed 24 August 2016).

93. Ministry of Community and Social Services. Health benefits: Dental coverage. Toronto: Queen's Printer for Ontario; 2012. http://www.mcss.gov.on.ca/en/mcss/programs/social/odsp/ (accessed 24 August 2016).

94. Ministry of Health and Long-Term Care. Oral and maxillofacial rehabilitation program. Toronto: Queen's Printer for Ontario; 2014. http://www.health.gov.on.ca/en/public/programs/omrp/ (accessed 25 August 2016).

95. Ministry of Health and Long-Term Care. Health services. Toronto: Queen's Printer for Ontario; 2012. http://www.health.gov.on.ca/en/public/publications/ohip/services.aspx (accessed 25 August 2016).

96. Ministry of Health and Long-Term Care. Dental health (CINOT). Toronto: Queen's Printer for Ontario; 2015. http://www.mhp.gov.on.ca/en/healthy-communities/dental/ (accessed 24 August 2016).

97. Ministry of Health and Long-Term Care. Healthy Smiles Ontario. Toronto: Queen's Printer for Ontario; 2016. http://www.health.gov.on.ca/en/pro/programs/dental/default.aspx (accessed 27 August 2016).

9. Care for Indigenous peoples

Cristina A. Mattison, Kody Doxtater and John N. Lavis

Key messages for citizens

- Indigenous peoples in Canada are made up of three groups – First Nations, Inuit and Métis – with historically important distinctions made between status and non-status and on- and off-reserve First Nations peoples.

- Of the 1.4 million Indigenous peoples living in Canadian provinces and territories, the largest proportion (22%) and number (301,425) live in Ontario, although they only make up 2% of the province's total population.

- Significant health disparities exist, both within and across Indigenous communities and compared to the non-Indigenous population.

- Indigenous peoples have access to the same programs and services as the rest of the population (although geographic location among other factors can make accessing these programs and services difficult), and to some programs and services designed specifically for them.

Key messages for health professionals

- Indigenous peoples have the same coverage and benefits as any other citizen in the province, but they can also be referred to dedicated facilities, programs and providers:

  - the Aboriginal Healing and Wellness Strategy created 'bricks and mortar' locations where Indigenous peoples can receive culturally and linguistically appropriate care (e.g., Aboriginal Health Access Centres, healing lodges, family shelters, and a birth centre), and specific programs focusing on health and wellness, crisis intervention and healing services, and healthy babies and children (e.g., mental health demonstration projects and the Aboriginal Healthy Babies Healthy Children program);

  - cultural supports (e.g., chiefs, elders and knowledge keepers) and linguistic supports (e.g., translators) can be drawn upon as needed; and

  - networks, resources and training programs on Indigenous cultural competency are available to health professionals.

Key messages for policymakers

- Intersecting with and complementing the programs offered by the federal government (i.e., making the most of a 'patchwork') creates challenges for the Government of Ontario, and these challenges will likely increase in the short term as the federal government responds to a Supreme Court decision that acknowledges similar rights for Métis and non-status First Nations.

- While the health status of Indigenous peoples in Ontario tends to be much worse than the non-Indigenous population, current strategies tend to adopt a positive, strengths-based approach to health improvement, and one rooted in Indigenous ways of knowing, governance and control.

- The 20-plus-year-old Aboriginal Healing and Wellness Strategy is recognized for being the first inclusive Indigenous-specific provincial strategy focusing on health.

· · ·

In this chapter we focus on care for a select population, Indigenous peoples, as it is handled in unique ways at both the provincial and federal levels, in what is often referred to as a 'patchwork' of care.(1; 2) We apply a health-system lens to examine Indigenous health and healthcare in the province, recognizing that this is a western perspective and requires sensitivity to the ongoing historical legacies of colonization and racism.(3) Complementary efforts led by or conducted in partnership with Indigenous peoples are necessary to appropriately understand and apply Indigenous perspectives to the health and healthcare of Indigenous peoples.

For the purposes of this chapter, our aim is to describe the context in which care is being provided to Indigenous peoples (historical, geographic and socio-demographic, political, economic, and health status), the governance, financial and delivery arrangements within which this care is being provided, the programs and services that comprise this care, and the places where the care is being provided and the people involved in providing it. As with other chapters in the book, we use 'Indigenous' as an inclusive term. Use of terms such as Aboriginal and Indian are in reference to specific acts, policies and/or programs and services.

We provide Ontario-specific data wherever possible, but in its absence we provide Canadian data. Data from Statistics Canada, which collects information on off-reserve Indigenous peoples, are referenced throughout the chapter. We note that there are limitations in the available data, including that the data do not capture the health of all Indigenous peoples. We recognize that data ownership is very important to Indigenous peoples, and where possible, we include data collected and stored by Indigenous groups (e.g., the First Nations Information Governance Centre, where on-reserve data are housed for First Nations communities, and the Métis Nation of Ontario, which collaborates with the Institute for Clinical and Evaluative Sciences to collect data on chronic diseases).

Context

Indigenous peoples in Canada are made up of three groups: First Nations, Inuit and Métis. In the past, distinctions have been made by the federal government between status and non-status First Nations and between First Nations peoples living on- and off-reserve. Only First Nations individuals registered under the *Indian Act, 1876* are recognized by the federal government as having status, and many are not recognized as such.(4) Each of these groups is also diverse in many ways. For example, First Nations in Canada are comprised of over 600 distinct Nations where over 60 languages are spoken.(5)

Historical context

The federal government's history and relationship with Indigenous peoples are described in the report of the Royal Commission on Aboriginal Peoples as one that moved from "partnership to domination, from mutual respect and co-operation to paternalism and attempted assimilation."(6) As the government moves to establish nation-to-nation relationships with Indigenous peoples, it is important to consider historical legacies of colonization and cultural dispossession. In the land that is recognized as Ontario, there were 14 different Nations before contact with European settlers: Algonquin, Anishinabe (the Anishinaabek Peoples), Cayuga, Chippewa, Delaware, Mississauga, Mohawk, Mushkegowuk (Cree), Odawa, Oneida, Onondaga (the Haudenosaunee - Onkwehonwe Peoples), Pottawotami, Seneca, and Tuscarora.(7) The colonization process included policies that enforced assimilation (e.g., *Indian Act, 1876*) and attendance at residential schools, and resulted in the alteration and fragmentation of the Nations. In Ontario there are currently 133 First Nations communities.

It is also important to consider the historical legacies of racism. There are different ways in which racism works, from the individual level to the structural.(8) Individual-level racism can introduce barriers to care, such as being denied treatment in a hospital based on assumptions about the Indigenous person.(3) Structural racism refers to the ways in which systems and institutional arrangements create and reinforce inequities between groups.(9) Policy legacies have reinforced structural racism (e.g., social segregation through the residential school system), resulting in inter-generational trauma that continues to affect the physical and mental health of Indigenous peoples.(10; 11)

Critical events dating back to the early 1100s have implications for how care is provided by and for Indigenous peoples today (Table 9.1). Some more recent key events at the federal government level include:
1) the *British North America Act, 1867* transferred obligations related to Indigenous peoples and their land from the British Crown to Canada's federal government;
2) the *Indian Act, 1876* established the terms under which the federal government engaged with First Nations peoples (e.g., Crown as 'guardian' of land and resources);
3) the Indian Health Policy (1979) led to the creation of Health Canada's First Nations and Inuit Health Branch, the development of the Non-Insured Health Benefits program (which provides supplementary health benefits to eligible First Nations and Inuit), and the establishment of a role (if not a fulsome role) for First Nations peoples in the governance and delivery of healthcare;
4) the *Constitution Act, 1982* recognized the existing rights of Indigenous peoples (First Nations, Inuit and Métis);
5) the Health Transfer Policy (1989) allowed Indigenous communities (below the 60th parallel) administrative control of community-based health programs;
6) the Royal Commission on Aboriginal Peoples (1991-96) documented, through public hearings and consultations, a range of inequities experienced by Indigenous peoples;(12)
7) the Truth and Reconciliation Commission of Canada (2015) doc-

umented the widespread removal of Indigenous children from their communities and families and their placement into residential schools from the 1800s to 1996, and created 94 calls to action to address the legacies of the schools and move towards reconciliation (including an inquiry into missing and murdered Indigenous women and girls);(13) and

8) the Supreme Court of Canada (2016), building on a 2013 decision, ruled that the federal government's fiduciary relationship to status First Nations extends to Métis and non-status Indigenous peoples.(14)

Table 9.1: Chronology of key events that have implications for how care is provided by and for Indigenous peoples

Year	Event	Why it matters	Precursors and subsequent affirmations or extensions
1142	Great Law of Peace (among the Five Nations of the Iroquois Confederacy)	Formalized the first democracy in North America, many centuries before the arrival of Europeans	Precursors • Undocumented
1763	Royal Proclamation	Established that the British Crown (later the Canadian federal government) would negotiate with First Nations on a nation-to-nation basis (e.g., to purchase land) and uphold specific rights for First Nations peoples	Precursors • Doctrine of Discovery (1493), which was used to assert European sovereignty over Indigenous lands • Kaswentha treaty (mid-1600s), which was one of the first treaties to establish inherent rights for Indigenous peoples • Previous Royal Proclamation (1755), which placed a bounty on First Nations peoples • British Board of Commissioners (1756), which redefined the bounty
1769	Jay Treaty	Established the right of First Nations peoples to claim duty-free passage across the Canada-U.S. border, which affects the treatment of tobacco to this day	Subsequent affirmations or extensions • Treaty of Ghent (1814), which reinstated the provisions of the Jay Treaty
1857	*Gradual Civilization Act*	Established requirements for 'Indian status' (e.g., a Christian surname) and hence for the inherent rights that were deemed to follow from status	

Continued on next page

Year	Event	Why it matters	Precursors and subsequent affirmations or extensions
1867	*British North America Act*	Transferred obligations to Indigenous peoples from the British Crown to the Canadian federal government	Subsequent affirmations or extensions • Numbered Treaties (1871-1921), which opened up additional land for development • *Constitution Act, 1982* affirmed the treaty rights of First Nations peoples
1876	*Indian Act*	Established the terms under which the federal government engaged with First Nations peoples (e.g., government as 'guardian' of land – in the form of 'reserves' – and resources; status Indians as Crown wards)	Precursors • *Indian Enfranchisement Act, 1869*, which replaced Indigenous forms of government (e.g., Iroquois Confederacy) with a new 'foreign' form (e.g., band councils) Subsequent affirmations or extensions • Amendments (1884), which banned traditional practices, including traditional medicine (which were reversed in 1951) • Amendments (1985), which established what happened to Indigenous status for women who married a non-status Indian (aspects of which were reversed in 2010)
1894-1996	Residential schools	Forcibly removed Indigenous children aged 3-16 from their communities to be educated in residential schools, where many died from infectious diseases, were subjected to physical and sexual abuse, and lost touch with their families and culture	Precursors • Davin report (1879), which set the stage for residential schools Subsequent affirmations or extensions • 'Sixties scoop' (1960s), which involved the adoption of First Nations (and other Indigenous) children by non-Indigenous parents
1979	Indian Health Policy	Initiated a role for First Nations peoples in the governance and delivery of healthcare, and established the Non-Insured Health Benefits program	Subsequent affirmations or extensions • Health Transfer Policy (1989), which allowed for the transfer of authority from the federal government to Indigenous communities willing to accept administrative control of community-based health programs
1990-94	Aboriginal Healing and Wellness Strategy	Established a cross-sectoral approach to providing culturally appropriate care in Ontario for Indigenous peoples	Subsequent affirmations or extensions • Aboriginal Health Policy (1994), which provided a mechanism through which the Ministry of Health and Long-Term Care could address inequities in access and prioritize areas in Indigenous health programming • Strategy renewal (2010)

Continued on next page

Year	Event	Why it matters	Precursors and subsequent affirmations or extensions
2013	Supreme court decision, Manitoba Métis Federation Inc. v. Canada	Established that Métis (of whom there are roughly 86,000 in Ontario) and non-status Indigenous peoples have the same rights as those with status	Subsequent affirmations or extensions • Federal court of appeals ruling (2014), which affirmed the rights of Métis but established that non-status Indigenous peoples would be dealt with on a case-by-case basis • Supreme Court of Canada's ruling (2016), that extends the federal government's fiduciary relationship from status First Nations peoples to include Métis and non-status Indigenous peoples
2015	Truth and Reconciliation Commission reports	Established that the Canadian federal government had committed cultural genocide through residential schools, and included six healthcare-related recommendations (e.g., acknowledge health status a result of past government policies, set measurable goals to improve health status, and provide cultural competency training for all professionals)	Precursors • Royal Commission on Aboriginal Peoples (1991-96), which documented, through public hearings and consultations, a range of inequities experienced by Indigenous peoples, including the legacy of residential schools and their health consequences • Federal government signs the United Nations Declaration on the Rights of Indigenous People (2000) Subsequent affirmations or extensions • Political Accord (2015), signed by the Chiefs of Ontario and the Government of Ontario, which guides their relationship and affirms First Nations' inherent right to self-government • Ontario's Commitment to Reconciliation (2016), which addresses the legacies of the residential-school system through various initiatives (e.g., mental health and wellness programs, child and family programs, justice programs, and cultural revitalization)

Sources: 1; 2; 13; 14; 61-66

A key event at the provincial level was the creation of the Aboriginal Healing and Wellness Strategy by the Government of Ontario (between 1990 and 1994) as a cross-sectoral and inclusive approach to Indigenous health. Through the Aboriginal Healing and Wellness Strategy, the Aboriginal Health Policy (1994) was developed as a broader mechanism through which the Ministry of Health and Long-Term Care could address inequities in access and prioritize areas in Indigenous health programming.(2) The Aboriginal Health Policy gave the first explicit recognition to Indigenous ways of knowing and is recognized as the most comprehensive Indigenous-focused health policy in Canada.(2)

Geographic and socio-demographic context

Just over half of all Indigenous peoples living in Canada (56%) live in urban areas, defined as areas with populations greater than 100,000.(15) Indigenous peoples living in rural and remote areas often face challenges associated with geographic remoteness, including low population density, challenging climate conditions and lack of infrastructure, that result in barriers to accessing services.(16)

Ontario has the largest proportion (22%) and number (301,425) of Indigenous peoples of any Canadian province or territory, although they only make up 2% of the province's total population.(5) The Indigenous population in Canada has increased by 20% (232,385) between 2006 and 2011, compared to 5% for the non-Indigenous population over the same time period.(5) The median age of the Indigenous population in Canada is young, at 28 years, compared to 40 years for the non-Indigenous population.(5) We now turn to the three groups that comprise Indigenous peoples living in Ontario.

A large First Nations population (201,100) makes up 67% of the total Indigenous population in the province and 24% of the First Nations population in the country.(5) Sixty-two percent of First Nations peoples in Ontario hold status, and 37% of First Nations peoples with status live on-reserve in the province, which is the lowest proportion in the country after Newfoundland and Labrador.(17) The Chiefs of Ontario is the Secretariat and organizing body for the 133 First Nations, four provincial territorial organizations (Association of Iroquois and Allied Indians, Grand Council Treaty #3, Nishnawbe Aski Nation, and the Union of Ontario Indians), as well as the Independent First Nations and several unaffiliated First Nations.(18; 19)

One in four First Nations communities in Ontario are remote, accessible only by ice roads in the winter or by air year-round (Figure 9.1).(20) Six Nations of the Grand River Territory, located 25 km southwest of Hamilton, has the largest population of First Nations in Canada (with a total band membership of 25,660).(21)

A small Inuit population (3,355, which accounts for 6% of all Inuit in the country) resides in Ontario, with the majority living in the Ottawa-Gatineau

Figure 9.1: Map of major roads in Ontario and First Nations communities

Source: Adapted from: 67

census metropolitan area.(17) While there are relatively few Inuit living in Ottawa, it is a major hub for healthcare for Inuit requiring certain medical procedures and coming from the Inuit Nunangat. The majority of Inuit in Canada live in the Inuit Nunangat – Nunatsiavut (northern Labrador), Nunavik (northern Quebec), Nunavut, and Inuvialuit Settlement Region (Northwest Territories) – but 38% live outside the Inuit Nunangat, typically in urban areas.(5)

Ontario is home to the second largest number (86,015) and proportion (19%) of Métis in a province or territory after Manitoba.(5) The majority of Métis in Ontario live in the Midland and Kenora areas. The Métis Nation of Ontario represents the Métis people and communities in Ontario.(22) Historically the Métis have not been recognized by the federal government, and it was not until the 1982 Charter of Rights and Freedoms that the Métis were formally recognized, and not until the 2013 and 2016 Supreme Court decisions that the federal government was confirmed to hold unique responsibilities with respect to them.(3; 14)

Political context

In addition to the political context for Ontario's health system covered in Chapter 1, other political considerations influence how care is provided by and for Indigenous peoples. These include:

1) a renewed nation-to-nation relationship between the federal government and Indigenous peoples in Canada;(23)
2) no single voice for Indigenous peoples in the province as a result of the mix of provincial and national groups representing diverse constituencies; and
3) different ways of knowing, with Indigenous knowledge systems being recognized as complementary to western knowledge systems.

Economic context

Indigenous peoples living in Canada have lower rates of high school completion (64%) than the non-Indigenous population (76%).(24) Compared to the non-Indigenous population, Indigenous peoples living in Canada have a higher unemployment rate (11% compared to 6%), and a lower employment rate (68% compared to 82%).(24) In addition, First Nations peoples living on-reserve have lower employment rates compared to those off-reserve, given limited work opportunities.(17) There are also differences in average weekly wage rates; Indigenous peoples in Ontario earn an average weekly wage of $823 compared to $940 in the non-Indigenous population.(25)

Health status and determinants of health

Indigenous peoples suffer significant health disparities when compared to the non-Indigenous population. For example, life expectancy is shorter and avoidable mortality rates are higher among Indigenous peoples.(26; 27) First Nations adults have more than double the risk of dying from avoidable causes (e.g., preventable or treatable deaths) when compared to non-Indigenous adults.(28) Rates of engagement in risk behaviours (e.g., smoking, drug and alcohol abuse) are also higher in Indigenous peoples, and such behaviours are linked to higher rates of cardiovascular disease and lung cancer.(29) Chronic diseases, such as asthma and diabetes, are also disproportionately higher in Indigenous peoples.(30; 31) Among Métis specifically, the prevalence of chronic obstructive pulmonary disease, diabetes, and osteoarthritis are higher than among the non-Indigenous population, and Métis are less likely to receive care from a specialist for these conditions.(32) National data show that there are differences in rates of heart disease and in the care of heart disease among Indigenous patients compared to non-Indigenous patients, including in the rate of heart attacks and in the hospital experiences of patients who suffered a heart attack.(33)

Mental illness and suicide rates are also higher in Indigenous peoples. Depression and post-traumatic stress disorder are particularly prevalent in First Nations living both on- and off-reserve.(34) The suicide rate among Indigenous peoples in Canada is much higher than in the non-Indigenous population and, along with self-injury, is the leading cause of death among First Nations youth and adults.(34-36) Higher rates of mental illness and suicidal ideation in First Nations have been linked to residential school attendance by the individual or their parent(s), as well as the social determinants of health.(34; 35). To varying degrees, these trends are also prevalent in Inuit and Métis peoples, however, we focus on First Nations as they make up the largest proportion of Indigenous peoples in Ontario.(11) A number of Ontario First Nations communities have declared states of emergency due to suicide.(37; 38) It is important to note, however, that this is not the case across all First Nations communities, and living in communities with higher levels of community control (e.g., increased control over community-based health services) has been found to be associated with improved health outcomes.(39; 40)

Appropriate housing conditions (e.g., acceptable number of people living in a dwelling, no major repairs needed to the home, and access to safe drinking water) and food security are additional concerns for Indigenous peoples. First Nations peoples living on-reserve (27%) are more likely to live in crowded dwellings (more than one person per room) compared to the non-Indigenous population (4%).(17) They are also more likely to live in homes in need of major repairs (43%) compared to the non-Indigenous population (7%).(17) Similarly, over one third (36%) of First Nations respondents to the First Nations Regional Health Survey (2008-10) reported that their water supply was not safe for consumption year-round.(41) Food security is also an issue: in Ontario 19% of respondents to Statistics Canada's Aboriginal Peoples Survey reported low or very low food security.(42) While these statistics help to put into context the living conditions of many Indigenous peoples, they do not do justice to describing the actual realities of these conditions or to Indigenous peoples' lived experience.

Governance, financial and delivery arrangements

Healthcare for Indigenous peoples is often referred to as a 'patchwork' due to the jurisdictional complexity in federal and provincial/territorial governmental roles in the delivery of healthcare for this population.(2) The federal government has policy authority for providing healthcare services for First Nations peoples and Inuit, where services are not provided by provincial/territorial health systems, through the First Nations and Inuit Health Branch of Health Canada. The First Nations and Inuit Primary Health Care program has an estimated budget in 2015-16 of $810 million ($579 per capita) for the provision of primary healthcare services across the country, which include:

- health-promotion and disease-prevention services in three key areas: healthy child development, mental wellness, and healthy living ($408 million);
- primary healthcare in 200 remote First Nations and Inuit communities, delivered by 675 nurses and 22 physicians, through contribution arrangements or direct spending ($304 million), as well as home and community care (in over 600 communities), on-reserve nursing stations (74 total and 29 federally funded nursing stations in Ontario), 223 health centres, 41 alcohol and drug treatment centres, nine solvent abuse centres, dental services, and two on-reserve hospitals; and

- public health focusing on communicable diseases (control and management) and environmental public health ($98 million).(43-45)

Supplementary health benefits are offered through the First Nations and Inuit Health Branch's Non-Insured Health Benefits program. This program acts as a supplement to the coverage provided by provincial/territorial healthcare programs. The program provides medically necessary products and services for status First Nations peoples and eligible Inuit. Coverage includes prescription drugs, medical supplies and equipment, transportation to medical services, dental and vision care, and short-term/crisis mental health counselling.(46) Benefits are delivered by registered healthcare providers in the private sector and claims are processed by an electronic claims system or regional Non-Insured Health Benefits offices.(47) The program is funded through a transfer payment and has an estimated budget of $1.13 billion for 2015-16.(47) Ontario has the largest number (197,092) and proportion (24%) of eligible client population, with the vast majority being First Nations (196,444) and very few being Inuit (648).(48) In Ontario, from 2013 to 2014, the program had a total expenditure of $194 million, which included $79 million in 'pharmacy' (prescription and over-the-counter drugs and medical equipment), $63 million in medical transportation, $44 million in dental services, $6 million in vision care, and $3 million in other healthcare claims.(48)

In addition to funding for the First Nations and Inuit Primary Health Care program and Non-Insured Health Benefits program, there are health infrastructure supports ($635 million in 2015-16) to build First Nations and Inuit capacity in the management and implementation of health programs and services, and support the integration of healthcare services.(45) The First Nations and Inuit Health System Transformation program ($29 million in 2015-16) focuses on systems integration and eHealth infrastructure.(45) Finally, as part of a broader effort and long-term policy goal of Health Canada, funding ($421 million in 2015-16) is provided for tripartite health governance (federal government, B.C. government, and B.C. First Nations) to integrate federal and provincial healthcare services, initially in B.C.(45)

Programs and services

In addition to the programs and services provided at the federal level and those available in the broader Ontario health system, Indigenous peoples in the province have access to targeted programs and services through the Aboriginal Healing and Wellness Strategy (Figure 9.2). The strategy, created in 1994 and renewed in 2010, brings together traditional and western programs and services with the aim of providing culturally and linguistically appropriate care to improve Indigenous health, healing and wellness, while reducing family violence and violence against Indigenous women and children.(49) It is the largest provincially funded Indigenous health initiative in the country. The strategy covers First Nations, Inuit and Métis, both on- and off-reserve, and is considered the first inclusive provincial strategy to focus solely on Indigenous health. The strategy is cross-ministerial and receives funding and support from the ministries of aboriginal affairs, children and youth services, community and social services, and health and long-term care and from the Ontario Women's Directorate.

The Aboriginal Healing and Wellness Strategy consists of three broad program types: 1) health and wellness, 2) crisis intervention and healing services, and 3) healthy babies and children. The strategy delivers care to approximately 42,000 Indigenous individuals each year.(49) A mix of community-based programs and services are available both on- and off-reserve, as well as in urban and rural settings (Table 9.2). Aboriginal Health Access Centres were created in 1994 and stem from the Aboriginal Health Policy, and in 2010 they transitioned from being a program within the Aboriginal Health and Wellness Strategy to contracts with the Ministry of Health and Long-Term Care.(50) Aboriginal Health Access Centres are based on a holistic framework, offering community-based primary healthcare and traditional healing, along with a range of other programs (i.e., mental wellness and cultural programs).(51) There are 10 Aboriginal Health Access Centres in the province, serving over 50,000 individuals annually, with an annual budget of $2 million per centre.(51) In addition to the programs and services offered through the Aboriginal Healing and Wellness Strategy, Cancer Care Ontario delivers targeted programs for cancer prevention, screening and information (see Chapter 7).

Longitudinal data were collected on the Aboriginal Healing and Wellness Strategy. The third and final phase of the strategy's longitudinal study

Figure 9.2: Care for Indigenous peoples

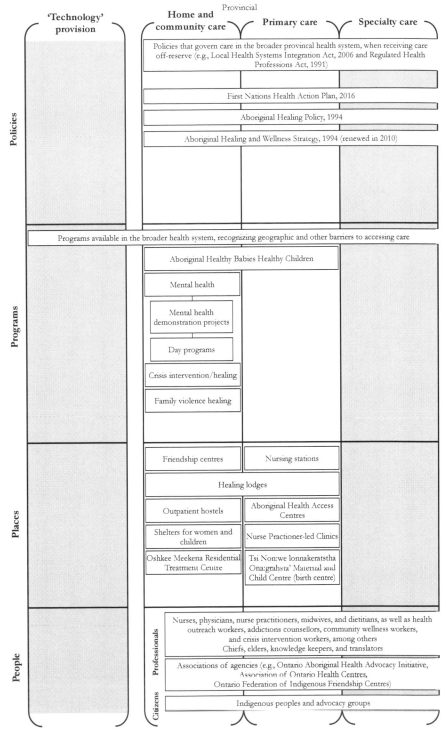

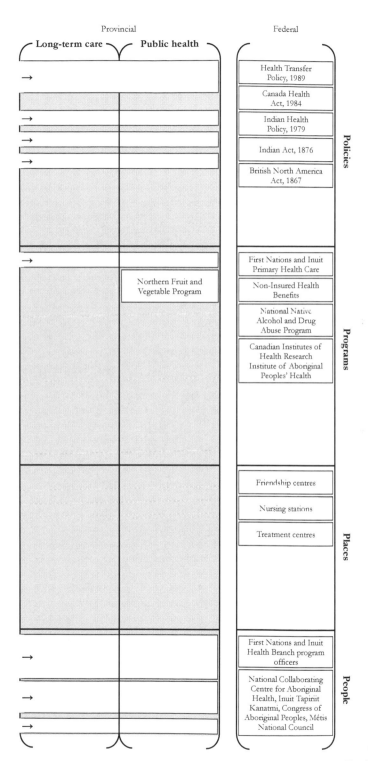

Provincial		Federal	
Long-term care	**Public health**		
→		Health Transfer Policy, 1989	**Policies**
		Canada Health Act, 1984	
→		Indian Health Policy, 1979	
→		Indian Act, 1876	
→		British North America Act, 1867	
→		First Nations and Inuit Primary Health Care	**Programs**
	Northern Fruit and Vegetable Program	Non-Insured Health Benefits	
		National Native Alcohol and Drug Abuse Program	
		Canadian Institutes of Health Research Institute of Aboriginal Peoples' Health	
		Friendship centres	**Places**
		Nursing stations	
		Treatment centres	
→		First Nations and Inuit Health Branch program officers	**People**
→		National Collaborating Centre for Aboriginal Health, Inuit Tapiriit Kanatmi, Congress of Aboriginal Peoples, Métis National Council	
→			

Sources: 44; 55-58; 68-80

Table 9.2: Programs specific to Indigenous peoples

Program[1]	Services	First Nations	Inuit	Métis
Health and wellness				
Health outreach workers	Personal support, education and information on health and wellness, disease prevention, and family violence prevention	✓	✓	✓ (urban areas)
Mental health	Two types of mental health programs: • mental health demonstration projects offer non-residential, culturally appropriate mental health services • day programs (four days in length) support individuals and their families with mental health issues	✓ ✓ (Ottawa, Victoria Harbour, Fort Severn, and Sioux Lookout)		✓ (available at 12 sites)
Tsi Non:we Ionnakeratstha Ona:grahsta' Maternal and Child Centre	Pre- and post-natal care to Indigenous women and families, providing a mix of traditional and contemporary midwifery services	✓ (Six Nations/southwestern Ontario)		
Outpatient hostels	Short-stay, outpatient hostel services are offered to those receiving medical treatment, including accommodation and meals, airport transfer, and translation	✓ (Timmins amd Kenora)		
Translation services	For individuals in need of translation assistance with health professionals and workers	✓	✓	✓ (Moose Factory, Sudbury and Fort Frances)
Crisis intervention and healing services				
Community wellness workers	Education and prevention programs in schools and communities, counselling referrals, case management, and outreach to Indigenous individuals and families who are in violent situations	✓		✓ (available through nine sites)
Shelters for women and children	Short-term residences and counselling supports for women and children leaving domestic abuse situations	✓ (seven shelters)		
Healing lodges	Focus on trauma (e.g., sexual assault, emotional and physical abuse, or family dysfunction) and are offered as residential programs	✓ (six healing lodges)		
Family violence healing	Combines traditional and mainstream counselling approaches, focusing on abusers or people at risk of abusing	✓ (Ohsweken and Cornwall)		
Crisis intervention workers	Services range from suicide prevention and intervention to counselling and treatment program referrals	✓ (based in two sites, servicing remote northern First Nations communities)		
Oshkee Meekena Residential Treatment Centre	Treatment for Indigenous youth with addiction issues	✓ (Sioux Lookout)		

Continued on next page

Program[1]	Services	Who is covered		
		First Nations	Inuit	Métis
Healthy babies and children				
Aboriginal Healthy Babies Healthy Children	Education, screening, coordination of services, home visits, and referral services	✓	✓	✓
		(available through 28 sites)		

Sources: 55-58; 71-78; 80-82

Notes:
[1] The programs are offered by the Ministry of Community and Social Services, through the Aboriginal Healing and Wellness Strategy, to First Nations, Inuit and Métis peoples living in Ontario. The Aboriginal Healing and Wellness Strategy was launched in 1994 and spans several ministries, with a focus on complementing traditional practices with western programs to support Indigenous healing and wellness, while reducing family violence and violence against Indigenous women and children. The programs are community-based and available to First Nations, Inuit and Métis, both on- and off-reserve, as well as in urban and rural settings. The strategy is offered through the ministries of aboriginal affairs, children and youth services, community and social services, health and long-term care, and the Ontario Women's Directorate.

(2005-08) collected data at 23 program sites. The results were positive, with the majority (93%) of program clients reporting that it respected cultural heritage and made a difference in their lives (95%).(52)

Complementing the Aboriginal Healing and Wellness Strategy, in May 2016 the Ministry of Health and Long-Term Care announced the First Nations Health Action Plan, which prioritizes four key areas: 1) primary care (e.g., increasing physician services and cultural competency training for health professionals); 2) public health and health promotion (e.g., expanding the Northern Fruit and Vegetable Program); 3) seniors care and hospital services (e.g., increasing hospital beds for seniors at the Meno Ya Win Health Centre in Sioux Lookout); and 4) life promotion and crisis support (e.g., expanding crisis prevention and management supports and telemedicine services).(53) The plan focuses primarily on northern First Nations, but also includes opportunities for improving Indigenous healthcare across the province. Over the next three years, the Ministry of Health and Long-Term Care will invest $222 million in the First Nations Health Action Plan, followed by sustained funding of $105 million annually.(53)

Places and people

While the places where care is provided for Indigenous peoples are broadly the same as for non-Indigenous peoples living in Ontario (see Chapters 6 and 7), there are specific places (both on- and off-reserve) where care is provided by and for Indigenous peoples (Figure 9.2). Community-based primary care is provided in nursing stations, Aboriginal Health Access

Centres, Nurse-Practitioner-led Clinics, and one birth centre (Tsi Non:we Ionnakeratstha Ona:grahsta' Maternal and Child Centre, which is located on-reserve at Six Nations of the Grand River). Twenty-eight off-reserve friendship centres offer a range of programs and services for Indigenous peoples.(54) Six healing lodges provide residential programs and incorporate traditional approaches to address trauma.(55) Three outpatient hostels are available for Indigenous peoples receiving medical treatment.(56) Six shelters for women and children offer crisis intervention services.(57) The places where mental health and addictions services are provided range from a treatment centre for Indigenous youth (Oshkee Meekena Residential Treatment Centre) to 10 treatment centres offered through the federal National Native Alcohol and Drug Abuse Program and 13 provincial mental health demonstration projects.(58; 59)

In addition to the regulated health professionals and unregulated health workers who have been described in previous chapters, some of the other healthcare providers involved in providing care include health outreach workers, addictions counsellors, community wellness workers, and crisis intervention workers. Chiefs, elders, knowledge keepers and translators are involved in providing cultural and linguistic supports.

Conclusion

Healthcare for Indigenous peoples in Canada is complex. Historical legacies mean that the way healthcare is handled for this population is different, in that it relies on a mix of federal and provincial government resources and infrastructure.(60) Moreover, Indigenous peoples continue to experience ongoing forms of colonization (including assimilationist policies, such as the ownership of who is able to define 'status') and the intergenerational effects of the process of colonization. They also continue to experience many forms of racism. These legacies have resulted in gaps in care within the health system, and in Indigenous peoples continuing to experience disparities in health outcomes, as well as the social determinants thereof, when compared to the non-Indigenous population.(29) The identification of the need for culturally and linguistically appropriate care, and the recognition of culture as a mechanism for healing, led to the creation of the Aboriginal Healing and Wellness Strategy in Ontario in the 1990s. A recent change in federal government leadership (2015) has prompted renewed discussion more broadly on nation-to-nation relationships. The 2016 Supreme Court decision has established a need for determining whether all existing healthcare programs and services for status First Nations and eligible Inuit should be extended to non-status First Nations and to Métis. This renewed discussion could help to further develop culturally appropriate care for Indigenous peoples in Ontario such that disparities are reduced.

References

1. Lavoie J, Gervais L, Toner J, Bergeron O, Thomas G. The Aboriginal health legislation and policy framework in Canada. Prince George: National Collaborating Centre for Aboriginal Health; 2011.

2. National Collaborating Centre for Aboriginal Health. Looking for Aboriginal health in legislation and policies, 1970 to 2008. A policy synthesis project. Prince George: University of Northern British Columbia; 2011.

3. Allan B, Smylie J. First Peoples, second class treatment: The role of racism in the health and well-being of Indigenous peoples in Canada. Toronto: The Wellesley Institute; 2015.

4. Indigenous and Northern Affairs Canada. Indian status. Ottawa: Indigenous and Northern Affairs Canada; 2013. http://www.aadnc-aandc.gc.ca/eng/1100100032374/1100100032378 (accessed 26 August 2016).

5. Statistics Canada. Aboriginal peoples in Canada: First Nations people, Métis and Inuit. National Household Survey, 2011. Ottawa: Statistics Canada; 2011.

6. Indigenous and Northern Affairs Canada. Highlights from the Report of the Royal Commission on Aboriginal Peoples. Looking forward looking back. Ottawa: Indigenous and Northern Affairs Canada; 2010. http://www.aadnc-aandc.gc.ca/eng/1100100014597/1100100014637 (accessed 26 August 2016).

7. Chiefs of Ontario. Understanding First Nation sovereignty. Toronto: Chiefs of Ontario; 2016. http://www.chiefs-of-ontario.org/faq (accessed 24 August 2016).

8. Jones CP. Levels of racism: A theoretic framework and a gardener's tale. *American Journal of Public Health* 2000;90(8): 1212-15.

9. Powell JA. Structural racism: Building upon the insights of John Calmore. *North Carolina Law Review* 2007;86: 791.

10. Gee GC, Ford CL. Structural racism and health inequities: Old issues, new directions. *Du Bois Review* 2011;8(1): 115-132.

11. Hackett C, Feeny D, Tompa E. Canada's residential school system: Measuring the intergenerational impact of familial attendance on health and mental health outcomes. *Journal of Epidemiology & Community Health* 2016;70(11): 1096-1105.

12. Royal Commission on Aboriginal Peoples. Report of the Royal Commission on Aboriginal Peoples. Volume 1 – Looking forward looking back. Ottawa: Canada Communication Group; 1996.

13. Truth and Reconciliation Commission of Canada. Honouring the truth, reconciling for the future: Summary of the final report of the Truth and Reconciliation Commission of Canada. Winnipeg: Truth and Reconciliation Commission of Canada; 2015.

14. Supreme Court of Canada. Daniels v. Canada (Indian Affairs and Northern Development). Ottawa: Supreme Court of Canada; 2016. http://scc-csc.lexum.com/scc-csc/scc-csc/en/item/15858/index.do (accessed 24 August 2016).

15. Indigenous and Northern Affairs Canada. Urban Indigenous peoples. Ottawa: Indigenous and Northern Affairs Canada; 2014. https://www.aadnc-aandc.gc.ca/eng/1100100014265/1369225120949 (accessed 24 August 2016).

16. National Collaborating Centre for Aboriginal Health. Access to health services as a social determinant of First Nations, Inuit and Métis health. Prince George: University of Northern British Columbia; 2010.

17. Statistics Canada. Aboriginal statistics at a glance: 2nd edition (Catalogue no. 89-645-x2015001). Ottawa: Statistics Canada; 2015.

18. Chiefs of Ontario. Provincial territorial organization (PTO) affiliations. Toronto: Chiefs of Ontario; 2016. http://www.chiefs-of-ontario.org/pto-affiliations (accessed 24 August 2016).

19. Chiefs of Ontario. Independent First Nations. Toronto: Chiefs of Ontario; 2016. http://www.chiefs-of-ontario.org/independent-nations (accessed 24 August 2016).

20. Indigenous and Northern Affairs Canada. Ontario region. Ottawa: Indigenous and Northern Affairs Canada; 2014. https://www.aadnc-aandc.gc.ca/eng/1100100020284/1100100020288 (accessed 24 August 2016).

21. Six Nations Council. Community profile. Ohsweken: Six Nations Council; 2013. http://www.sixnations.ca/CommunityProfile.htm (accessed 24 August 2016).

22. Métis Nation of Ontario. Governing structure. Ottawa: Métis Nation of Ontario; 2016. http://www.metisnation.org/governance/governing-structure/ (accessed 24 August 2016).

23. Liberal Party of Canada. A new nation-to-nation process. Ottawa: Liberal Party of Canada; 2016. https://www.liberal.ca/realchange/a-new-nation-to-nation-process/ (accessed 24 August 2016).

24. Statistics Canada. Table 282-0228 - Labour force survey estimates (LFS), by Aboriginal group, educational attainment and age group, Canada and selected regions, annual (persons unless otherwise noted), CANSIM (database). Ottawa: Statistics Canada; 2016. http://www5.statcan.gc.ca/cansim/a26?lang=eng&retrLang=eng&id=2820228&&pattern=&stByVal=1&p1=1&p2=-1&tabMode=dataTable&csid= (accessed 24 August 2016).

25. Statistics Canada. Table 282-0233 - Labour force survey estimates (LFS), average hourly and weekly wages and average usual weekly hours by Aboriginal group and age group, Canada, selected provinces and regions, annual (number unless otherwise noted), CANSIM (database). Ottawa: Statistics Canada; 2016. http://www5.statcan.gc.ca/cansim/a26?lang=eng&retrLang=eng&id=2820233&&pattern=&stByVal=1&p1=1&p2=-1&tabMode=dataTable&csid= (accessed 25 August 2016).

26. Adelson N. The embodiment of inequity: Health disparities in Aboriginal Canada. *Canadian Journal of Public Health* 2005;96 Suppl 2: S45-61.

27. Statistics Canada. Table 109-5401 - Life expectancy at various ages, by population group and sex, Canada, occasional (years), CANSIM (database). Ottawa: 2011. http://www5.statcan.gc.ca/cansim/a26 (accessed 18 February 2016).

28. Park J, Tjepkema M, Goedhuis N, Pennock J. Avoidable mortality among First Nations adults in Canada: A cohort analysis (Catalogue no. 82-003-X). Ottawa: Statistics Canada; 2015.

29. Reading CL, Wien F. Health inequalities and social determinants of aboriginal peoples' health. Prince George: National Collaborating Centre for Aboriginal Health; 2009.

30. Dyck R, Osgood N, Lin TH, Gao A, Stang MR. Epidemiology of diabetes mellitus among First Nations and non-First Nations adults. *Canadian Medical Association Journal* 2010;182(3): 249-56.

31. Gershon AS, Khan S, Klein-Geltink J, et al. Asthma and chronic obstructive pulmonary disease (COPD) prevalence and health services use in Ontario Métis: A population-based cohort study. *PLoS One* 2014;9(4): e95899.

32. Métis Nation of Ontario. Chronic Disease Surveillance Project. Key findings. Ottawa: Métis Nation of Ontario; 2016. http://www.metisnation.org/media/578079/key findings-factsheet-en_6.pdf (accessed 24 August 2016).

33. CIHI. Hospital care for heart attacks among First Nations, Inuit and Métis. Ottawa: Canadian Institute for Health Information; 2013.

34. Public Health Agency of Canada. First Nations and Inuit mental health and addictions – Cluster evaluation 2005/06–2009/10. Ottawa: Health Canada; 2012.

35. Kumar M. Lifetime suicidal thoughts among First Nations living off reserve, Métis and Inuit aged 26 to 59: Prevalence and associated characteristics (Catalogue no. 89-653-X2016008). Ottawa: Statistics Canada; 2016.

36. Peters PA, Oliver LN, Kohen DE. Mortality among children and youth in high-percentage First Nations identity areas, 2000-2002 and 2005-2007. *Rural Remote Health* 2013;13(3): 2424.

37. Fontaine T. Cree communities launched and funded own inquiry into 'suicide pandemic'. CBC News. 16 March 2016.

38. Thompson N. Northern Ontario First Nations community declares state of emergency after suicide attempts. The Globe and Mail. 10 April 2016.

39. Lavoie JG, Forget EL, Prakash T, Dahl M, Martens P, O'Neil JD. Have investments in on-reserve health services and initiatives promoting community control improved First Nations' health in Manitoba? *Social Science and Medicine* 2010;71(4): 717-24.

40. Lavoie JG, Dwyer J. Implementing Indigenous community control in health care: Lessons from Canada. *Australian Health Review* 2015;40(4): 453-458.

41. First Nations Information Governance Centre. First Nations Regional Health Survey (RHS) 2008/10: National report on adults, youth and children living in First Nations communities. Ottawa: First Nations Information Governance Centre; 2012.

42. Statistics Canada. Table 577-0009 - Aboriginal peoples survey, food security, by Aboriginal identity, age group, sex, and number of persons in household, population aged 6 years and over, Canada, provinces and territories, occasional, CANSIM (database). Ottawa: Statistics Canada; 2015. http://www5.statcan.gc.ca/cansim/a26?lang=eng&retrLang=eng&id=5770009&&pattern=&stByVal=1&p1=1&p2=-1&tabMode=dataTable&csid= (accessed 25 August 2016).

43. Auditor General of Canada. 2015 spring reports of the Auditor General of Canada. Report 4: Access to health services for remote First Nations communities. Ottawa: Auditor General of Canada; 2015.

44. First Nations and Inuit Health Branch. Fact sheet - First Nations and Inuit Health Branch Ottawa: Health Canada; 2008. http://www.hc-sc.gc.ca/ahc-asc/branch-dirgen/fnihb-dgspni/fact-fiche-eng.php (accessed 25 August 2016).

45. Health Canada. Health Canada 2015-16 report on plans and priorities. Strategic Outcome 3: First Nations and Inuit communities and individuals receive health services and benefits that are responsive to their needs so as to improve their health status. Ottawa: Health Canada; 2016. http://www.hc-sc.gc.ca/ahc-asc/performance/estim-previs/plans-prior/2015-2016/report rapport-eng.php - a2.3 (accessed 25 August 2016).

46. First Nations and Inuit Health Branch. Non-Insured Health Benefits for First Nations and Inuit. Ottawa: Health Canada; 2016. http://www.hc-sc.gc.ca/fniah-spnia/nihb-ssna/index-eng.php (accessed 25 August 2016).

47. Health Canada. Health Canada 2015-16 report on plans and priorities. Strategic Outcome 3: First Nations and Inuit communities and individuals receive health services and benefits that are responsive to their needs so as to improve their health status. Program 3.2: Supplementary health benefits for First Nations and Inuit. Ottawa: Health Canada; 2016. http://www.hc-sc.gc.ca/ahc-asc/performance/estim-previs/plans-prior/2015-2016/report-rapport-eng.php - a2.3 (accessed 25 August 2016).

48. Health Canada. Non-Insured Health Benefits program. First Nations and Inuit Health Branch. Annual report 2013/14. Ottawa: Health Canada; 2014.

49. Ministry of Community and Social Services. Ontario's Aboriginal Healing and Wellness Strategy. Toronto: Queen's Printer for Ontario; 2014. https://news.ontario.ca/mcss/en/2014/11/ontarios-aboriginal-healing-and-wellness-strategy.html (accessed 24 August 2016).

50. Ontario's Aboriginal Health Access Centres. 2016 Ontario budget submission from the Aboriginal Health Access Centres of Ontario. Toronto: Association of Ontario Health Centres; 2016.

51. Ontario's Aboriginal Health Access Centres. Our health, our seventh generation, our future. 2015 Aboriginal Health Access Centres report. Toronto: Association of Ontario Health Centres; 2015.

52. Aboriginal Healing and Wellness Strategy. Aboriginal Healing and Wellness Strategy: Phase III longitudinal study. Final report. Toronto: Aboriginal Healing and Wellness Strategy; 2009.

53. Government of Ontario. Ontario launches $222 million First Nations Health Action Plan. Toronto: Queen's Printer for Ontario; 2016. https://news.ontario.ca/mohltc/en/2016/05/ontario-launches-222-million-first-nations-health-action-plan.html (accessed 23 August 2016).

54. Ontario Federation of Indigenous Friendship Centres. Find a Friendship Centre. Toronto: Ontario Federation of Indigenous Friendship Centres; 2016. http://www.ofifc.org/about-fc/centres/list (accessed 4 November 2016).

55. Ministry of Community and Social Services. Programs and supports for Aboriginal individuals and families. Crisis intervention/healing services. Healing lodges. Toronto: Queen's Printer for Ontario; 2012. http://www.mcss.gov.on.ca/en/mcss/programs/community/ahws/individuals/healing_lodges.aspx (accessed 24 August 2016).

56. Ministry of Community and Social Services. Programs and supports for Aboriginal individuals and families. Health and wellness. Outpatient hostels. Toronto: Queen's Printer for Ontario; 2012. http://www.mcss.gov.on.ca/en/mcss/programs/community/ahws/individuals/outpatient_hostels.aspx (accessed 24 August 2016).

57. Ministry of Community and Social Services. Programs and supports for Aboriginal individuals and families. Crisis intervention/healing services. Family violence healing program. Toronto: Queen's Printer for Ontario; 2012. http://www.mcss.gov.on.ca/en/mcss/programs/community/ahws/individuals/family_violence_healing_program.aspx (accessed 24 August 2016).

58. Ministry of Community and Social Services. Programs and supports for Aboriginal individuals and families. Health and wellness. Mental health programs. Toronto: Queen's Printer for Ontario; 2012. http://www.mcss.gov.on.ca/en/mcss/programs/community/ahws/individuals/mental_health_programs.aspx (accessed 24 August 2016).

59. National Native Alcohol and Drug Abuse Program. Addictions treatment for First Nations and Inuit. Ottawa: First Nations and Inuit Health; 2016. http://healthycanadians.gc.ca/healthy-living-vie-saine/substance-abuse-toxicomanie/help-aide/treatment-centres-traitement-eng.php - a5 (accessed 4 November 2016).

60. Paradies Y. Colonisation, racism and Indigenous health. *Journal of Population Research* 2016;33(1): 83-96.

61. Government of Ontario. The journey together. Ontario's commitment to reconciliation with Indigenous peoples. Toronto: Queen's Printer for Ontario; 2016.

62. Government of Ontario. First Nations, Ontario sign political accord. Toronto: Queen's Printer for Ontario; 2015. https://news.ontario.ca/opo/en/2015/08/first-nations-ontario-sign-political-accord.html (accessed 23 August 2016).

63. Health Canada. Indian Health Policy 1979. Ottawa: Health Canada; 2014. http://www.hc-sc.gc.ca/ahc-asc/branch-dirgen/fni-hb-dgspni/poli_1979-eng.php (accessed 25 August 2016).

64. Indigenous and Northern Affairs Canada. A history of Indian and Northern Affairs Canada. Ottawa: Indigenous and Northern Affairs Canada; 2011. https://www.aadnc-aandc.gc.ca/eng/1314977281262/1314977321448 (accessed 24 August 2016).

65. National Collaborating Centre for Aboriginal Health. An overview of Aboriginal health in Canada. Prince George: University of Northern British Columbia; 2013.

66. Supreme Court of Canada. Manitoba Métis Federation Inc. v. Canada. Ottawa: Supreme Court of Canada; 2013. https://scc-csc.lexum.com/scc-csc/scc-csc/en/item/12888/index.do (accessed 24 August 2016).

67. Centre for Rural and Northern Health Research. Ontario - Diversity of northern populations [maps]. Created by JE Sherman using ESRI ArcGIS 10.1. Sudbury: Centre for Rural and Northern Health Research; 2015.

68. Chiefs of Ontario. A guide for First Nations in Ontario: Navigating the Non-Insured Health Benefits & Ontario health programs benefits. Toronto: Chiefs of Ontario; 2013.

69. Government of Canada. The federal role in health and healthcare. Ottawa: Government of Canada; 2005. http://www.lop.parl.gc.ca/content/lop/researchpublications/prb0858-e.pdf (accessed 26 August 2016).

70. Government of Ontario. Aboriginal peoples in Ontario. Toronto: Queen's Printer for Ontario; 2015. http://www.ontario.ca/aboriginal/aboriginal-peoples-ontario (accessed 24 August 2016).

71. Health Canada. First Nations and Inuit Health Branch. Ottawa: Health Canada; 2013. http://www.hc-sc.gc.ca/ahc-asc/branch-dirgen/fnihb-dgspni/index-eng.php (accessed 25 August 2016).

72. Health Canada. Non-Insured Health Benefits for First Nations and Inuit. Ottawa: Health Canada; 2015. http://www.hc-sc.gc.ca/fniah-spnia/nihb-ssna/index-eng.php (accessed 25 August 2016).

73. Ministry of Community and Social Services. Programs and supports for Aboriginal individuals and families. Health and wellness. Health outreach workers. Toronto: Queen's Printer for Ontario; 2012. http://www.mcss.gov.on.ca/en/mcss/programs/community/ahws/individuals/health_outreach_workers.aspx (accessed 24 August 2016).

74. Ministry of Community and Social Services. Programs and supports for Aboriginal individuals and families. Health and wellness. Maternal and child centre. Toronto: Queen's Printer for Ontario; 2012. http://www.mcss.gov.on.ca/en/mcss/programs/community/ahws/individuals/maternal_health.aspx (accessed 24 August 2016).

75. Ministry of Community and Social Services. Programs and supports for Aboriginal individuals and families. Crisis intervention/healing services. Community wellness workers. Toronto: Queen's Printer for Ontario; 2012. http://www.mcss.gov.on.ca/en/mcss/programs/community/ahws/individuals/community_wellness_workers.aspx (accessed 24 August 2016).

76. Ministry of Community and Social Services. Programs and supports for Aboriginal individuals and families. Crisis intervention/healing services. Community intervention workers. Toronto: Queen's Printer for Ontario; 2012. http://www.mcss.gov.on.ca/en/mcss/programs/community/ahws/individuals/crisis_intervention_workers.aspx (accessed 24 August 2016).

77. Ministry of Community and Social Services. Programs and supports for Aboriginal individuals and families. Toronto: Queen's Printer for Ontario; 2012. http://www.mcss.gov.on.ca/en/mcss/programs/community/ahws/individuals/youth_treatment_centre.aspx (accessed 24 August 2016).

78. Ministry of Community and Social Services. Programs and supports for Aboriginal individuals and families. Healthy babies and children. Aboriginal Healthy Babies Healthy Children program. Toronto: Queen's Printer for Ontario; 2012. http://www.mcss.gov.on.ca/en/mcss/programs/community/ahws/individuals/healthy_babies.aspx (accessed 24 August 2016).

79. Ministry of Community and Social Services. Supporting Aboriginal people. Toronto: Queen's Printer for Ontario; 2013. http://www.mcss.gov.on.ca/en/mcss/programs/community/programsforaboriginalpeople.aspx (accessed 24 August 2016).

80. Six Nations of the Grand River Territory. Tsi Non:we Ionnakeratstha Ona:grahsta' Maternal and Child Centre. Ohsweken: Six Nations Council; 2006. http://www.snhs.ca/bcBackground.htm (accessed 24 August 2016).

81. Government of Ontario. Aboriginal peoples in Ontario. Toronto: Queen's Printer for Ontario; 2015. http://www.ontario.ca/aboriginal/aboriginal-peoples-ontario (accessed 25 August 2016).

82. Ministry of Community and Social Services. Supporting Aboriginal people. Toronto: Queen's Printer for Ontario; 2013. http://www.mcss.gov.on.ca/en/mcss/programs/community/programsforaboriginalpeople.aspx (accessed 24 August 2016).

.

10. Reforms

Michael G. Wilson, Cristina A. Mattison and John N. Lavis

Key messages for citizens

- The health system was reformed in 2007 to make healthcare more responsive to local needs by creating 14 Local Health Integration Networks that assumed a substantial portion of the responsibility for planning and integrating the delivery of services, and for funding the organizations (each typically overseen by its own board of directors) that deliver these services.

- Reforms have been implemented to enhance care for priority populations, such as those with complex health needs and those living with mental health and substance use problems.

- Privacy rules for personal health information were enhanced in 2004, and again in 2016.

- Planned reforms articulated in the *Patients First Act, 2016* seek to make care more patient-centred through an expansion of the role of the Local Health Integration Networks for planning and integrating primary care and home and community care.

Key messages for professionals

- The *Excellent Care for All Act, 2010* included a requirement for many types of health organizations (e.g., hospitals and Family Health Teams) to submit annual Quality Improvement Plans to Health Quality Ontario.

- Some reforms have been implemented for managing the health workforce in the province, including strengthening the nursing workforce, expanding the scope of practice for many regulated health professionals, and enhancing coordination between the education and health systems in training health professionals.

- The way that some professionals practise (e.g., as part of interprofessional teams in primary care) and are paid (e.g., using a payment mechanism called Quality-Based Procedures to reimburse hospitals based on the type and quantity of patients they treat) has been changed, and additional changes seem to be on the horizon through the *Patients First Act, 2016* (e.g., as a result of Local Health Integration Networks taking on responsibility for planning primary care) and through negotiations between the Government of Ontario and the Ontario Medical Association on the terms of a new Physician Services Agreement.

Key messages for policymakers

- The last decade and a half has been a time of many health-system changes that have moved the province towards more of a true 'system' (i.e., one that takes a coordinated approach to planning, integrating and funding care across sectors).

- The most significant changes appear to have emerged due to factors related to electoral processes, most notably a change in governing party in 2003 that led to 13 of the 31 recent reforms identified in this chapter (six of which represented significant changes), and a new leader for a majority government in 2014 that led to the *Patients First Act, 2016* that amended 20 pieces of existing legislation (and significantly expanded the role of Local Health Integration Networks in planning and integrating primary care and home and community care).

- One notable area where significant reforms have not been implemented is prescription drugs, where no changes have been made since the introduction of the Trillium Drug Program, despite prescription drugs being the second-largest health expenditure in Ontario.

. . .

This chapter about recent health-system reforms is the first of two chapters that address change and progress, with the second focusing on assessments of the health system that can inform decisions about future reforms. Government decisions to introduce reforms are typically the result of there being: 1) agreement among key decision-makers that there is a compelling problem that needs to be addressed at the level of: risk factors, diseases or conditions; the programs, services or drugs currently being used to address risk factors, diseases or conditions; the governance, financial or delivery arrangements within which these programs, services or drugs are provided; and/or the current degree of implementation of an agreed upon course of action; 2) one or more viable solutions to address the problem (which need to target the right level(s) of the problem); and 3) a determination that the 'politics' are conducive to taking action.(1)

For this chapter we identified recent reforms to the Ontario health system (which we defined very liberally to mean reforms introduced since 2000) by summarizing policy changes that we identified and described in detail in each of the previous chapters of the book. We supplement this with an overview of proposed reforms to the health system. We analyze recent and proposed reforms in terms of both their nature and where they have and have not happened.

To understand why larger structural reforms to the health system have happened (or may happen in future), the findings from a large empirical study of policymaking processes for a purposively selected sample of six policy issues in five different provinces (Alberta, Saskatchewan, Ontario, Quebec, and Newfoundland and Labrador) are helpful. This study found that two variables were consistently associated with 'large reforms': 1) electoral processes (new government or government leader, campaign commitment to reform during an election, appointment of a champion once in power, and a policy announcement in the first half of a mandate); and 2) presence of a perceived fiscal crisis.(2) Moreover, the study found that the Ontario case – when compared to the other four provinces – is perhaps best characterized as the tortoise in the fable of the tortoise and the hare, since the Government of Ontario took a slow-and-steady approach whereas other provincial governments at times experimented with bold policy changes such as regionalization (which Ontario ended up pursuing, in a much less dramatic form, much later than other provinces).(3) The metaphor still appears apt.

Recent reforms

Since 2000, 31 reforms have been introduced to Ontario's health system. These reforms can be described in relation to the year in which they were implemented, the type and focus of reforms, and the levels of the system that they affected (which is our focus in Table 10.1) and in relation to whether they changed the ways in which the health-system building blocks are used (which is our focus on Table 10.2). We address the timing of the reforms before turning to the nature of the reforms.

In the same time period (i.e., since 2000), there have been four general elections in Ontario (2003, 2007, 2011 and 2014), with the first leading to a new governing party (Dalton McGuinty's majority Liberal government in 2003) and the last involving a new Liberal leader (Kathleen Wynne's majority Liberal government) after three years of a Liberal minority government. In addition, this time period included two significant

Table 10.1: Overview of reforms since 2000

Year	Reform[1]	Type of reform	Focus of the reform	Level of reform
2000-12	Regulation of health professions	Legislation	Enhanced regulations for healthcare providers that were implemented over a period of 12 years for eight health professions or categories of health workers (nurse practitioners, opticians, psychologists, homeopathy, naturopathy, traditional Chinese medicine, personal support workers, and physician assistants), as well as established regulations for new health professions as parts of the *Health System Improvements Act, 2007* (see below)	Profession
2000	*Bill 168, Brian's Law (Mental Health Legislative Reform)*	Legislation	Modified assessment and committal criteria for seriously mentally ill people to enable earlier intervention by their families and health professionals, and to enable their treatment in the community rather than in a psychiatric facility	Cross-sectoral
2001	*Community Care Access Corporations Act*	Legislation	Established the mandate, governance and accountabilities of Community Care Access Centres (CCACs)	Sector
2001	Good Nursing, Good Health: A Good Investment	Strategy/ recommendations/ framework	Provided eight recommendations from the Nursing Task Force focused as part of its mandate "to examine the impact of healthcare reform on both the delivery of nursing services and the nursing profession in Ontario and to recommend strategies to ensure and enhance quality of care through effective use of nursing human resources"(13)	Profession
2003	Mental Health Accountability framework ('Making it Happen')	Strategy/ recommendations/ framework	Developed a guide for mental health accountability in four areas (performance domains, transfer payments from the Ministry of Health and Long-Term Care to agencies, an operating manual for mental health and addiction agencies, and hospital accountability)	Cross-sectoral
2004	*Commitment to the Future of Medicine Act*	Legislation	Established an organization (that became what is now known as Health Quality Ontario, or HQO) to publicly report on health-system performance and support continuous quality improvement	System
2004	*Personal Health Information Protection Act*	Legislation	Enshrined patient confidentiality as an individual right by outlining rules for collecting, using and disclosing personal information about individuals that protect confidentiality while also providing effective healthcare	System

Continued on next page

Year	Reform[1]	Type of reform	Focus of the reform	Level of reform
2004-05	Cancer Care Ontario (CCO) restructuring	Contracts	Restructured CCO between 2004 and 2005 from a provider of a limited scope of cancer services to give it a broader role that includes overseeing the regional delivery of an expanded range of services through 14 regional cancer programs that align with the 14 Local Health Integration Networks (LHINs) (this included transferring assets to hospitals but retaining the funding levers for services delivered, as well as a model for performance accountability)	Cross-sectoral
2005	Health human resource initiatives	Program	Enhanced coordination between the education and health systems in the training of health professionals through a joint initiative between the Ministry of Health and Long-Term Care and the then Ministry of Training, Colleges and Universities	Profession
2005	Family Health Teams	Contracts	Implemented an interprofessional team-based primary care model consisting of physicians, nurse practitioners and other clinicians working in collaboration, with extended hours of care provided	Sector
2006[2]	Nurse Practitioner-led Clinics	Contracts	Implemented a primary-care model where nurse practitioners assess, diagnose, treat and monitor a wide range of health problems	Sector
2006	Program Framework for Mental Health and Court Support Services	Strategy/ recommendations/ framework	Developed a framework for guiding individuals from the criminal justice system to mental health services	Cross-sectoral
2006	*Transparent Drug System for Patients Act*	Legislation	Established the Ontario Public Drug Programs as part of the public drug system reform and includes consumer and patient engagement, transparency, and basing funding decisions on clinical and economic evidence	Cross-sectoral
2006	*Local Health Integration Network Act*	Legislation	Created 14 geographically defined LHINs that have responsibility for the planning, integration and funding of healthcare in their regions, and for ensuring that the different parts of the health system in their regions work together Reduced the number of CCACs from 43 to 14, aligned their boundaries with those of the LHINs, and established the LHINs as their funder	System

Continued on next page

Year	Reform[1]	Type of reform	Focus of the reform	Level of reform
2006-07	Health-Force-Ontario and Health-Force-Ontario Marketing and Re-cruitment Agency	Program	Developed a provincial strategy (HealthForce-Ontario) to address the supply and mix of health professionals Created the HealthForceOntario Marketing and Recruitment Agency, which focuses on the recruitment, distribution and retention of health professionals	Profession
2007	*Health System Improve-ments Act*	Legislation	Introduced several changes (through omnibus legislation that affected a number of existing acts) including: • four new regulated health professions (homeopathy, kinesiology, naturopathy and psychotherapy) • new requirements for regulatory colleges (e.g., to establish their own websites with mandated information such as summaries of disciplinary decisions) • allocation of responsibility for some public health activities in the province (e.g., for an enhanced approach to emergency manage-ment and for public health laboratories) to a newly created agency (Ontario Agency for Health Protection and Promotion, which was later renamed to Public Health Ontario) that provides leadership and support for all public health activities (including an enhanced ap-proach to emergency management and public health laboratories in Ontario)	Profession Sector
2007	*Long-Term Care Homes Act*	Legislation	Expanded the Residents' Bill of Rights, updated regulations and strengthened the inspection process (including rules for inspectors to enforce compliance)	Sector
2010 (re-newed original 1994 strategy)	Aboriginal Healing and Wellness Strategy	Strategy/ recommen-dations/ framework	The largest provincially funded Indigenous health initiative in the country, which brings together traditional and western programs and services with the aim of providing culturally and linguis-tically appropriate care to improve Indigenous health, and support Indigenous healing and well-ness, while reducing family violence and violence against Indigenous women and children (14)	Cross-sectoral
2010	*Excellent Care for All Act*	Legislation	Created the requirement for many types of health organizations to submit annual Quality Improve-ment Plans to HQO, and for research evidence to be used to inform policy decisions about the health system	System

Continued on next page

Year	Reform[1]	Type of reform	Focus of the reform	Level of reform
2010	*Narcotics Safety and Awareness Act*	Legislation	Established a monitoring system for the prescribing and dispensing of narcotics and other monitored drugs, in order to reduce the misuse and abuse of these types of drugs (15)	Cross-sectoral
2011	*Health Protection and Promotion Amendment Act*	Legislation	Established the authority of the provincial chief medical officer of health to direct boards of health and their medical officers of health in cases of a pandemic, public health event or emergency with health impacts	Sector
2011	Open Minds, Healthy Minds	Strategy/ recommendations/ framework	Developed a strategy focused on supporting mental health and addictions throughout the life span	Cross-sectoral
2012	Community Health Links	Contracts	Support the delivery of coordinated care in the community for those with complex health needs	Cross-sectoral
2012	Health system funding reform	Contracts	As of 2015-16 two new funding approaches make up 70% of the total funding provided to hospitals: 1) Health-Based Allocation Model (40% of total funding to hospitals) that allocates funding based on a number of inputs that can be used to predict how many services will be needed each year and the costs of those services (e.g., historical service volumes, expected population growth, and healthcare access patterns in a specific region); and 2) Quality-Based Procedures (30% of total funding to hospitals) that allocates funding based on the costs of all of the services required as part of an optimal clinical pathway for an episode of care (or for a discrete part of the clinical pathway)\n\nA similar approach is now being used for CCACs	Sector
2012	Moving on Mental Health: A System that Makes Sense for Children and Youth	Strategy/ recommendations/ framework	Created the action plan for community-based mental health for care for children and youth	Cross-sectoral
2013	Make No Little Plans	Strategy/ recommendations/ framework	Developed a strategic plan for restructuring the public health sector with a focus on addressing early childhood development, infectious diseases, prevention, healthy environments, and infrastructure and emergency preparedness	Sector

Continued on next page

Year	Reform[1]	Type of reform	Focus of the reform	Level of reform
2013	Community-based specialty clinics	Contracts	Formalized the process for shifting the site of service delivery from hospitals to community-based specialty clinics for low-risk diagnostic and therapeutic procedures that do not require an overnight hospital stay	Sector
2014	Midwifery-led birth centres	Contracts	Launched two new community-based birth centres with one located in Ottawa (Ottawa Birth and Wellness Centre) and the other in Toronto (Toronto Birth Centre)	Sector
2015 (updated from 2012)	Action plan for health care	Strategy/recommendations/framework	Focused on patient-centred care in the most recent version, and provided four overarching goals for the health system that have been used to shape subsequent reforms: 1) improving access; 2) connecting services; 3) informing people and patients; and 4) protecting the universal public health system	System
2016	Ontario Palliative Care Network	Program	Committed in the March 2016 budget to establish the Ontario Palliative Care Network, a partnership among CCO, LHINs, HQO and other partners (e.g., patients, caregivers and clinical representatives) to develop provincial end-of-life care standards, and to support the regionally focused networks that already exist	Cross-sectoral
2016	*Health Information Protection Act*	Legislation	Amended the *Personal Health Information Protection Act, 2004*, and other acts to establish a framework for the electronic health record, and provide increased accountability, transparency and privacy protection for personal health information	System

Sources: 16-40

Notes:
[1] This table does not include legislation that has been proposed or recently passed, the most noteworthy of which is the *Patients First Act, 2016*
[2] The first Nurse Practitioner-led Clinic was approved in Sudbury in 2006 and implemented in 2007. This was followed by the approval of 25 Nurse Practitioner-led Clinics between February 2009 and August 2010.

Table 10.2: Analysis of where reforms did and did not change the ways in which the health-system building blocks are used

Sector, treatment or population	Where did reform happen?	Nature of changes to health-system building blocks			Where did reform not happen?
		Governance	Financial	Delivery	
Care by sector (Chapter 6)					
Home and community care	• Responsibility for planning, integration and funding shifted to the Local Health Integration Networks (LHINs) • Regulation of and increased funding for personal support workers • Shift in approach to funding Community Care Access Centres (e.g., Health-Based Allocation Model) • Coordinated delivery of care for people with complex conditions in their communities (Health Links)	✓	✓	✓	• First-dollar coverage as is provided for hospital-based and physician-provided care (although additional investments have been made)
Primary care	• Enhanced accountability for providers working in Family Health Teams • Introduction of interprofessional team-based care (Family Health Teams) that included alternative remuneration models • Expanded role for nurse practitioners and pharmacists (e.g., through prescribing), and midwives (e.g., through the introduction of birth centres) in primary care	✓	✓	✓	• Accountability for providing primary care to a geographically defined population as opposed to patients on the roster of primary-care clinics (although this is called for in the *Patients First Act, 2016*) • Broader roll-out of alternative remuneration models (most family physicians still work in traditional fee-for-service models) • Requirement for physicians not in Family Health Teams to submit Quality Improvement Plans to Health Quality Ontario (HQO)

Continued on next page

Sector, treatment or population	Where did reform happen?	Nature of changes to health-system building blocks			Where did reform not happen?
		Governance	Financial	Delivery	
Specialty care	• Responsibility for planning, integration and funding shifted to the LHINs • Requirement to submit annual Quality Improvement Plans to HQO • Shift in approach to hospital funding (e.g., Health-Based Allocation Model and Quality-Based Procedures) • Some low-risk procedures shifted to community-based speciality clinics	✓	✓	✓	• Removal of hospital boards of directors as has been done in other provinces
Rehabilitation care	• Expansion of Ontario Health Insurance Plan coverage for physiotherapy clinics		✓		• First-dollar coverage for all medically necessary rehabilitation services
Long-term care	• Responsibility for planning, integration and funding for some long-term care homes shifted to the LHINs • Implementation of the *Long-Term Care Act, 2007* that strengthened regulations and enhanced the patients' bill of rights	✓			• None identified
Public health	• Creation of a new public health agency	✓			• Connecting local public health agencies to the LHINs and to primary care (although this had been included in an early draft of the *Patients First Act, 2016*) • Needs-based funding of public health agencies

Continued on next page

Sector, treatment or population	Where did reform happen?	Nature of changes to health-system building blocks			Where did reform not happen?
		Governance	Financial	Delivery	
Care for select conditions (Chapter 7)					
Mental health and addictions	• Enhanced accountability • Development of assessment and committal criteria for seriously mentally ill individuals • Increased collaboration between the criminal justice system and mental health services • Monitoring for prescribing and dispensing narcotics • Development of a strategy focused on supports over the life span	✓		✓	• Mental health and addictions continues to be treated separately from 'physical health' • Defining core services to be available to adults in communities across the province, establishing a lead agency that can serve as a 'way in' to these services, creating a new funding model for the agencies that deliver services, and building a legal framework for these agencies (although significant progress has been made in these directions)
Work related injuries and diseases	• Workplace Safety and Insurance Board (WSIB) has taken an active role in commissioning care to achieve better health and return-to-work outcomes • A network of providers and organizations has evolved to meet the demand induced by WSIB's enhanced role		✓	✓	• Change of approach to treating work-related injuries and diseases such that these are now treated differently than other injuries and diseases
Cancer	• Fourteen regional cancer programs established in 2005 that align with each of the LHINs	✓			• None identified

Continued on next page

Sector, treatment or population	Where did reform happen?	Nature of changes to health-system building blocks			Where did reform not happen?
		Governance	Financial	Delivery	
Care for select conditions (Chapter 7) – continued					
End of life	• Commitment to establish the Ontario Palliative Care Network • Federal 'medical assistance in dying' legislation approved			✓	• Medical assistance in dying not available to those who do not have a 'reasonably foreseeable death' (e.g., persons with long-term conditions that cause them to live in substantial pain or discomfort)
Care using select treatments (Chapter 8)					
Prescription and over-the-counter drugs	• Strengthened consumer/patient engagement, transparency, and use of evidence in decision-making • Increased scope of practice for pharmacists • Established a monitoring system for narcotics prescribing and dispensing	✓		✓	• Increased public coverage for prescription drugs • Further expanded scope of practice for pharmacists (as promised in the 2014 Liberal Party platform)
Complementary and alternative therapies	• Enhanced regulation of health professions (e.g., naturopathy, traditional Chinese medicine)	✓			• None identified
Dental services	• *Long-Term Care Homes Act, 2007* established requirements for oral care for residents			✓	• Integration of care with the health system (beyond limited intersection with hospitals and long-term care homes) or expansion of public coverage
Care for Indigenous peoples (Chapter 9)					
	• Renewal of existing commitment (Aboriginal Healing and Wellness Strategy)	✓	✓	✓	• Extension of coverage to non-status First Nations and to Métis

recessions, one that began in 2001 and the other being the global economic crisis that began in 2008.

When considered in light of these electoral and financial factors, as well as Ontario's slow-and-steady approach to health-system reform, Tables 10.1 and 10.2 reveal that the previous finding that major electoral changes are supportive of significant reform appears to be borne out again in Ontario during this time. A four-year span following the 2003 election of a Liberal majority government after two terms of a majority Progressive Conservative government resulted in 13 of the 31 reforms (close to half of the reforms that took place over 16 years). Of these, six could be seen as constituting 'large' reforms, which included (in chronological order) the:

- *Commitment to the Future of Medicare Act, 2004* that established an organization that became what is now known as Health Quality Ontario (HQO) to publicly report on health-system performance and support continuous quality improvement;
- *Personal Health Information Protection Act, 2004* that enshrined patient confidentiality as an individual right;
- introduction of interprofessional team-based primary care in the form of Family Health Teams (2005) and a new approach to physician remuneration (blended capitation and fee-for-service payment) after decades of recommendations to move in this direction;
- expansion of the nurse role and team-based primary care through the introduction of Nurse Practitioner-led Clinics in 2006;
- creation of 14 geographically defined Local Health Integration Networks (LHINs) that were given responsibility for the planning and funding of healthcare in their regions, and for ensuring that the different parts of the health system in their regions work together (see Figure 1.1); and
- *Health Systems Improvement Act, 2007* that produced (through omnibus legislation) several notable changes including:
  - a restructured 'public health' sector, including the creation of a new agency (Ontario Agency for Health Protection and Promotion, which was later renamed Public Health Ontario) that supports emergency management and operates public health laboratories in Ontario;
  - four new regulated health professions (naturopathy, homeopathy, kinesiology and psychotherapy); and
  - new requirements for regulatory colleges (e.g., to establish their

own websites with mandated information such as summaries of disciplinary decisions).

Three other reforms that happened later could be considered as 'large.' These include the:

- *Excellent Care for All Act, 2010* that created the requirement for many types of health organizations (e.g., Family Health Teams and hospitals) to submit annual Quality Improvement Plans to HQO;
- health-system funding reform in 2012 that implemented a Health-Based Allocation Model that provides organization-level funding for hospitals and Community Care Access Centres (CCACs), as well as a payment system called Quality-Based Procedures that reimburse providers based on the type and quantity of patients they treat; and
- formalization of the process for shifting the site of service delivery from hospitals to community-based specialty clinics for low-risk diagnostic and therapeutic procedures that do not require an overnight stay (although this is 'large' in the sense of a change in direction, not in the volume of procedures now being provided in these clinics).

Interestingly these three reforms also appear to align with important factors related to electoral processes, with the *Excellent Care for All Act* being implemented in the lead up to an election, and the implementation of health-system funding reform and introduction of community-based specialty clinics being key pieces of the province's Action Plan For Health Care that was released after the election (in 2012). As noted in the next section about future reforms, the *Patients First Act, 2016,* which will make significant changes to the health system (particularly for planning and funding home and community care and primary care), also appears to fit this pattern.(4)

The foundation for each of three of these reforms (the move to interprofessional team-based primary care with an alternative remuneration model, regionalized planning and funding of healthcare, and community-based specialty clinics) was laid much earlier in the province, further supporting the characterization of the approach to Ontario's health reforms as slow and steady. For the move to interprofessional team-based care, the foundation was laid through the pilot Primary Care Networks that started in 1998 through a collaboration between the Government of Ontario and the Ontario Medical Association. For regionalized planning and funding, the foundation was not in the form of a pilot, but rather a 'wait-and-see' approach, given that all provinces other than Ontario had moved forward with some form of regionalized healthcare in the early 1990s. Lastly, a series of decisions beginning in 1990 supported the development of the infrastructure needed to implement community-based specialty clinics. These past decisions included amending the *Independent Health Facilities Act, 1990*, as well as allowing for the development of private for-profit delivery of medically necessary 'high-tech' diagnostic services in 1996. While these changes were eventually identified as potentially leading to parallel (i.e., public and private) tiers of access to services, this never occurred given subsequent changes in governments with different priorities, but it facilitated the creation of infrastructure for community-based specialty clinics.

We now turn to the nature of the 31 reforms to Ontario's health system. We group them according to the level of the system that each reform affected, namely system, profession, sector, and cross-sectoral (Table 10.1), before turning to where reforms did not happen (Table 10.2). By sector we mean the six sectors described in Chapter 6, namely home and community care, primary care, specialty care, rehabilitation care, long-term care, and public health. For the purpose of this exercise we have considered 'sub-systems' of care (e.g., care for mental health and addictions and cancer care, which we address in Chapter 7) and prescription and over-the-counter drugs (which we address in Chapter 8) to be cross-sectoral.

System-level reforms

Six system-level reforms have been implemented in Ontario since 2000, which provided for far-reaching changes to the health system in the areas of protecting patient confidentiality, strengthening governance and accountability, and providing strategic areas of focus for future reforms. These reforms include:

- enshrining patient confidentiality as an individual right through the *Personal Health Information Protection Act, 2004*, which was recently amended through the *Health Information Protection Act, 2016* to provide a framework for electronic health records and to provide increased accountability, transparency and privacy protection for personal health information (two reforms listed in Table 10.1);
- moving to a regionalized system in 2007 as a result of passing the *Local Health Integration Network Act, 2006*, whereby 14 LHINs are

responsible for planning and integrating the delivery of services at the local level, and for funding the organizations (each typically overseen by its own board of directors) that deliver these services (as opposed to funding these services directly, as other provinces have done, in part to avoid the challenges that can come from high-profile boards focusing only on 'pieces of the puzzle');

- strengthening governance, quality improvement (e.g., with some organizations such as hospitals and Family Health Teams required to submit Quality Improvement Plans to HQO) and evidence-based decision-making first through the *Commitment to the Future of Medicare Act, 2004* and more comprehensively later through the *Excellent Care for All Act, 2010* (two reforms listed in Table 10.1); and

- creating an action plan for healthcare in 2015 (updated from a previous plan in 2012), which articulated four overarching goals:
  - improving access (i.e., providing faster access to the right care),
  - connecting services (i.e., delivering better coordinated and integrated care in the community and closer to home),
  - informing people and patients (i.e., providing the education, information and transparency they need to make the right decisions about their health), and
  - protecting our universal public health system (i.e., making evidence-based decisions on value and quality, to sustain the system for generations to come).

Profession-level reforms

Five profession-level reforms have been implemented in the province since 2000. They focused on:

- expanding scopes of practice for regulated health professions, and introducing new regulated health professions, through legislative changes and direction to regulatory colleges, based on advice from the Health Professions Regulatory Advisory Council – an arm's-length council that provides independent policy advice on the regulation of health professions (two reforms listed in Table 10.1, the first of which is listed in the first row and the second appears in the row describing the *Health System Improvements Act, 2007*);

- developing a nursing strategy in 2001, which created 12,000 new permanent nursing positions, reformed nursing education, and implemented a nursing recruitment and retention strategy;

- enhancing coordination between the education and health systems in the training of health professionals through a joint initiative between the Ministry of Health and Long-Term Care and the then Ministry of Training, Colleges and Universities; and
- developing a provincial strategy (HealthForceOntario) to address the supply and mix of health professionals, which was followed by the creation of the HealthForceOntario Marketing and Recruitment Agency, which focuses on the recruitment, distribution and retention of health professionals.

Sector-based reforms

Ten sector-based reforms have been implemented in the province since 2000. These reforms focused on five of the six sectors covered in Chapter 6, namely home and community care, primary care, specialty care, long-term care, and public health, with one of the reforms (health sector funding reform) affecting two of the sectors. Starting with the home and community care sector, the mandate, governance and accountabilities of CCACs were established in 2001, and the funding model for CCACs (and as noted below, for hospitals as well) began to be shifted as part of health-system funding reform in 2012. Turning to the primary-care sector, an inter-professional team-based primary-care model (Family Health Teams) was launched in 2005, Nurse Practitioner-led Clinics were launched in 2006, and two midwifery-led birth centres were launched in 2014. In specialty care, health-system funding reform was introduced for hospitals (as noted above) and in 2013 (a year later) the process was formalized for the shifting of the site of service delivery from hospitals to community-based specialty clinics. In the long-term care sector, the reform in 2007 expanded the Residents' Bill of Rights, updated regulations, and strengthened the inspection process. In the public health sector, the reforms included creating (as part of the omnibus *Health System Improvement Act, 2007*) what is now known as Public Health Ontario, establishing in 2011 the authority of the provincial chief medical officer of health (through the *Health Protection and Promotion Amendment Act, 2011*), and developing a strategic plan for the public health sector in 2013 (Make No Little Plans).

Cross-sectoral reforms

Since 2000, 10 cross-sector reforms have been implemented, with five of them involving conditions described in Chapter 7 (mental health and addictions, cancer, and end of life), two of them involving treatments described in Chapter 8 (prescription and over-the-counter drugs), and one of them involving Health Links, which we discuss in many chapters. Four of the five reforms involving mental health and addictions were what we labelled 'strategy/recommendations/framework:' 1) the 'Mental Health Accountability' framework (2003); 2) the 'Program Framework for Mental Health and Court Support Services' (2006); 3) the 'Open Minds, Healthy Minds' strategy to address mental health and addictions across the life-span (2011); and 4) the 'Moving on Mental Health' action plan for mental health services for children and youth (2012). The one other reform in this domain was *Bill 168, Brian's Law (Mental Health Legislative Reform), 2000*. The one reform in cancer care was the significant restructuring of cancer care in 2004-05.(5; 6) The reform related to end-of-life care involved the creation of the Ontario Palliative Care Network in 2016. The two reforms related to prescription drugs were the *Transparent Drug System for Patients Act, 2006*, and the *Narcotics Safety and Awareness Act, 2010*. The final cross-sectoral reform involved the creation of Health Links in 2012 to support the delivery of coordinated care in the community for those with complex needs.

Where reform did not happen

As outlined in the last column in Table 10.2, there are many areas where reform could have happened, but did not. Several of these relate to the continued provision of first-dollar coverage (i.e., full coverage, without deductibles or cost-sharing) for care provided in hospitals or by physicians, but not for any other parts of the health system. This includes what many would identify as either sectors that provide essential care such as home and community care (although increased investments have been made in this sector) and rehabilitation care, and forms of treatment that many patients require access to as part of their care plans (most notably pre-scription drugs), or as part of primary care (dental services). Another area where reform has not happened is the implementation of a comprehensive approach to address the overuse of health services, where most action has taken the form of focused profession-led initiatives, such as Choosing

Wisely Canada.

While reforms to the types of services receiving first-dollar coverage may seem particularly difficult to implement given the finite resources available, several areas where reforms have not happened seem to be on the horizon. For example, as noted in the next section, the *Patients First Act, 2016* will address many of the accountability and planning gaps noted for home and community care (other than first-dollar coverage) and primary care, and to a lesser extent public health.(4) Moreover, while mental health and addictions continues to be treated separately from 'physical health,' Ontario's slow-and-steady approach to reform may yet result in progress towards efforts such as defining core services to be available in communities across the province, establishing a lead agency that can serve as a 'way in' to these services, creating a new funding model for the agencies delivering these services, and building a legal framework for them (although significant progress has been made in these directions).

Proposed reforms

Health-system reform priorities in Ontario for a 10-year period (2014-24) have been articulated through both the Liberal government's 10-year plan for the health system and Premier Kathleen Wynne's mandate letter to the Minister of Health and Long-Term Care following the 2014 election in Ontario,(7; 8) which we summarize in Table 10.3. As can be seen from the table, the priorities focus on:

- system-level, profession-level, sector-level and cross-sectoral reforms to strengthen governance, financial and delivery arrangements, and to strengthen seniors care (including for their families and caregivers); and
- sector-level reforms to strengthen services for maternal and child health.

While several priorities have already been addressed (e.g., increasing funding for infertility services and home care, increasing wages for personal support workers, and creating a strategy for end-of-life care), others are in the process of being implemented (e.g., launching the remaining Health Links), or first steps have been taken toward implementing them (e.g., passing the *Health Information Protection Act, 2016* to establish a framework for electronic health records as part of using technology more effectively). No 'large' reforms, however, were formally proposed as part of this agenda

Table 10.3: Overview of health-system reform priorities, 2014-24

Priorities[1]	Type of reform			
	System-level	Profession-level	Sector-level	Cross-sectoral
Strengthen governance arrangements by: • supporting institutional collaboration • providing a patient ombudsman • ensuring Ornge's (i.e., air ambulance and medical transport service) accountability and transparency	✓		✓	
Strengthen financial sustainability (as an aspect of financial arrangements) of the health system by: • maintaining annual health spending growth at 3% • increasing funding for Ontario's Mental Health and Addictions Strategy	✓			✓
Strengthen delivery arrangements by: • using technology more effectively • guaranteeing that every Ontarian has access to a primary-care provider • reducing wait times on referrals to specialists by 50% • coordinating delivery of care between healthcare providers as well as between Local Health Integration Networks, Community Care Access Centres and local public health agencies • providing culturally appropriate care by building community wellness • creating 36 additional Health Links • expanding scopes of practice (e.g., nurses and pharmacists) • advocating for a national drug insurance program • coordinating and expediting drug-approval processes	✓	✓	✓	✓
Strengthen maternal and child health by: • increasing funding for infertility services • providing access to free vaccinations • implementing a newborn screening program			✓	
Strengthen seniors care, including families/caregivers by: • increasing funding for home care • increasing wages for personal support workers • creating a palliative care and end-of-life care strategy • supporting family caregivers • increasing funding for activity and community grant programs • creating 25 new 'memory clinics'	✓	✓	✓	✓

Sources: 7; 8

Note:
[1] Priorities have been drawn from both the Liberal government's 10-year plan for the health system (released in 2014) and Premier Kathleen Wynne's mandate letter to Eric Hoskins, Minister of Health and Long-Term Care.

until recently. Specifically, the Liberal government passed the *Patients First Act, 2016*, (4) which involves amendments to 20 existing pieces of legislation, with key changes including an expansion of the role of the LHINs in planning and integrating primary care and home and community care.(4) The key goals outlined in the legislation include:

- improving access to primary care for patients;
- improving local connections and communication among home and community care, primary care, and hospitals to ensure equitable access and a smoother patient experience;
- ensuring that patients only have to tell their story once, by enabling healthcare providers to share and update their healthcare plans;
- making it easier for physicians, nurses, and other primary-care providers to connect their patients to the healthcare they need;
- providing smoother patient transitions among home and community, primary, specialty, and long-term care, and with mental health and addictions care;
- improving consistency of home and community care across the province so that people know what to expect and receive good care regardless of where they live in the province;
- strengthening health planning and accountability by monitoring performance;
- ensuring public health practitioners have a voice in health-system planning by establishing a formal relationship between LHINs and local boards of health; and
- facilitating local healthcare planning to ensure decisions are made by people who best understand the needs of their communities, and that LHIN boards reflect the communities they serve.

Similar to the other recent 'large' reforms outlined earlier, this proposed reform seems to have emerged due to several factors related to the electoral process, including:
- a new leader of the governing party (Kathleen Wynne);
- commitments that came from a campaign (the priorities in Table 10.2 that were articulated shortly after the election);
- appointment of champions once in power (Eric Hoskins as the new minister of health and Robert Bell as the new deputy minister of health); and
- an announcement of the legislation in the first half of a political mandate.

Moreover, this reform has been proposed during a time of fiscal crisis, when much attention has been paid to doing things differently to reduce the government's large budget deficit (although this does not appear to include providing LHINs with any influence over spending on prescription drugs or physicians, and it fails to align the boundaries of local public health agencies to those of the LHINs, both of which have presumably been the focus of significant resistance by key stakeholders).

Also, Ontario's slow-and-steady approach to health-system reform seems to have played a role, as the foundation for many of the proposed changes were put in place much earlier. The most notable earlier reforms that made the *Patients First Act, 2016* possible include the implementation of inter-professional team-based primary care (which is proposed to be expanded on in order to provide population-level coverage for primary care), and the establishment of LHINs (which, under the new legislation, will have their role expanded to include home and community care – although payment for physicians will still come from the Ministry of Health and Long-Term Care). Moreover, the priorities assimilated in the *Patients First Act, 2016* were extensively 'road tested' through the 2012 and 2015 Action Plans for Health, and more recently through a discussion paper that was published in December 2015 by the ministry about strengthening patient-centred healthcare. The latter included much of what is contained in the now passed legislation.(9)

Conclusion

This chapter shows that the last decade and a half has been a time of many health-system changes that have moved the province towards more of a true 'system' (i.e., a system that takes a coordinated approach to planning and funding care across sectors). The most significant changes appear to have emerged due to factors related to electoral processes (most notably a change in governing party in 2003 and a new leader for a majority government in 2014). Moreover, many of the significant reforms that have either taken place more recently or have been proposed have been made possible by a 'slow-and-steady' approach to health-system reform, whereby policies put in place much earlier (or not put in place, in the case of a regionalized approach to planning and funding the system) have laid a foundation for larger reforms later.

Perhaps the most notable areas where significant reforms have not been implemented, and which therefore represent barriers to a true 'system' of integrated care, are strengthening care for mental health and addictions and enhancing prescription-drug funding. The former has seen the development of legislation, programs and several frameworks and strategies, but none that would be considered significant changes (at least on the scale of implementing the LHINs, Family Health Teams, restructuring public health or the changes articulated in the *Patients First Act, 2016*). Given the pattern of health-system reform, it would seem that Ontario appears poised to build on this steady process of foundation building towards more significant changes (e.g., to defining core mental health and addictions services to be available in communities and establishing a lead agency for these services). Moreover, given that progress towards these larger policy goals seems to have been made in the first half of a political mandate, the prospects for such reform appear high.(10; 11) However, for prescription-drug funding, which constitutes the second largest healthcare expenditure in the province,(12) the picture seems quite different, as there has been little activity. The last substantive funding change was the introduction of the Trillium Drug Program in 1995, which may point to the need for an external impetus to change, such as the increasing emphasis being put on moving towards a national pharmacare plan. This was included as a priority in the Liberal government's 10-year plan for the health system.

For those interested in keeping abreast about new reforms that have been proposed or implemented, many sources can be used, including: media coverage (e.g., by following specific media sources or by systematically searching indexes of media coverage, such as LexisNexis); government media releases; transcripts of parliamentary debates (i.e., Hansard); and statements of intent to introduce reforms (e.g., electoral platforms of the governing party, speeches from the Throne, budget announcements, mandate letters from the premier to the minister of health, and ministry action plans). For analyses of the factors leading to specific reforms, and their consequences, *Health Reform Observer - Observatoire des Réformes de Santé* periodically publishes articles about reforms in Ontario.

References

1. Kingdon JW. Agendas, alternatives, and public policies. Updated second edition Boston: Longman; 2011.

2. Lazar H, Lavis JN, Forest P-G, Church J. Paradigm freeze: Why it is so hard to reform health care in Canada. Montreal and Kingston: McGill-Queen's University Press; 2013.

3. Lavis JN, Pasic D, Wilson MG. Health-care reform in Ontario: More tortoise than hare? In: Lazar H, Lavis JN, Forest P-G, editors. Paradigm freeze: Why it is so hard to reform health-care policy in Canada. Montreal and Kingston: McGill-Queen's University Press; 2013.

4. Legislative Assembly of Ontario. Bill 41, Patients First Act, 2016. Toronto: Queen's Printer for Ontario; 2016. http://www.ontla.on.ca/web/bills/bills_detail.do?locale=en&Intranet=&BillID=4215 (accessed 7 October 2016).

5. Bytautas J, Dobrow M, Sullivan T, Brown A. Accountability in the Ontario cancer services system: A qualitative study of system leaders' perspectives. *Healthcare Policy* 2014;10(SP): 10.

6. Sullivan T. Improving quality and performance in Ontario's cancer services: Lessons for constructing a learning healthcare system. *Healthcare Quarterly* 2015;17 (SP): 4.

7. Ontario Liberal Party. Kathleen Wynne's plan for Ontario. Access to the right health care, at the right time, in the right place. Toronto: Ontario Liberal Party; 2014. https://www.aohc.org/sites/default/files/documents/Access-to-the-Right-Health-Care-at-the-Right-Time-in-the-Right-Place.pdf (accessed 24 August 2016).

8. Wynne K. 2014 mandate letter: Health and long-term care. Premier's instructions to the Minister on priorities for the year 2014. Toronto: Queen's Printer for Ontario; 2014. https://www.ontario.ca/government/2014-mandate-letter-health-and-long-term-care (accessed 24 August 2016).

9. Ministry of Health and Long-Term Care. Patients first. A proposal to strengthen patient-centred health care in Ontario. Toronto: Queen's Printer for Ontario; 2015. http://www.health.gov.on.ca/en/news/bulletin/2015/docs/discussion_paper_20151217.pdf (accessed 25 August 2016).

10. Bullock H, Waddell K, Lavis JN. Evidence brief: Defining the mental health and addictions 'basket of core services' to be publicly funded in Ontario. Hamilton: McMaster Health Forum; 2016.

11. Bullock H, Waddell K, Lavis JN. Dialogue summary: Defining the mental health and addictions 'basket of core services' to be publicly funded in Ontario. Hamilton: McMaster Health Forum; 2016.

12. CIHI. National health expenditure trends, 1975 to 2015. Series D table D.3.6.1, public sector health expenditure, by use of funds, Ontario, 1975 to 2015 - Current dollars ($' 000,000). Ottawa: Canadian Institute for Health Information; 2015.

13. Joint Provincial Nursing Committee. Good nursing, good health: A good investment. Toronto: Queen's Printer for Ontario; 2001. http://www.health.gov.on.ca/en/common/ministry/publications/reports/nurserep01/616209_moh_good_nursing.pdf (accessed 25 August 2016).

14. Ministry of Community and Social Services. Ontario's Aboriginal Healing and Wellness Strategy. Toronto: Queen's Printer for Ontario; 2014. https://news.ontario.ca/mcss/en/2014/11/ontarios-aboriginal-healing-and-wellness-strategy.html (accessed 24 August 2016).

15. Legislative Assembly of Ontario. Narcotics Safety and Awareness Act, 2010, S.O. 2010, c. 22. Toronto: Queen's Printer for Ontario; 2016. https://www.ontario.ca/laws/statute/10n22?search=Narcotics+Safety+and+Awareness+Act,+2010&_ga=1.730513 47.1103199844.1444060626 (accessed 24 August 2016).

16. Legislative Assembly of Ontario. Local Health System Integration Act, 2006. S.O. 2006, c. 4. Toronto: Queen's Printer for Ontario; 2010. https://www.ontario.ca/laws/statute/06l04 (accessed 25 August 2016).

17. Ministry of Health and Long-Term Care. Personal Health Information and Privacy Act. Toronto: Queen's Printer for Ontario; 2000.

18. Ministry of Health and Long-Term Care. Ontario's personal health information privacy legislation for the health sector (health sector privacy rules). Toronto: Queen's Printer for Ontario; 2000. http://www.health.gov.on.ca/en/common/ministry/publications/reports/phipa/phipa_mn.aspx (accessed 25 August 2016).

19. Ministry of Health and Long-Term Care. Mental health accountability framework. Toronto: Queen's Printer for Ontario; 2003.

20. Ministry of Health and Long-Term Care. Program policy framework and service standards for mental health services and supports. Toronto: Queen's Printer for Ontario; 2003.

21. Ministry of Health and Long-Term Care. Laying the foundation for change. A progress report on Ontario's health human resources initiatives. Toronto: Queen's Printer for Ontario; 2005.

22. Ministry of Health and Long-Term Care. Building an innovative foundation: A plan for Ontario's new Public Health Agency. Toronto: Queen's Printer for Ontario; 2006.

23. Ministry of Health and Long-Term Care. Regulation of health professions in Ontario: New directions - Use of titles in the profession of psychology. Toronto: Queen's Printer for Ontario; 2006.

24. Ministry of Health and Long-Term Care. Regulation of health professions in Ontario: New directions - The regulation of personal support workers. Toronto: Queen's Printer for Ontario; 2007.

25. Government of Ontario. Open minds, healthy minds: Ontario's comprehensive mental health and addictions strategy. Toronto: Queen's Printer for Ontario; 2011. http://www.health.gov.on.ca/en/common/ministry/publications/reports/mental_health2011/mentalhealth.aspx (accessed 25 August 2016).

26. Ministry of Health and Long-Term Care. The health profession assistant: Consideration of the physician assistant application for regulation. Toronto: Queen's Printer for Ontario; 2012.

27. Ministry of Health and Long-Term Care. Ontario's action plan for health care. Better patient care through better value from our health care dollars. Toronto: Queen's Printer for Ontario; 2012.

28. Ontario Hospital Association. Toolkit to support the implementation of Quality-Based Procedures. Toronto: Ontario Hospital Association; 2013. http://www.oha.com/CurrentIssues/Issues/HSFR/Pages/QBPResources.aspx (accessed 24 October 2016).

29. Ministry of Health and Long-Term Care. Health system funding reform (HSFR). Toronto: Queen's Printer for Ontario; 2014. http://www.health.gov.on.ca/en/pro/programs/ecfa/funding/hs_funding.aspx (accessed 25 August 2016).

30. Canadian Health Services Research Foundation. Hospital payment mechanisms: An overview and options for Canada. Vancouver: CHSRF; 2011.

31. Ministry of Health and Long-Term Care. About Health Links. Toronto: Queen's Printer for Ontario; 2012. http://news.ontario.ca/mohltc/en/2012/12/about-health-links.html (accessed 26 August 2016).

32. Health Progessions Regulatory Advisory Council. Archived HPRAC reports. Toronto: Queen's Printer for Ontario; 2014. http://www.hprac.org/en/reports/archivedreports.asp (accessed 24 August 2016).

33. Ministry of Health and Long-Term Care. Community-based specialty clinics. Toronto: Queen's Printer for Ontario; 2014. http://www.health.gov.on.ca/en/pro/programs/ihf/specialtyclinics/ (accessed 25 August 2016).

34. Ministry of Health and Long-Term Care. Nurse Practitioner-led Clinics. Toronto: Queen's Printer for Ontario; 2015. http://www.health.gov.on.ca/en/common/system/services/npc/ (accessed 25 August 2016).

35. Ministry of Health and Long-Term Care. Family Health Teams. Toronto: Queen's Printer for Ontario; 2016. http://health.gov.on.ca/en/pro/programs/fht/ (accessed 26 August 2016).

36. Ministry of Health and Long-Term Care. The Transparent Drug System for Patients Act progress. Toronto: Queen's Printer for Ontario; 2013. http://www.health.gov.on.ca/en/pro/programs/drugs/plan_reform_ods/strengt_transparent_drug.aspx (accessed 25 August 2016).

37. Legislative Assembly of Ontario. Bill 119, Health Information Protection Act, 2016. Toronto: Queen's Printer for Ontario; 2016. http://www.ontla.on.ca/web/bills/bills_detail.do?locale=en&BillID=3438 (accessed 24 August 2016).

38. Ministry of Health and Long-Term Care. Province strengthens end-of-life care with $75 million investment. Toronto: Queen's Printer for Ontario; 2016. https://news.ontario.ca/mohltc/en/2016/3/province-strengthens-end-of-life-care-with-75-million-investment.html (accessed 25 August 2016).

39. Legislative Assembly of Ontario. Transparent Drug System for Patients Act, 2006, R.S.O. 2006, c. 14. Toronto: Queen's Printer for Ontario; 2006. http://www.ontla.on.ca/web/bills/bills_detail.do?locale=en&BillID=412 (accessed 24 August 2016).

40. Legislative Assembly of Ontario. Personal Health Information Protection Act, 2004, S.O. 2004, c. 3, Sched. A. Toronto: Queen's Printer for Ontario; 2004. http://www.e-Laws.gov.on.ca/html/statutes/english/elaws_statutes_04p03_e.htm (accessed 24 August 2016).

11. Performance

Kaelan A. Moat and John N. Lavis

Key messages for citizens

- Ontario's health system seeks to achieve the 'triple aim' of improving the patient experience and population health while keeping the amount spent per person manageable.

- Timely access to care has been improving in some domains (e.g., home care, primary care, and some surgeries), albeit unequally across the province. And while Ontarians are generally satisfied with the care they receive, care coordination could be improved, as could accountability and transparency.

- Most Ontarians will live longer, healthier lives than previous generations, although they do not exercise as much as the average Canadian.

- The amount of money spent on prescription and over-the-counter drugs for each Ontarian is among the highest in the world and continues to rise.

Key messages for professionals

- Existing evaluations of whether the health system is achieving the 'triple aim' of improving the patient experience and population health while keeping per capita costs manageable do not provide a balanced picture of performance across sectors (with more emphasis on specialty care), conditions (with more focus on cancer care), treatments (with more focus on prescription drugs) or populations (with limited focus on marginalized groups).

- Although most Ontarians are satisfied with the care they receive from their family physician and in hospital, they often have difficulty accessing needed services in a timely manner, and variations in access have been reported in all sectors.

- While the health of Ontarians is improving in many ways, the incidence of certain diseases is increasing (e.g., cancer) and protection against communicable diseases through immunization is decreasing.

- Like most other jurisdictions in Canada and internationally, the amount spent on healthcare (both public and private) for each Ontarian continues to increase, although compared to the rest of Canada, Ontario has the third-lowest per capita expenditure.

Key messages for policymakers

- Recent policy developments (e.g., *Excellent Care for All Act, 2010* and *Patients First Act, 2016*) and monitoring frameworks have established a commitment to addressing the 'triple aim' of improving the patient experience and population health while keeping per capita costs manageable.

- Existing evaluations suggest that improvements are being realized in terms of improving the patient experience and population health, although this progress is not equally distributed across regions. While overall healthcare spending per person in Ontario is lower than in other provinces, rising per capita drug spending and inefficiencies continue to be a challenge.

- These evaluations do not address the 'triple aim' features comprehensively or address all sectors, conditions, treatments or populations comprehensively, and they typically lack the longitudinal data to assess whether progress is being made over time.

. . .

In this second of two chapters focused on change and progress, we provide a brief overview of what we are learning from evaluations of the health system's performance. We first discuss how health-system goals can be defined, which directly influences how performance is measured, and introduce the 'triple aim' – enhancing the patient experience, improving population health, and keeping per capita costs manageable – as an orienting framework for goal definition and performance measurement. We then provide an overview of how Ontario's stated health-system goals align with the 'triple aim.' In the remainder of the chapter we present a summary of what is being learned from formal evaluations of performance against the 'triple aim' by sector and for select conditions, treatments and populations.

Stated goals of the health system

The stated goals of any health system can change to reflect shifts in the political orientation of the government in power, trends in population health, and the realities of the socio-economic context. As such, evaluations of whether the existing governance, financial and delivery arrangements in a particular health system (i.e., its 'building blocks') are achieving stated goals can be hampered by moving targets. However, health systems around the world are increasingly aligning their reform goals with the 'triple aim' framework, either implicitly or explicitly.(1) This framework was developed by the Institute for Healthcare Improvement in the U.S., and states that health-system transformation initiatives need to simultaneously pursue three broad goals:

1) improving the patient experience of care;
2) improving population health; and
3) keeping per capita costs manageable.(2)

Given the increasingly widespread use of the 'triple aim,' we organized this chapter around these three broad goals, acknowledging that the specific ways in which they are operationalized in other countries, across provinces and territories in Canada, and in Ontario specifically, can vary tremendously. In an attempt to ensure the contents of this chapter are relevant to as many of these different approaches to operationalization as possible, we adopted broad, rather than narrow, definitions of each goal.

In addressing the first dimension of the 'triple aim' – improving the patient experience of care – we focused on Ontarians' access to care (including how timely access is, and whether access is equitable), how care is experienced once accessed (including whether care is coordinated, evidence-based, safe and effective) and Ontarians' satisfaction with these experiences, as well as whether the processes underpinning the planning and delivery of care are transparent, and whether those responsible for planning and delivering care are held accountable for performance. We also focused on aspects of provider experience in this dimension, which is increasingly being referred to as a 'fourth aim' and which is seen as an essential component of ensuring a good patient experience (while also having potential implications for health outcomes and per capita costs).(3)

In addressing the second dimension of the 'triple aim' – improving population health – we focused on both measurable health outcomes (e.g., disease burden, life expectancy, health-related quality of life, and mortality rates) and measurable risk factors that can lead to poor health outcomes in a population (e.g., rates of obesity and smoking). However, as we note in the corresponding section of the chapter, many measures of population health can be affected by factors such as housing, income and social supports, which are beyond the control of the health system per se, and shaped in powerful ways by both governments and markets.

In addressing the third dimension of the 'triple aim' – keeping per capita costs manageable – we focused on the total amount spent per person (i.e., per capita costs), efficiency (i.e., getting the most out of every dollar spent), financial protection (i.e., the measures in place to ensure citizens avoid bankruptcy when they need care), and equity in financing (i.e., ensuring financial protections are in place for those who need them most).

Provincial goals

In Ontario, like many other jurisdictions around the world, the 'triple aim' has increasingly worked its way into many of the most important strategic plans and system reforms, although the language used is often unique to the province. We will focus on three important examples here: 1) the *Excellent Care for All Act, 2010*; 2) Health Quality Ontario's (HQO) definition of quality care and the dimensions of its Common Quality Agenda; and 3) 'Patients first: A proposal to strengthen patient-centred care in Ontario,' which has since been operationalized as the *Patients First Act, 2016*. While the 'triple aim' framework is not mentioned explicitly in the stated goals contained within these strategic plans and system reforms, they align in a number of ways. Below, we briefly outline the ways in which the stated goals in the health system align with the dimensions of the 'triple aim,' and provide a summary of these linkages in Table 11.1.

The *Excellent Care for All Act, 2010* articulated a number of health-system goals in the preamble to the legislation. A paraphrased list of these goals include:
1) improving the patient experience;
2) promoting high-quality care that is accessible, appropriate, safe, effective, efficient, equitable, integrated, patient-centred and population-health focused;
3) supporting healthcare providers to use the best available research evidence;
4) promoting transparency in the system;
5) ensuring healthcare organizations are accountable to the public;
6) ensuring patients and their caregivers realize their best health; and

7) ensuring that the system is sustainable, and that Ontarians continue to receive publicly funded care.(4; 5)

Table 11.1: Stated goals of the health system in relation to the 'triple aim'

Examples of how stated health-system goals align with dimensions of the 'triple aim'		
Dimension 1: improving patient experience of care (access, care experience, transparency and accountability)	Dimension 2: improving population health (health outcomes and risk factors that can lead to poor health outcomes)	Dimension 3: keeping per capita costs manageable (total amount spent per person, efficiency, financial protection and equity in financing)

Excellent Care for All Act, 2010

• Improving the patient experience is an explicitly stated goal • Several goals outlined in the preamble to the legislation relate to patient experience, including ensuring care is accessible, appropriate, effective, equitable, integrated, patient-centred, and safe • Promoting transparency in the system is an explicitly stated goal • Ensuring healthcare organzations are accountable to the public is an explicitly stated goal • Supporting healthcare providers to use the best available scientific evidence is an explicitly stated goal	• Ensuring patients and their care-givers realize their best health is an explicitly stated goal • Focusing on population health is an explicitly stated component of the goal of ensuring high-quality care	• Ensuring health-system sustainability is an explicitly stated goal • Efficiency is an explicitly stated component of the goal of ensuring high-quality care

Health Quality Ontario's definition of quality, and their Common Quality Agenda framework

• Adopted definition of quality states that quality care is safe, effective, patient-centred, timely and equitable • Patient experience included as a key component of quality-monitoring framework (particularly in the home and community care sector and the specialty sector – specifically in hospitals) • Access and timely care included as a key component of quality-monitoring framework	• Several dimensions of population health outcomes and risk factors included as a key component of quality-monitoring framework	• Adopted definition of quality states that quality care is efficient • Per capita system spending a key component of quality-monitoring framework

Continued on next page

Examples of how stated health-system goals align with dimensions of the 'triple aim'		
Dimension 1: improving patient experience of care (access, care experience, transparency and accountability)	Dimension 2: improving population health (health outcomes and risk factors that can lead to poor health outcomes)	Dimension 3: keeping per capita costs manageable (total amount spent per person, efficiency, financial protection and equity in financing)
Patients First proposal		
• Improving access, connecting services and supporting people and patients to make the right decisions about their health are explicitly stated as goals	• Improving health outcomes listed as one of the ways that meeting the goals of 'Patients First' will benefit Ontarians	• Protecting the universal public health system is explicitly stated as an objective, while realizing efficiencies is listed as one of the potential ways that meeting the goals of 'Patients First' will benefit Ontarians

Sources: 4-7

The 'triple aim' dimension that most closely aligns with the goals described in the *Excellent Care for All Act, 2010* is the first: improving the patient experience of care. This dimension aligns with goal 1 (patient experience), seven of the nine parts of goal 2 (accessible, appropriate, safe, effective, equitable, integrated and patient-centred), goal 3 (evidence-based), goal 4 (transparency), and goal 5 (accountability). The second dimension of the 'triple aim' – improving population health – is aligned with goal 6 (health of patients and caregivers) and with part of goal 2 (population-health focused), while the third dimension – keeping per capita costs manageable – is aligned with goal 7 (sustainable) and part of goal 2 (efficient).(1; 5)

Our second example of provincial health-system goals come from HQO, which is a government agency mandated to advise the Government of Ontario on how to ensure high-quality care in the province, as well as to monitor progress and report on it to the public. In its early years, HQO used a nine-element definition of quality care that effectively matched the list provided in goal 2 above, with the one key difference being that 'appropriate' was changed to 'appropriately resourced.'(4) More recently, however, it has used a 'streamlined operational definition of quality' from the Institute of Medicine, which defines six aims of quality care:
1) safe;
2) effective;
3) patient-centred;
4) timely;

5) efficient; and
6) equitable.(4)

The fifth aim aligns with the third dimension of 'triple aim' (keeping per capita costs manageable) while the rest align with the first dimension (improving the patient experience of care) as we have conceived it here.

The framework adopted by HQO to assess quality in the health system – known as the Common Quality Agenda – contains several elements that align closely with the 'triple aim.'(6) For instance, HQO's approach to monitoring home and community care and specialty (specifically hospital) care (which involves surveys of patients about their satisfaction with services), as well as its measures of access to and timeliness of care, are related to the first dimension of the 'triple aim' (patient experience). The health of Ontarians is also measured in terms of health risk factors (e.g., smoking, physical inactivity, obesity, and inadequate fruit and vegetable intake), broad health outcomes (e.g., life expectancy, infant mortality, self-reported health status, and potentially avoidable deaths), and health outcomes specific to a sector, set of conditions or population (e.g., suicide rates), all of which align with the second dimension of the 'triple aim' (improving population health). The Common Quality Agenda also measures per capita system spending, which relates to the third dimension of the 'triple aim' (keeping per capita costs manageable).

Our third example involves the goals that were introduced through 'Patients first: A proposal to strengthen patient-centred care in Ontario,' which has since been operationalized in the *Patients First Act, 2016.* The proposal provides the most current vision for the health system, and will have broad influence across many sectors for years to come (see Chapter 10 for more details on this and other recent reforms).(7) The goals outlined in the proposal include:
1) improve access (provide faster access to the right care);
2) connect services (deliver better coordinated and integrated care in the community, closer to home);
3) support people and patients (provide the education, information and transparency Ontarians need to make the right decisions about their health); and
4) protect the universal public health system (make decisions based on value and quality to sustain the system for generations to come).

The most explicit connections between the proposal's goals and the 'triple aim' can be found in the first three of the goals stated above, which align with the 'triple aim' dimension of patient experience, while the last goal aligns with the first and third 'triple aim' dimensions (patient experience and per capita costs). Additionally, the proposal clearly states that, by focusing on these goals, health outcomes can be improved (the second 'triple aim' dimension) and efficiencies realized (the third 'triple aim' dimension), while a number of other health-system strengthening approaches (e.g., modernizing delivery) are also positioned as ways to achieve facets of the 'triple aim.'

In sum, this broad overview of the ways in which recently established health-system goals align with the 'triple aim' framework provides a clear indication that, like many other jurisdictions around the world, policymakers in the province want to improve the patient experience of care, improve population health, and keep per capita costs manageable.

Assessment and reporting

In the sections that follow, we draw on formal evaluations of the health system to describe how well the system is performing in terms of achieving the 'triple aim.' Given the large number of organizations in the province engaged in collecting and reporting indicators (see Table 4.12), it was a challenge to piece together all of the relevant formal evaluations. In an attempt to be as systematic and transparent as possible, we used searches of Ontario's health-system documents in Health Systems Evidence (www.healthsystemsevidence.org), as well as frequent screenings of email listservs and websites (e.g., HQO), to find Ontario-focused health-system evaluations. We prioritized recent sources when possible (i.e., from the last two years), as well as sources with a clear intention to evaluate health-system performance.

The two sources of assessments we most consistently drew from were those published by HQO (particularly its annual 'Measuring up' reports and its one-off publications focused on specific sectors, conditions and treatments) and the provincial auditor general (particularly the annual reports). We also found that, while the Commonwealth Fund's International Health Policy Survey results are consistently published and often the centre of media attention because they provide international comparisons of health-system performance, they were frequently covered by other reports we drew from – particularly HQO's 'Measuring up' series. As such, we did not place additional emphasis on publications from the Commonwealth Fund when the results relevant to Ontario were published elsewhere.

Other sources of evaluations we drew on for this chapter include the Cancer Quality Council of Ontario (most notably the Cancer System Quality Index) and the Institute for Clinical Evaluative Sciences (most notably its one-off reports and stroke report-card series), as well as one-off reports from the Canadian Cancer Society, the Conference Board of Canada, and the Institute for Competitiveness & Prosperity.

Three important observations were made during the process of identifying and reading through evaluations of the health system. First, when limited to documents in the public domain, it is difficult to determine whether all of the potentially relevant information has been identified. There are almost certainly evaluations addressing some of the dimensions of the 'triple aim' that are only available to internal staff at places like the Ministry of Health and Long-Term Care.

The second major observation is that there are imbalances in the coverage of the publicly available evaluations of the health system. Certain 'triple aim' dimensions are not routinely featured, either implicitly or explicitly. For example, we found few evaluations focused on financial protection and equity within the 'keeping per capita costs manageable' dimension of the 'triple aim.' There are also sectors for which few formal assessments exist, and the few that do exist often do not focus on any of the 'triple aim' goals (particularly rehabilitation care and public health). Within sectors, there also are imbalances in terms of which conditions are focused on by publicly available evaluations. For example, in the specialty care sector, while there are numerous reports with an evaluative component published each year, in addition to a monitoring and reporting framework for cancer care (e.g., through the Cancer System Quality Index), the same cannot be said for most other conditions (see Chapter 7 for an overview of these select conditions). There are also few evaluations for select treatments such as dental services (covered in Chapter 8) or for specific populations of interest, such as Indigenous peoples (covered in Chapter 9).

The third major observation emerged as the result of having to extract information retrospectively from formal evaluations published by other stakeholders: evaluations of the health system seldom present indicators in consistent or comparable ways. Related to this is the fact that a number of reports and evaluations are prepared as a 'one-off' initiative, with insights that can only be taken as a performance snapshot. As such, it is not always possible to provide insights about trends in health-system performance across sectors or over time, and hence to draw conclusions about relative performance or changes over time.

Improving the patient experience of care

Improving the patient experience of care – the first dimension of the 'triple aim' – is an important aspiration for the health system, as evidenced by the number of stated goals that align with this dimension (Table 11.1). In this section, we provide brief overviews of what has been learned in each sector about three key aspects of this 'triple aim' dimension: 1) access to care; 2) care experience; and 3) transparency and accountability. In the corresponding tables, points are preceded by a symbol indicating whether the assessments we drew from framed them as positive (✓) or negative (✗) observations.

Access to care

Overall, existing assessments of access to care suggest that performance is mixed (Table 11.2). While improvements have been noted in all sectors, inequities continue to exist, and in most sectors access to care depends on where a person lives. Furthermore, the maldistribution of healthcare providers in favour of urban areas over rural areas continues to be highlighted, particularly for physicians, while factors such as socio-economic status and

Table 11.2: Access to care

Summary of findings related to access to care
Cross-sectoral
✗ The maldistribution of physicians has created access challenges for some citizens, particularly those living in rural areas   • As of 2011, 95% of physicians practised in urban areas and 5% practised in rural areas, despite the fact that 14% of Ontarians live in rural areas (8)

Continued on next page

Home and community care

✓ Among patients referred to a Community Care Access Centre (CCAC) by their family physician, 90% receive their first in-home service within 28 days (8)

✓ From 2007 to 2015, Local Health Integration Network (LHIN) performance measurements showed that there were improvements in wait times for CCAC-funded in-home services (8)

✓ In 2013-14, 94% of home-care patients received nursing services within five days (which was the same as reported in 2012-13) (9)

✗ There are regional variations in access to personal support services, and whether Ontarians in need receive the right amount of support depends on where they live in the province
   • Patients referred to a CCAC by their family physician receive their first in-home visit in as short as 12 days in some regions, and as long as 82 days in others (8)

✗ There is variation across regions with respect to the percentage of home-care patients who receive nursing services within five days, ranging from 90% in the North West CCAC region to 97% in the Central West CCAC region (9)

✗ Care coordinators in CCACs do not assess and/or reassess client needs in a timely way, causing delays in access to the most appropriate level of care needed (8)
   • In 2015, 65% of initial home care assessments and 32% of reassessments for chronic and complex clients were not conducted within the required time frame
   • The average time between referral and initial contact assessments was six to eight days (rather than the Ministry of Health and Long-Term Care, or MOHLTC, standard of three days), and 25 to 28 days between initial assessment and home-care assessment (rather than the MOHLTC standard of seven to 14 days) in regions audited in 2014

✗ Access to respite care for caregivers varies across regions, and services are only provided within the hours allocated to the primary client (8)

Primary care

✓ From January 2013 to October 2014, there was an increase in the number of patients enrolled in the 25 Nurse Practitioner-led Clinics established to provide access to prim-ary care in underserved communities, from 33,000 to 48,544 (8)

✓ From 2009 to 2012, Family Health Teams (which serve close to 25% of Ontarians) improved access to most health services, with wait times reduced through the establishment of interprofessional primary-care teams, telephone support and after-hours coverage
   • e.g., 82% of patients reported they definitely or probably would have no difficulty getting care when they needed it, and that they definitely or probably could have got an appointment the same day when they became ill (15)

✗ While 94% of Ontarians have a primary-care provider, only half can get a timely appointment when they are sick, and this varies greatly by region
   • Only 44% of adults are able to see their primary-care provider on the same day or next day when they are sick
   • The proportion of people who report being able to get a same- or next-day appointment for primary care when they are sick varies from 28% in the North West LHIN to 57% in the Central West LHIN (9)

✗ 56% of citizens report difficulty accessing care after hours (9)

Continued on next page

Specialty care

✓ From 2009-10 to 2013-14, the median 'maximum time' patients spent in the emergency department decreased from five (4.7) hours to four hours for low-acuity patients, and from 12 hours to 10 hours for high-acuity patients (9)

✓ From 2008-09 to 2014-15, the percentage of urgent hip replacements completed within the recommended maximum wait time of 42 days increased from 62% to 67%, and the percentage of semi-urgent hip replacements completed within the recommended maximum wait time of 84 days increased from 67% to 72% (9)

✓ From 2008-09 to 2014-15, the percentage of urgent knee replacements completed within the recommended maximum wait time of 42 days increased from 60% to 67%, and the percentage of semi-urgent knee replacements completed within the recommended maximum wait time of 84 days increased from 63% to 73% (9)

✓ The percentage of urgent cardiac procedures completed within access targets from 2009-10 to 2014-15 remained high or improved
   • The percentage of those receiving percutaneous coronary intervention within the recommended seven days stayed at 95%
   • The percentage of those receiving diagnostic cardiac catheterization within the recommended seven days improved from 94% to 95%
   • The percentage of those receiving coronary artery bypass graft surgery within the recommended 14 days improved from 97% to 99% (9)

✗ Between 2012 to 2014, only 60% of the 50 municipalities met the provincial target of an ambulance responding to 90% of emergency calls within 15 minutes (8)

✗ Emergency response-time standards vary significantly across the province, as each municipality sets its own standards for urgent cases that are not choking or cardiac arrest
   • e.g., some rural municipalities establish a target of 9% of responses within eight minutes, while other municipalities establish a target of 85% within eight minutes (8)

✗ There are variations across LHINs with respect to how long patients wait for hip- and knee-replacement surgeries (8)
   • In 2015, the best-performing LHIN in the Toronto area provided hip-replacement surgeries within the targeted 182 days for 97% of patients, whereas this target was only met for 49% of patients in the province's lowest-performing LHIN
   • In 2015, the best-performing LHIN achieved the 182-day target for knee replacements for 95% of its patients, and the worst-performing LHIN met this target for only 44% of patients

✗ Hospital use among Ontarians with low family income was 171% higher than those classified as high family income, with less than half of this attributable to variations in the extent to which they engaged in unhealthy behaviours (31 bed-days in hospital for adults in lower socio-economic groups compared to 13 days for those in higher groups) (10)

Rehabilitation care

✗ There is variation across LHINs in the supply of regular inpatient rehabilitation beds, which may result in inequitable access to rehabilitation services across the province
   • The number of beds ranges from 57 per 100,000 people in the Toronto Central LHIN, to only six per 100,000 in the Central West LHIN (with a provincial average of 18 per 100,000) (8)

✗ Patients who are ready to be discharged from an acute-care bed into a rehabilitation bed may not have timely access to the right care, given 25% of the 2,300 alternate-level-of-care patients waiting in acute-care hospital beds in 2014 were waiting for a regular rehabilitation or restorative rehabilitation bed (8)

Continued on next page

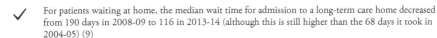

Long-term care

✓ For patients waiting at home, the median wait time for admission to a long-term care home decreased from 190 days in 2008-09 to 116 in 2013-14 (although this is still higher than the 68 days it took in 2004-05) (9)

✗ For patients waiting in hospital, the median wait time for admission to a long-term care home increased from 18 days in 2004-05 to 69 days in 2013-14 (although fewer people are now applying from hospitals given additional home support programs),(9) and wait times for long-term care vary substantially across the province
  • In 2013-14, the median wait for admission from home was 243 days in the Toronto Central LHIN, and 50 days in the North East LHIN
  • In 2013-14, the median wait for admission from hospital was 197 days in the Mississauga Halton LHIN and 34 days in the South West LHIN (9)

✗ Timely access to long-term care homes depends on clients' ability to pay, with clients who are able to pay for private or semi-private rooms in a long-term care home getting access to beds more quickly, given such beds constitute up to 60% of available beds in homes, but are only applied for by 40% of people who need a bed (14)

Public health

— No assessments identified

Select conditions

✗ From 2008-09 to 2014-15, the percentage of cancer surgeries completed within the target time improved for all priority levels
  • the percentage of patients who required and received surgery within 14 days increased from 54% to 78%
  • the percentage of patients who required and received surgery within 28 days increased from 68% to 83%
  • the percentage of patients getting surgery within the 84-day maximum recommended wait increased from 88% to 95% (9)

✗ There is significant variation across the regions in the province in terms of wait times from cancer diagnosis to treatment, suggesting much room for improvement
  • e.g., 48% of lymphoma patients started chemotherapy within 30 days following diagnosis from 2010 to 2013, although this was as high as 61% in some LHINs, and as low as 37% in others (11)

✗ Access to palliative-care beds differs by region, as there are large discrepancies in the total number (both in hospital and in publicly funded hospices) across LHINs (8)
  • While one LHIN audited in 2014 had 5.9 beds per 100,000 Ontarians, another had triple the amount (18.5 per 100,000), which could not be fully explained by population characteristics or increased demand

Select treatments

— No assessments identified

Select populations

— No assessments identified

Sources: 8-11; 15

ethnicity still influence which patients have access to the services they need.

In home and community care, wait times for CCAC-funded in-home services have been decreasing, but access to care varies significantly across Local Health Integration Networks (LHINs): wait times for a first in-home visit can differ by as much as 70 days between the best- and worst-performing regions.(8) Variations also exist across regions with respect to how long it takes to get nursing services, the amount of time it takes care coordinators to undertake assessments (and reassessments) for service eligibility, and whether caregivers have access to respite care.(8; 9)

In primary care, there have been improvements in access to interprofessional, team-based care as a result of the introduction and scale-up of new models of delivery that emphasize patient enrolment (e.g., Family Health Teams and Nurse Practitioner-led Clinics). However, despite 94% of Ontarians reporting that they have access to a primary-care provider (which is above the Canadian average, but lower than many other countries), less-than half report being able to get a same- or next-day appointment when sick, and access to after-hours care is still difficult for many Ontarians.(9) Furthermore, it is clear that same- or next-day access varies across LHINs.(9)

In the specialty care sector, the story is much the same, with improvements being realized, but not equally across the province. For example, the total time spent in emergency departments per visit has been decreasing since 2009, and wait times for urgent hip replacements, knee replacements and cardiac procedures (which are areas that were prioritized in the National Wait Times Initiative and that benefited from substantial investments) have all been improving, but this progress varies significantly across regions. Variation still exists in wait times for emergency services, wait times for hip- and knee-replacement surgeries, and time from cancer diagnosis to treatment. Furthermore, access to surgical care has also been noted as a challenge for certain populations. In particular, there is some evidence to suggest that those with lower incomes have fewer referrals to surgery, despite the fact that those with low family incomes are hospitalized more (those with a low income have a 171% higher rate of hospital use than those classified as high income). While this holds true in many instances, comparisons within some regions (e.g., the Toronto Central LHIN) have also found that both low-income and high-income earners use hospital services more than middle-income earners.(10)

Few assessments that were identified focused on rehabilitation care, although those that did (e.g., the auditor general's annual report from 2015) identified challenges in the sector with respect to access that were similar to those identified for other sectors. For instance, significant variation across LHINs was noted in terms of the number of (and access to) inpatient rehabilitation beds, with the number ranging from as many as 57 per 100,000 in the Toronto Central LHIN, to six per 100,000 in the Central West LHIN. Additionally, timely access to rehabilitation care from acute-care hospital beds has been highlighted as a major challenge.(8)

In the long-term care sector, reductions in wait times suggest that access to long-term care is improving for individuals waiting at home for admission (or placement, as it is commonly called in the sector). However, there are also many challenges that still exist: wait times have increased for those waiting for long-term care home admissions while in hospital, wait times vary across LHINs, and access may depend on individuals' ability to pay for care.

For select conditions, and particularly for cancer care, while wait times are improving for surgeries, there is significant variation across regions.(11) Additionally, there are large variations across regions with respect to the availability of palliative-care beds.(8)

No health-system assessments that focused on access to public health services (e.g., community-based health promotion/disease prevention programs) were identified, nor were any identified in relation to select treatments (e.g., dental services) or populations (e.g., Indigenous peoples).

Patient experience

As Table 11.3 shows, citizen surveys and a number of other measures related to the patient experience (e.g., getting the right care in the right place at the right time), suggest the health system is performing relatively well despite the need for improvement in some areas within each sector.

In home and community care, the vast majority (90%) of patients across the province are satisfied with the services they receive, although care

Table 11.3: Care experience

Summary of findings related to the care experience

Home and community care

✓ More than 90% of patients surveyed report having a positive experience with their home care, and satisfaction remains high across regions despite small variations (from 91% in the Mississauga Halton, Central and Central West Local Health Integration Networks, or LHINs, to 94% in the South West and South East LHINs) (9)

✗ The percentage of distressed caregivers increased from 16% in 2009-10 to 33% in 2013-14 (9)

✗ Care coordinators working in Community Care Access Centres (CCACs) experience challenges in appropriately refering clients to needed services, given a lack of centralized information-sharing among service providers (8)

Primary care

✓ 86% of adults in 2014 said their provider 'always or often involves them in decisions about their health-care' (9)

✓ 90% of family physicians say they always or often receive a report back from specialists with all relevant health information about their patients, which is higher than the Canadian average (85%) and many other Organisation for Economic Cooperation and Development (OECD) countries (although the proportion is 94% and 96% in Switzerland and France, respectively) (12)

✓ 71% of family physicians say they always or often receive a notification from the hospital when their patient is discharged (which is higher than the Canadian average of 65%, and in the middle when compared to other OECD countries) (12)

✗ Internationally, Ontario has one of the lowest reported percentages of physicians communicating with home and community services, with only 29% saying that they, or other personnel in their practice, routinely communicate with their patient's case manager or home care provider about the patient's needs and services to be provided (12)
  • This is lower than the Canadian average (32%) and, while it is higher than Quebec (22%), it is much lower than many other provinces (e.g., family physicians in Saskatchewan reported they communicated 62% of the time, New Brunswick 47% of the time, and Nova Scotia and Manitoba both reported communicating 39% of the time)

Specialty care

✓ 74% of inpatients surveyed would 'definitely recommend to family and friends the hospital where they received care' (9)

✓ Hospital admissions for conditions that can be managed outside of hospital (ambulatory-care sensitive conditions) decreased by one third from 2003-04 to 2013-14, from 341 per 100,000 people to 233 per 100,000 people (9)

✓ Progress continued to be made from 2013-14 to 2014-15 in a number of domains related to stroke care, including a reduction in the proportion of alternate-level-of-care days to total length of stay from just over 28% to 26% (13)

✗ From 2007 to 2015, the percentage of patients remaining in a hospital bed despite no longer needing the type of resources and services provided there because no appropriate care settings are available (i.e., alternate-level-of-care days) increased (8)

Continued on next page

Specialty care – continued

 While low-acuity emergency department visits declined slightly, high-acuity emergency department visits increased from 2,914,944 in 2009-10 to 3,571,327 in 2013-14, which accounted for nearly 66% of all emergency department visits, indicating an increase in the number of patients requiring more urgent care (9)

✗ The health system performs worse on some measures of system integration and continuity of care compared to other countries, with 10% of respondents surveyed in the province indicating that their specialist physician did not have test results or basic information about the reason for their appointment (compared to 3-5% in other countries) (21)

Rehabilitation care

 Progress (or the maintenance of good performance) continues to be made in a number of domains related to stroke rehabilitation care, and from 2013-14 to 2014-15 (13)
- the median number of days between stroke onset and admission to inpatient rehabilitation remains at nine
- the proportion of inpatient stroke rehabilitation patients achieving the active-length-of-stay target has increased from 53% to 60%
- the mean number of CCAC visits provided to stroke patients on discharge from inpatient acute care or inpatient rehabilitation rose from six to 7.3
- the proportion of patients admitted to inpatient rehabilitation with severe strokes increased from 38% to 41%

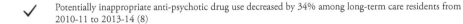

Long-term care

✓ The daily use of physical restraints in long-term care homes decreased from 16% in 2010-11 to 7% in 2014-15, which was better than B.C. and Alberta (11% and 9%, respectively) (9)

✓ Potentially inappropriate anti-psychotic drug use decreased by 34% among long-term care residents from 2010-11 to 2013-14 (8)

✗ The rates of daily physical restraint use vary substantially across the province, with a low of 2.7% in the Toronto Central LHIN to a high of 14.4% in the North West LHIN (9)

Public health

— No assessments identified

Select conditions

 From 2010 to 2013, 57% of stage III colon cancer patients aged 65 and older were treated with guide-line-recommended chemotherapy (although for patients 80 and older, these rates were lower) (11)

✓ More than three quarters (78%) of people who attended a 'Diagnostic Assessment Program' to improve care coordination during the diagnostic phase of the cancer journey rated their care as 'excellent', while 76% and 78% of patients surveyed about cancer education at their regional cancer centre stated that they received sufficient information to help them understand their cancer and to manage their care, respectively (11)

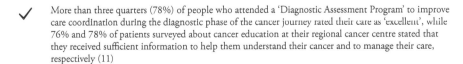 Average patient-satisfaction scores for outpatient care have remained high over the last three years for 'respect for patient preferences' (81% reported being satisfied in both 2013-14 and 2015-16) and for 'physical comfort' (79% reported being satisfied in both 2013-14 and 2015-16), and there have been slight improvements in satisfaction with 'coordination and continuity of care' (increased from 69% in 2013-14 to 71% in 2015-16) (11)

Continued on next page

Select conditions – continued

X   Approximately 25% of patients who undergo lung, prostate and colorectal surgery have an unplanned hospital visit following surgery (11)

X   The rate of emergency-department visits for cancer patients in the last two weeks of life is 40%, indicating lack of timely advanced care planning, lack of community and after-hours care, and lack of appropriate end-of-life supports (11)

X   Since 2013-14, satisfaction with 'emotional support' in outpatient cancer care has remained the lowest of all aspects of care rated, with just over half of patients reporting being satisfied (53% in 2013-14 and 55% in 2015-16) (11)

X   There is variation in patient experience and satisfaction across regional cancer centres, with the highest satisfaction with three components of care (communication, self-management and support for shared decision-making) being 78% and the lowest 59% (11)

Select treatments

—   No assessments identified

Select populations

—   No assessments identified

Sources: 8; 9; 11-13; 21

coordination remains sub-optimal and there is an increasing number of caregivers who are distressed.(9)

In primary care, satisfaction with services is also high, with most patients (86%) reporting that they feel involved in decisions about their care, and the number of family physicians in Ontario who report receiving adequate information about their patients from other sectors (e.g., specialty care) is greater than the Canadian average and comparable to or higher than other Organisation for Economic Cooperation and Development countries.(9; 12) However, there also appears to be room for improvement in Ontario in ensuring primary-care services are coordinated with home and community care services, based on low rates of communication between providers in the two sectors.(12)

In the specialty care sector, three quarters of inpatients are satisfied with their hospital services, while a growing number of people are being treated in more comfortable settings outside of the hospital when appropriate.(9) While these are positive developments, health-system leaders continue to grapple with increasing numbers of 'alternate-level-of-care' days (when a patient remains in a hospital bed, despite no longer needing the type of resources and services provided there, because no appropriate care settings are available), as well as high and growing rates of emergency department visits and hospital readmissions among a number of patient groups (e.g., high-acuity patients).(8; 9) This is in addition to a number of integration challenges.

While few assessments were identified that focused on care experience in the rehabilitation sector, those that were identified indicated that there have been improvements in a number of domains related to stroke rehabilitation (e.g., days between stroke onset and admission to rehabilitation, length-of-stay targets, and the number of home and community care visits after discharge).(13) Similarly, while few sources were identified that captured care experience in long-term care explicitly, the use of daily physical restraints and potentially inappropriate anti-psychotic drugs in long-term care homes have declined. This could be an indication that the patient experience is improving in this sector, although variations across LHINs also indicate that this is not the case for all long-term care home residents in the province.(8; 9)

For select conditions, results are also mixed. For instance, assessments showed that the majority of cancer patients are satisfied with various aspects of their care (e.g., diagnostic-assessment programs, patient education, and outpatient services), and that they are increasingly being treated with guideline-recommended chemotherapy.(11) However, results also show that emotional support continues to be the lowest-rated aspect of outpatient services.(11) Furthermore, there are regional variations in patient satisfaction with outpatient services, and there is still a significant proportion who are making unplanned visits to hospital after surgery and are accessing emergency departments instead of appropriate community and after-hours care at the end of life.(11)

No assessments that directly or indirectly focused on citizens' experience with public health services were identified, nor were any identified that focused on select treatments or populations.

Transparency and accountability

There were no assessments identified in which specific measures were used to evaluate progress in the health system within the domains of transparency and accountability (Table 11.4). As such, it is not possible to present findings about how well the system performs in these domains per se. However, a number of auditor general reports were identified that did provide insights from select sectors (primary care and rehabilitation excluded), about how each performs in this domain through specific critiques of system monitoring, oversight and compliance – although the majority of these sources pointed to challenges, rather than progress. For example, the lack of transparency around how the Ministry of Health and Long-Term Care measures LHIN performance, and the lack of consistent enforcement of mechanisms established to hold each of these regional planning units accountable, were highlighted in the 2015 auditor general's report as areas that need improvement.(8)

Table 11.4: Transparency and accountability

Summary of findings related to transparency and accountability
Cross-sectoral
X In overseeing the function of Local Health Integration Networks (LHINs), the Ministry of Health and Long-Term Care (MOHLTC) has not defined what constitutes a 'fully integrated health system,' when it should be achieved, or how to measure how LHINs are performing as planners, funders and system integrators (8)   • The MOHLTC has not set timelines for when all LHINs are expected to meet their long-term performance targets, and as of 2015 only four of the 11 provincial targets were met   • Little action is taken to hold LHINs accountable when low performance continues year after year with respect to measured performance indicators, and the MOHLTC responds differently to different LHINs when challenges are faced (e.g., in some instances performance targets were reduced, and in others they were tightened or maintained)
X No common complaint-management process has been established across LHINs, and there are no processes to ensure patient complaints are appropriately resolved   • At least three LHINs did not track complaints at all (or only partially tracked them) as of 2014 (8)
Home and community care
X LHINs do not consistently monitor the quality of health services provided, and performance information submitted by health-service providers is not verified
X Non-performing health-service providers are not consistently dealt with in accordance with guidelines established by the MOHLTC (8)
X Community Care Access Centres (CCACs) are not providing adequate oversight of contracted services, and do not consistently ensure service providers are complying with contract requirements (8)   • Missed visits and failures to provide needed services on time are not routinely or accurately reported

Continued on next page

Home and community care – continued

X   Some of the costs reported by CCACs as 'direct patient care' do not involve actual interactions with patients (e.g., providers' overhead and profit) (18)
- On average 72% of total expenditures involve direct patient care that includes interactions with patients

Primary care

X   There is an expectation that interprofessional primary-care teams submit annual Quality Improvement Plans to Health Quality Ontario,(16) but the extent to which Family Health Teams in Ontario engage in quality-improvement planning and standardized reporting varies significantly across the province (15)

Specialty care

X   As of March 2012, 12% of Independent Health Facilities have not been assessed by the College of Physicians and Surgeons of Ontario within the past five years, to help ensure that diagnostic images are being read correctly by the physicians working there (14)

X   As of March 2012, 60% of facilities providing X-ray services had not been inspected as frequently as required to ensure safety of the machines (14)

Rehabilitation care

—   No assessments identified

Long-term care

✓   The *Long-Term Care Homes Act, 2007* has made it a requirement that every long-term care home has an unannounced inspection at least once per year (although not all inspections have to be comprehensive) (8)
- In 2013 the MOHLTC committed to ensuring that each long-term care home be subject to a comprehensive inspection each year, and by December 2014 the commitment had largely been met, with 95% of long-term care homes in the province having been subject to a comprehensive assessment that year (the remaining 5% were completed by January 2015)

X   The MOHLTC does not provide clear guidance on how much time long-term care homes should be given to comply with orders, and practice varies across regions (8)
- In 2014, homes in one region were given an average 34 days to comply with orders, while inspectors in another region gave an average of 77 days to comply

X   There are no processes in place for the MOHLTC to monitor compliance with orders requiring follow-up, which may place residents at risk (8)
- Approximately two thirds of compliance orders due in 2014 had not been followed up within 30 days, and it took an average of two months for the MOHLTC to perform a follow-up inspection
- Non-compliance remains high among homes in certain regions (with 40% non-compliance reported among homes in one region in 2014)
- Timeliness of the inspection process varies across regions, with some regions experiencing significant delays

X   The backlog of complaints and critical incidents that required MOHLTC follow-up more than doubled from December 2013 to March 2015, from 1,300 to 2,800 (8)
- Nearly 40% of high-risk and critical complaints took longer than three days to inspect, and a quarter of these took between one and nine months
- Sixty per cent of medium-risk cases that should have taken 30 days took 62 days to inspect

Continued on next page

Long term care – continued

X   In 2014 there were a total of 9,520 enforcement actions taken by the MOHLTC against long-term care homes, including:
- 4,030 written notifications;
- 4,450 voluntary plans of correction collected from homes; and
- 1,040 compliance orders (8)

Public health

X   There is minimal coordination among, and oversight of, the 36 municipally governed local public health agencies with respect to the delivery of the immunization program in the province, with each acting independently and with no accountability to the Chief Medical Officer of Health (14)

Select conditions

—   No assessments identified

Select treatments

—   No assessments identified

Select populations

—   No assessments identified

Sources: 8; 14-16; 18

In home and community care, a lack of consistent oversight of Community Care Access Centres (CCACs) by LHINs, and of service providers by both LHINs and CCACs, in addition to inconsistent use of accountability measures, were highlighted in the sector.(8) In specialty care, the oversight of physicians working in Independent Health Facilities and of the facilities themselves was identified as a challenge.(14)

The only strongly positive assessment made by the auditor general was for the long-term care sector, where efforts by the Ministry of Health and Long-Term Care to inspect all long-term care homes in the province annually have been quite successful, achieving a 95% inspection rate in the first year of the initiative.(8) However, like the other sectors, there are also challenges in ensuring non-performers are held accountable, including:
- a lack of clarity around timelines for compliance with ministry orders following inspections;
- no processes to monitor compliance with orders (e.g., no follow-up and variation in inspection timelines);
- a growing backlog of complaints and critical incidents requiring ministry follow-up; and
- a high number of enforcement actions on the books.(8)

In public health, the major challenge that was noted relates to a lack of coordination between municipally governed local public health agencies, as well as a lack of oversight of the province's immunization programs.(14) No assessments were identified that addressed transparency and accountability in primary care – although there are indications that despite expectations that interprofessional care teams in primary care submit annual Quality Improvement Plans, engagement in quality improvement and standardized reporting varies significantly across established Family Health Teams in the province (15; 16) – and no assessments were identified for rehabilitation care or for select conditions, treatments or populations.

Improving population health

Improving population health is the second dimension of the 'triple aim,' and is central to some health-system goals. Within this objective, addressing risk factors for poor health is also important, and in many health systems, including Ontario's, these are the focus of many assessments. That said, many measures of population health are affected by factors beyond the control of the health system (e.g., housing, income and social supports), in which case they may be poor measures of health-system performance per se. Also, interpreting some of these measures as indicators of either good or poor performance can be a challenge: rising cancer cases may be the result of better detection (which could be interpreted as good performance), but may also be the result of inadequate efforts to support lifestyle and other changes that raise the risk of cancer (which could be interpreted as poor performance). In this section, we highlight some of the key themes that can be drawn from identified assessments of population health outcomes and risk factors for poor health, with additional detail provided in Table 11.5. Points are again presented in each table depending on whether the assessments we drew from framed them as positive (✓) or negative (✗) observations.

Overall, assessments of health outcomes paint a generally positive picture of health. Life expectancy has risen over the last decade, and two thirds of Ontarians say they are in very good or excellent health.(9) People are dying less frequently from stroke, and five-year cancer survival ratios (i.e., comparing survival between cancer patients and members of the general

Table 11.5: Population health outcomes

Summary of findings related to population health outcomes

Health outcomes

✓ Life expectancy rose from 80.5 years in 2003-05 to 81.5 years in 2007-09 (9)

✓ Nearly 66% of Ontarians say their health is 'excellent or very good' (9)

✓ Ontario's rate of potentially avoidable deaths (183 per 100,000 people) is the second lowest in Canada (9)

✓ Risk-adjusted stroke mortality rates dropped from 11.7 to 10.6 per 100 patients from 2013-14 to 2014-15 (13)

✗ Cancer survival ratios are among the highest in the world, and from 2005 to 2009, five-year relative survival ratios for the most common cancers were either the highest in the world (e.g., 65% for colon cancer and 68% for rectal cancer), or similar to the jurisdictions with the highest rates in the world (e.g., 86% for female breast cancer compared to 89% in the U.S., and 95% for prostate cancer, compared to 97% in the U.S.) (11)

✗ While the rate of potentially avoidable deaths in Ontario (163 per 100,000) is lower than the Canadian average (171 per 100,000), it varies significantly across the province (9)
  • The highest rate is 258 per 100,000 people (North West Local Health Integration Network, or LHIN) and the lowest rate is 114 (Central LHIN)

✗ The annual number of new cancer cases has more than doubled since 1984, with roughly 85,600 new cases estimated to be diagnosed in 2016 (11)

✗ In 2012, mortality rates for the most common cancers were higher (and in some cases much higher) than the best performing jurisdictions internationally (11)

✗ From 2010-11 to 2013-14, patient outcomes in long-term care homes worsened (8)
  • There was a 7% increase in the number of residents who experienced worsened pressure ulcers
  • There was a 6% decrease in the number of residents experiencing improved physical functioning, and a 5% increase in the number experiencing worsened physical functioning
  • Number of falls and worsened depressive mood both increased by 2% among long-term care home residents

Risk factors for poor health

✓ Among the provinces, Ontario has the second-lowest smoking rate (18%), and this decreased by 3% from 2007 to 2013 (9)

✓ The rate of obesity in Ontario (17%) is among the lowest in Canada, although it slightly increased (by 0.5%) between 2007 and 2013 (9)

✓ Fruit and vegetable intake has slightly increased, from 58% in 2007 to 61% in 2013 (9)

✗ While physical inactivity declined from 50% to 45% from 2007 to 2013, this is higher than the Canadian average of 44% (9)

✗ Among Ontarians aged 65 and older, there was a reduction in immunization rates from 75% in 2007 to 71% in 2012 (22)

Continued on next page

Risk factors for poor health – continued

 Early-childhood immunization rates have fallen below federal government targets, and in most cases below the level of immunization required to prevent the transmission of disease (14)
- Diphtheria has dropped to 75% coverage (99% target), measles and mumps immunization coverage have both fallen to 88% (99% target), and polio has fallen to 74% (99% target)

Sources: 8; 9; 11; 13; 14; 22

population) are among the best in the world for the most common cancers (e.g., breast, colon, prostate and rectal cancers).(11; 13)

However, there are still challenges that have been highlighted. For instance, while the average Ontarian is living longer than ever before, potentially avoidable deaths are much higher in some regions than others. The number of new cancer cases continues to increase, and while five-year survival ratios are some of the best internationally, we cannot say the same for cancer mortality rates (i.e., the number of deaths due to cancer).(11) Additionally, the health of residents of long-term care homes appears to be getting worse (although this could be because, with Ontarians being cared for at home longer than in the past, long-term care residents are older and have more complex health conditions), and there has been an increase in depressive moods, pressure ulcers and falls, and a decrease in physical functioning.(8; 9)

There is a lot to be positive about in terms of risk factors for poor health in Ontario. Smoking and obesity rates are among the lowest in the country, and more Ontarians are incorporating fruit and vegetables in their diets.(9) However, Ontarians are less physically active than the average Canadian, and immunization rates among children and the elderly continue to decline, reducing the ability of Ontario's immunization program to protect citizens against a range of communicable diseases.(8; 9)

Keeping per capita costs manageable

The third dimension of the 'triple aim' focuses on keeping the amount of money spent per person on the health system (i.e., per capita costs) manageable. In this section, we consider what publicly available assessments tell us about how the health system is performing in this domain, and when information was available we also sought to highlight findings for two related dimensions:

1) whether the money spent on healthcare is being used efficiently (i.e., maximizing the outcomes we are getting for every dollar spent); and
2) whether Ontarians are financially protected (i.e., what out-of-pocket costs they face), and whether this protection is equitably distributed.

In this section, the intention is not to review in detail how the health system is financed and how this money is spent, which is covered in detail in Chapter 3. Rather, we aim to provide high-level 'snapshots' of what formal evaluations tell us about performance in these domains. Readers are encouraged to review Chapter 3 for additional details not covered here. As in previous sections, points are presented in each table depending on whether the assessments we drew from framed them as positive (✓) or negative (✗) observations. When it was not clear from an assessment whether an observation was positive or negative, we used a chevron (❯).

Per capita spending and efficiency

Overall, the most consistent message related to per capita spending is that, like most other jurisdictions in Canada and internationally, the amount spent on healthcare for each individual citizen continues to increase, and this includes both public spending (i.e., government) and private spending (i.e., private insurance and out-of-pocket). When compared to the rest of Canada, Ontario has the third lowest per capita expenditure (after Quebec and B.C.), and it spends approximately $450 more per person than Quebec (the province with the lowest per capita expenditure) and $1,000 less per person than Newfoundland and Labrador (the province with the highest per capita expenditure).(9) While there are few assessments of overall health-system efficiency, technical efficiency shortfalls have been noted in the province, particularly as these relate to how technology is leveraged (e.g., use of electronic health records).(17)

Few sector-specific assessments were identified that focus on per capita spending and/or efficiency, although some trends might be gleaned from the results presented in Table 11.6. In home and community care, costs are increasing as more patients with complex health conditions are receiving care outside of hospital settings.(18) In primary care, shifts in how physicians are paid have likely contributed to an increase in spending in that sector.(19) In specialty care, assessments point to mixed results, with efficiency found to be improving in some areas (e.g., radiation treatment

Table 11.6: Efficiency and per capita costs

Summary of findings related to efficiency and per capita costs

Cross-sectoral

> Based on 2012 data, Ontario spends less per capita than the Canadian average, and has the third lowest per capita health expenditure in the country, spending an average of $450 more per person than Quebec (the lowest-spending province) and about $1,000 less than Newfoundland and Labrador (the highest-spending province) (9)
> - Total per capita spending increased from $3,115 per person in 2000, to $4,022 per person in 2012 (9)
> - In the same time period, public per capita spending increased from $2,072 to $2,661, and private per capita spending increased from $1,043 to $1,361

✗ The health system lags in technical efficiency (17)
- The large scale adoption and implementation of information technology has the potential to enhance efficiency as well as increase safety and quality
- eHealth Ontario data (from fiscal year 2012-13) indicate that 66% of family physicians use electronic medical records (EMRs), whereas EMRs are used by 92-98% of physicians in some comparator countries (e.g., the Netherlands, Norway, and the U.K.)

Home and community care

> From 2009-10 to 2013-14 Community Care Access Centre expenses increased by 26% to provide more hours of care to a patient population with more complex chronic health conditions (18)

Primary care

> In 2007-08, physicians participating in alternate funding arrangements were being paid at least 25% more than their fee-for-service counterparts, and by 2009-10 the 66% of family physicians participating in alternate funding arrangements received 76% of the total amount paid to physicians, although no analyses about whether these arrangements are more beneficial have been conducted (19)

✗ In 2009-10 there were approximately 8.6 million patients enrolled in either a Family Health Organization or Family Health Group, and although 1.9 million (22%) did not visit their physician that year, physicians in these practices received $123 million just for having them enrolled (19)
- Nearly half of these enrolled patients visited a different physician, and the Ontario Health Insurance Plan was billed separately for these visits

✗ In 2009-10 nearly 27% of all services provided to patients enrolled in a Family Health Organization were not covered by the capitation arrangements established between the Ministry of Health and Long-Term Care (MOHLTC) and physicians, so an additional $72 million was billed by physicians for providing these services (30% of which were flu shots and Pap-smear technical services that may have been more cost-effective as an inclusion in the routine package of care covered under capitation payments) (19)

Specialty care

✗ From 2004-05 to 2011-12, MOHLTC funding to municipalities for land ambulance services nearly doubled, although the number of patients transported only increased by 18% over the same period (and it was not clear if the increase in funding contributed to faster response times or better patient outcomes). MOHLTC funding increased a further 17% from 2011-12 to 2014-15, with the number of patients only increasing by 6% over the same period (8)

✗ From 2008-09 to 2012-13, the MOHLTC paid $40 million for a 'patient offload nurse' program to reduce ambulance wait times at hospitals, but during this same period ambulance wait times while stationed at hospitals funded under this initiative increased by 20% (8)

Continued on next page

Specialty care – continued

X   From 2006-07 to 2013-14, one in four low-risk births and one in five very low-risk births (i.e., those for which caesarean may be unnecessary) were caesarean deliveries (9)

Rehabilitation care

X   In two sites audited, nearly one third of patients receiving inpatient rehabilitation care in stroke programs might have been better served in less costly outpatient programs if they were available in the province, given they were assessed as having only mild functional impairment (8)

Long-term care

—   No assessments identified

Public health

>   The total operating cost of the immunization program was approximately $250 million in 2013-14 (which was the same as it was the previous year) (14)
- The MOHLTC does not track the information required to determine the total costs of delivering the immunization program, and as a result cannot ensure that the program is being delivered in a cost-effective manner (14)
- There has been no assessment of whether costs incurred by local public health agencies in implementing the immunization program are reasonable, and there are significant variations in the amount of funding received by each unit (ranging from $2 to $16 per person across regions)
- During the 2013-14 flu season, the MOHLTC paid physicians and pharmacists for administering the flu vaccine more than once to the same person nearly 21,000 times

X   Nearly $3 million in vaccines expired before their use (and were wasted) due to over-ordering in 2013-14, and there is no cost to agencies or providers who over-order vaccines (14)

Select conditions

✓   Between 2006 and 2015 the capacity and efficient use of radiation machines has increased along with increases in new capital investment and radiation equipment (11)
- e.g., the number of treated cancer cases increased by 32%, wait times decreased from 14 to seven days, and the number of patients treated per linear accelerator increased from 329 patients per machine in 2013 to 350 patients per machine in 2015

X   In 2014, 90% of imaging tests (4,561) for stage 1 breast cancer patients may have been unnecessary based on clinical practice guidelines (11)

Select treatments

X   Average per capita spending on drugs in Ontario is among the highest in the world, with nearly U.S.$800 dollars spent in total per person, which is lower than the U.S., but higher than Australia, France, Germany, Netherlands, Norway, Sweden and Switzerland (9)

X   The health system has shown an inability to control pharmaceutical spending (17)
- From 2000 to 2011, Canadian Institute for Health Information data indicate that Ontario's per capita drug spending increased at an average annual rate of 3.5%, which is greater than the average annual rate in similar Organisation for Economic Cooperation and Development countries (2.5%)

Select populations

—   No assessments identified

Sources: 8; 9; 11; 14; 17-19

for cancer), and poor efficiency reported in other areas (e.g., emergency services).(8; 9)

In rehabilitation care, efficiency may also be a challenge given many patients are still receiving care in settings that are more resource-intensive than their conditions require, and while the public health sector's immunization costs have remained steady, there are many examples of waste that have been highlighted by the auditor general.(8)

For select conditions, efficiencies in cancer care are being realized in some aspects of care (e.g., use of radiation equipment) while challenges remain in others (e.g., unnecessary imaging tests).(11) With respect to select treatments, assessments suggested that controlling drug spending is an ongoing challenge: Ontario's total per capita spending on drugs is among the highest in the world and, as we describe in Chapter 8, health-system leaders continue to struggle to reign in pharmaceutical spending.(9)

No assessments were identified that focused on efficiency and per capita costs in long-term care or for select populations.

Financial protection and equity in financing

There were very few systematic evaluations of health-system performance in terms of financial protection and equity in financing (Table 11.7). Overall the main messages that can be distilled are similar to those already mentioned several times throughout this book (see Chapter 3, for example): compared to many other jurisdictions around the world, public coverage in Ontario is relatively narrow given the focus on full financial protection only for hospital-based and physician-provided services, with inequitable protection for many other services (e.g., select treatments including prescription drugs and dental services).(17) Additionally, while not commonly highlighted, the rapidly aging population has also been identified as a source of intergenerational inequity in financing. In particular, the 'pay-as-you-go' financing model, where younger generations pay for the healthcare consumed by older generations, means that an increasingly higher proportion of costs are being borne by younger people through their taxes.(17)

Table 11.7: Financial protection and equity in financing

Summary of findings related to financial protection and equity in financing

Cross-sectoral

> Relative to comparator jurisdictions (excluding the U.S.), Ontario's public healthcare spending is considered 'low' due to narrow public coverage (17)

> Intergenerational inequities exist as a result of the current 'pay-as-you-go' healthcare financing model, where tax revenue is allocated toward healthcare expenditures that arise within the same year (17)
> - The growth in the number of adults 65 and older relative to the working-age population means government revenues are being extracted at increasingly higher proportions from the younger, smaller working population to provide for healthcare services
> - "As a result, the working generation is financially obliged to fund the healthcare cost for the generation that precedes it, carrying a disproportionately high financial burden."(p. 31)

Home and community care

— No assessments identified

Primary care

✗ The percentage of diabetes patients receiving a routine eye exam declined from 72% to 67% from 2003-04 to 2012-13, which may be associated with the confusion created when routine eye exams were delisted (while still covered for diabetes patients) (9)

Rehabilitation care

— No assessments identified

Long-term care

— No assessments identified

Public health

— No assessments identified

Select conditions

— No assessments identified

Select treatments

— No assessments identified

> Inequitable drug access results from the limited scope of public insurance (17)

✗ In 2014, 8% of Ontarians aged 55 or older (approximately one in 12) skipped medications because of cost, which is three to four times higher than many comparable countries (e.g., France, Germany, the Netherlands, Norway, Sweden, Switzerland and the U.K.) (9)

Select populations

— No assessments identified

Sources: 9; 17

Conclusion

While a review of the stated goals for the health system makes it clear that the pursuit of the 'triple aim' is important in the province, existing sources provide neither definitive nor comprehensive answers about whether each sector and the system as a whole are making progress towards achieving these goals. It can be said that progress is being made in improving some elements of the patient experience in a number of sectors, that the health of Ontarians is improving (although not all such improvements can be attributed to the health system), and that despite increases in the amount being spent on healthcare, the growth in per capita spending is similar to that in many other jurisdictions in Canada and internationally. It can also be said that significant challenges remain – and in some instances performance appears to be getting worse – within each of the 'triple aim' dimensions.

What is perhaps the most important take-away message from this chapter, however, is that the existing health-system performance evaluation landscape is not conducive to undertaking comprehensive assessments of system performance, particularly when measured against high-level system goals tied to the 'triple aim'. Some of the specific issues noted while preparing this chapter include:

- the lack of a centralized repository that enables access to systematically and transparently conducted health-system performance evaluations;
- the inconsistencies with which existing evaluations – even if published by the same organization – measure and report performance, including the indicators used, as well as the sectors, conditions, treatments and populations that are assessed;
- an imbalance in reporting, with some sectors getting more attention than others in assessments (e.g., specialty care), some conditions getting more attention than others (e.g., cancer), and some treatments getting more attention than others (e.g., drugs);
- notwithstanding initiatives such as HQO's 'Measuring up,' there are few routinely conducted performance evaluations that align indicators with stated health-system goals in order to provide information about whether progress is being made over time;
- critical health indicators that may be most appropriate from a patient perspective, such as health-related quality of life, are rarely measured and reported on (and there are no evaluations, to our knowledge, that

have measured this indicator over time);(20) and

- there is an abundance of one-off evaluations and reports that can only provide health-system performance 'snapshots.'

On a positive note, the *Patients First Act, 2016* presents a unique opportunity for health-system policymakers and stakeholders to converge upon a core set of goals that can be used to inform monitoring and evaluation efforts. Furthermore, efforts like HQO's 'Measuring up' reports and its Common Quality Agenda framework for integrated performance measurement, as well as the Cancer System Quality Index, suggest that those responsible for monitoring and evaluating system performance in Ontario are increasingly aware of the importance of ensuring consistency and comparability of indicators over time, as well as the importance of framing evaluations within stated goals. One challenge that remains to be addressed is the need to ensure the indicators selected to assess health-system performance are the right ones, and that focusing on some dimensions does not lead to the neglect of other dimensions. Regardless of any potential challenges, with time and the right investments, a clearer picture will likely emerge about how the system is performing, which will benefit the policymakers making decisions about how to improve the system, the health professionals working in the system, and the citizens whom the system serves.

References

1. Verma A, Bhatia S. A policy framework for health systems to promote triple aim innovation. *Healthcare Papers* 2016;15(3): 9-23.

2. Institute for Healthcare Improvement. IHI Triple Aim initiative. Cambridge: Institute for Healthcare Improvement; 2016. http://www.ihi.org/Engage/Initiatives/TripleAim/Pages/default.aspx (accessed 24 August 2016).

3. Bodenheimer T, Sinsky C. From triple to quadruple aim: Care of the patient requires care of the provider. *Annals of Family Medicine* 2014;12(6): 573-6.

4. Health Quality Ontario. Quality matters: Realizing excellent care for all. Toronto: Queen's Printer for Ontario; 2016.

5. Legislative Assembly of Ontario. Excellent Care for All Act, 2010, S.O. 2010, c. 14. Toronto: Queen's Printer for Ontario; 2010. https://www.ontario.ca/laws/statute/10e14#BK0 (accessed 24 August 2016).

6. Health Quality Ontario. Common quality agenda 2015. Toronto: Queen's Printer for Ontario; 2015.

7. Ministry of Health and Long-Term Care. Patients first: Action plan for health care. Toronto: Queen's Printer for Ontario; 2015.

8. Office of the Auditor General of Ontario. 2015 annual report of the Office of the Auditor General of Ontario. Toronto: Office of the Auditor General of Ontario; 2015.

9. Health Quality Ontario. Measuring up: HQO's 2015 yearly report. Toronto: Queen's Printer for Ontario; 2015.

10. Institute for Clinical Evaluative Sciences. 900,000 days in hospital: The annual impact of smoking, alcohol, diet and physical activity on hospital use in Ontario. Toronto: Institute for Clinical Evaluative Sciences; 2014.

11. Cancer Quality Council of Ontario. Cancer System Quality Index (CSQI) 2016. Toronto: Cancer Quality Council of Ontario; 2016. http://www.csqi.on.ca (accessed 25 August 2016).

12. Health Quality Ontario. Connecting the dots for patients. Family doctors' views on coordinating patient care in Ontario's health system. Toronto: Queen's Printer for Ontario; 2016.

13. Institute for Clinical Evaluative Sciences. Ontario and LHIN 2014/15 stroke report cards and progress reports: Active knowledge exchange to drive system integration and stroke best practices. Toronto: Institute for Clinical Evaluative Sciences; 2016.

14. Office of the Auditor General of Ontario. 2014 annual report of the Office of the Auditor General of Ontario. Toronto: Office of the Auditor General of Ontario; 2014.

15. The Conference Board of Canada. Final report: An external evaluation of the Family Health Team (FHT) initiative. Ottawa: The Conference Board of Canada; 2014.

16. Health Quality Ontario. Engaging with patients. Stories and successes from the 2015/2016 Quality Improvement Plans. Toronto: Health Quality Ontario; 2016. http://www.hqontario.ca/portals/0/documents/qi/qip/engaging-with-patients-en.pdf (accessed 7 October 2016).

17. Institute for Competitiveness & Prosperity. Building better health care: Policy opportunities for Ontario. Toronto: Institute for Competitiveness & Prosperity; 2014.

18. Office of the Auditor General of Ontario. Special report: Community Care Access Centres - Financial operations and service delivery. Toronto: Office of the Auditor General of Ontario; 2015.

19. Office of the Auditor General of Ontario. 2013 annual report of the Office of the Auditor General of Ontario. Toronto: Office of the Auditor General of Ontario; 2013.

20. Feeny D. Health-related quality-of-life data should be regarded as a vital sign. *Journal of Clinical Epidemiology* 2013;66(7): 706-9.

21. Health Quality Ontario. Experiencing integrated care. Ontarians' views of health care coordination and communication. Toronto: Queen's Printer for Ontario; 2015.

22. Health Quality Ontario. Measuring up: HQO's 2014 yearly report. Toronto: Queen's Printer for Ontario; 2014.

12. Conclusion

John N. Lavis

The primary goal in writing this book was to help to make Ontario's health system more understandable to the citizens who pay for it and are served by it, the professionals who work in it (and future professionals who will one day work in it), and the policymakers who govern it. The preceding 11 chapters have tried to do just that, and in each chapter we've distilled the key messages for each of these three groups. In this conclusion, we've distilled the key messages even further – to two per chapter – and emphasized points that are important for all three groups to understand. If someone asked any of the chapter authors how the Ontario health system works, Table 12.1 would be our 22-point response.

Table 12.1: Key features of the health system

Domain	Features
Introduction and overview	The health system is largely the responsibility of the Government of Ontario, albeit within certain broad rules set by the federal government (which apply only to medically necessary hospital-based and physician-provided care).
	Home and community care, acute specialty care, rehabilitation care and long-term care are increasingly being planned and integrated on a regional basis (and this is not yet true for primary care), with each region overseen by a Local Health Integration Network, or LHIN (and in the case of public health, with each local unit overseen by a board of health).
Building blocks of the system	
Governance arrangements	The Government of Ontario makes decisions in some areas (e.g., who is eligible for what prescription drugs as part of the Ontario Drug Benefit Program), and delegates decisions in other areas (e.g., to LHINs about planning, integrating and – with much less discretion – funding many types of care, to regulatory colleges about professional practice, and to government agencies about performance monitoring and in some cases performance management).
	Many of the organizations that provide care are private organizations – some not-for-profit (like almost all hospitals) and others for-profit (like community pharmacies and the facilities that perform blood tests and X-rays) – and these private organizations have a fair amount of discretion in many aspects of how they operate.
Financial arrangements	The money spent on the health system each year ($5,877 on average per Ontarian in 2013) comes largely from taxes paid to government (two thirds, much of which is spent on free-at-the-point-of-use hospital-based and physician-provided care) and from private sources like employer-sponsored insurance plans or out-of-pocket fees (one third, much of which is spent on prescription drugs).
	Many physicians are paid a set fee for each service they provide, although up to one third of all income received by physicians is now paid to them in other ways, whereas nurses and many other health professionals and workers are typically paid through salaries.

Continued on next page

Domain	Features

Building blocks of the system – continued

Delivery arrangements 1 • Infrastructure	The health system's infrastructure includes both the places where care is delivered (e.g., clinics, hospitals and long-term care homes) and the supports for that care (e.g., a tele-triage system called Telehealth Ontario, videoconferencing to provide clinical care at a distance through the Ontario Telemedicine Network, and electronic health records). Some infrastructure is the focus of formal capacity planning and capital spending by government (e.g., 151 private not-for-profit hospitals), whereas other parts are not (e.g., >800 community support service agencies, 184 Family Health Teams, and 934 Independent Health Facilities).
Delivery arrangements 2 • Workforce	The ranks of most of the 28 regulated health professions (e.g., nurses and physicians) and of many categories of unregulated health workers (e.g., personal support workers) have increased in number over the past decade, both in absolute number and in their density for every 100,000 Ontarians. The majority of Ontarians (94%) are registered with a primary-care provider (typically a physician), however, less than half (44%) report that they are able to see that provider the same or next day when they are sick.

Using the building blocks to provide care

Care by sector	Five of the system's six sectors have a 'key player,' which include Community Care Access Centres (the gateway to government-funded home care), primary-care teams or family physicians (for primary care), hospitals (for acute specialty care), long-term care homes, and local public health agencies. Rehabilitation care is an exception, both in lacking a key player and in being less a sector in its own right than an element of many other sectors.
Care for select conditions	Care for three groupings of conditions – mental health and addictions, work-related injuries and diseases, and cancer – operate to varying degrees within separate sub-systems of care, with cancer care being an almost fully parallel sub-system centred around an arm's-length provincial agency (Cancer Care Ontario) and 14 regional cancer centres. Key 'pieces' are in place for care at the end of life – nursing and personal support workers providing palliative home care services, primary-care providers delivering palliative care with the support of specialist palliative-care teams, and interprofessional palliative-care teams providing care in residential hospices, palliative-care units, and hospitals – but regional networks are just beginning to bring consistency to what can be expected from one community or region to the next.
Care using select treatments	Three broad categories of treatments – prescription and over-the-counter drugs, complementary and alternative therapies, and dental services – are paid for largely or almost entirely (65% for the first and 99-100% for the second and third) by private insurers or out-of-pocket. Prescription drugs are paid for by government, in whole or in part, when provided as part of home care, in hospital or in a long-term care home, but otherwise only if eligibility criteria are met for the Ontario Drug Benefit Program or select other drug and/or disease-specific programs (and drug program costs have grown dramatically in recent years).

Continued on next page

Domain	Features
Using the building blocks to provide care – continued	
Care for Indigenous peoples	Indigenous peoples have the same coverage and benefits as other citizens in the province (although geographic location, among other factors, can make accessing these programs and services difficult), and they can also access dedicated facilities (e.g., Aboriginal Health Access Centres), programs (e.g., Aboriginal Healthy Babies Healthy Children program), providers, and cultural and linguistic supports.
	While the health status of Indigenous peoples in Ontario tends to be worse than the non-Indigenous population, current strategies tend to adopt a positive, strengths-based approach to health improvement, and are rooted in Indigenous ways of knowing, governance and control.
Change and progress	
Reforms	The last decade and a half has been a time of many reforms, often initiated after key electoral events (especially the 2003 election), that have started to create a more integrated system.
	Planned reforms articulated in the *Patients First Act, 2016* include expanding the role of the LHINs in planning and integrating primary care and home and community care.
Performance	Evaluations of whether the health system is achieving the 'triple aim' of improving the patient experience and population health while keeping per capita costs manageable do not provide a balanced picture of performance across sectors (with more emphasis on acute specialty care), conditions (with more focus on cancer care), treatments (with more focus on prescription drugs) or populations (with limited emphasis on marginalized groups).
	These evaluations suggest that some improvements are being realized in terms of improving the patient experience and population health, although the unequal distribution of this progress across regions and rising per capita drug spending (which is among the highest in the world) continue to be a challenge.

The secondary goal in writing the book was to highlight some features of the health system that perhaps do not need to be that way. In the preface we called these features 'taken for granted' because, for the most part, they are features that many of us simply accept as 'the way things are' in the health system. However, they are features that struck us, individually or collectively, as curious as we drafted the chapters and acted on the feedback from the 41 policymakers, stakeholders and researchers who reviewed chapters or sections of chapters. We've again stuck to the 'two features per chapter' rule, so Table 12.2 offers 22 features for debate.

Identifying such features is in some ways a risky venture for us at the McMaster Health Forum. Two of our values – quality/excellence and inclusiveness – lead us to focus on the best available data and evidence and to respect all stakeholders' unique perspectives, not to impose our own values and preferences or to take a side in deliberations. By singling out these features, our hope is to start a discussion among citizens, professionals and policymakers, not to suggest that we have the answers or that the politics

Table 12.2: Some features of the health system that perhaps do not need to be that way

Domain	Features
Introduction and overview	Something has been lost in the movement away from the 'Ontario Health Insurance Plan' brand, which clearly conveyed a sense that Ontarians have pooled their risks of illness and injury through a publicly administered insurance plan (e.g., we now have a generic 'health' card instead of an Ontario Health Insurance Plan card).
	The public messaging about 'what is covered and the proportion of costs covered' that is used for hospital-based and physician-provided care (i.e., all medically necessary care, which is admittedly easier to convey) is lacking or confusing for key sectors (e.g., home care), 'conditions' (e.g., end of life), treatments (e.g., prescription drugs), and populations (e.g., Indigenous peoples).
Building blocks of the system	
Governance arrangements	The local community leaders sitting on hospital boards that operate with narrow perspectives (e.g., acute specialty care), many staff and volunteer supports, and significant fundraising capacity (and in many cases, direct access to elected politicians), are perhaps contributing less than they could if their perspectives were aligned with 'triple aim' objectives and their supports and capacity were spread across sectors (and especially in support of Local Health Integration Networks, or LHINs, home and community organizations, and community-governed primary-care teams).
	An uneven playing field in the standards for and accountabilities of the organizations that provide (or could provide) high volumes of low-risk diagnostic and therapeutic procedures (e.g., hospitals, Independent Health Facilities, and Out of Hospital Premises), and the lack of constraints on consolidation in laboratories and (to a lesser extent) pharmacies, among other factors, constrain the system's ability to benefit from competitive forces.
Financial arrangements	The purchaser-provider split (i.e., having independent organizations purchase products and services from providers, with process and outcome standards established through contracts) that has been used for cancer care, and to a lesser extent for home care and care for work-related injuries and diseases, has not been fully supported in LHINs (given so much of their expenditures are set through provincial formulae) and not considered for primary care.
	Sector-based bargaining over wages, benefits and employment conditions (e.g., for hospital nurses), and a historically rooted attachment to being small-business owners (e.g., among family physicians) complicate efforts to move beyond silos and towards a more integrated and equitable health system.
Delivery arrangements 1 • Infrastructure	Limited infrastructure data are available on key sectors (e.g., primary-care offices/clinics), conditions (e.g., mental health and addictions) and treatments (e.g., dental services), much capacity planning and capital spending takes place without public oversight, and despite significant capital spending on eHealth relatively few citizens can access all of their own health information or interact with health professionals online.
	Performance reporting is highly fragmented (across 21 hosts of publicly reported performance indicators for the health system) with unclear objectives, and infrastructure investments in healthcare-utilization data have not been matched by investments in collecting data related to most 'triple aim' objectives, or in harnessing the centres and initiatives that can inform how to address problems identified through healthcare-utilization data and 'triple aim' monitoring.

Continued on next page

Domain	Features

Building blocks of the system – continued

Delivery
arrangements 2
• Workforce

The 25-year-old legislation that created the (now) 26 regulatory colleges that oversee the 28 self-regulating health professions has been tinkered with but not comprehensively reviewed, and it leaves many categories of unregulated health workers requesting similar self-regulatory status (even if the public interest is already protected through regulations governing their workplace or other mechanisms).

Workforce planning is not yet needs-based, attentive to effective demand or regionally sensitive, continues to focus primarily on nurses and physicians, and still leaves many Ontarians with challenges in accessing timely primary and specialty care.

Using the building blocks to provide care

Care by sector

The health system's six sectors – home and community care, primary care, specialty care, rehabilitation care, long-term care, and public health – largely work in isolation from one another, with only limited recent efforts to actively support integration (instead of relying on the individual efforts of patients, caregivers and health professionals), including: 1) care coordination (though Health Links) across home, primary and specialty care for patients with complex needs; 2) 'bundled care' (a form of case-mix) funding of home and specialty care for patients receiving select treatments; and 3) the proposed LHIN sub-regional integration called for in the *Patients First Act, 2016* across home and primary care and public health.

The historical legacy of the hospital and medical (physician) insurance system has meant that the specialty sector is considered synonymous with hospitals and specialty physicians, and primary care is synonymous with family physicians, and the historical legacy of municipal government control over local public health agencies has meant that public health unit boundaries do not overlap with LHIN boundaries, and the agencies are not funded using a needs-based formula or challenged to focus more on population-based strategies (and less on the individual services that primary-care teams could bid on to provide).

Care for select
conditions

Care for three conditions or groupings of conditions – mental health and addictions, work-related injuries and diseases, and cancer – function in large part or almost fully as separate sub-systems of care, which can be seen as key to a high-performing sub-system (e.g., cancer care), a reflection of potentially unhelpful siloing (e.g., caring for mental and physical health separately), a contributor to inequities in access (e.g., buying preferential access to care when injuries are work-related), or some combination of all of these.

End-of-life care works well for some, but the system has been slow in standardizing models of palliative care and ensuring equitable access to these models.

Care using
select treatments

Prescription drugs can be very expensive and many Ontarians cannot afford the drugs prescribed for them despite the large and growing sums of money spent on public drug programs, which can lead them to forgo cost-effective treatments.

With only about 1% of dental-service expenditures paid for by government and no talk of connecting dental health professionals with interprofessional primary-care teams (including in the *Patients First Act, 2016*), dental services continue to be delivered in isolation of the broader health system.

Continued on next page

Domain	Features
Using the building blocks to provide care – continued	
Care for Indigenous peoples	Much care for Indigenous peoples does not recognize the legacies of colonization and racism or place western approaches alongside Indigenous approaches, which continue to contribute to shortfalls in care and disparities in health outcomes when compared to the non-Indigenous population.
	The 2016 Supreme Court decision effectively removed the historical distinction between on- and off-reserve First Nations, and between Métis and First Nations and Inuit, in terms of the federal government's fiduciary relationship with Indigenous peoples, which offers the opportunity for more integrated care for and in partnership with all Indigenous peoples.
Change and progress	
Reforms	The Government of Ontario's slow-and-steady approach to reforms (the 'tortoise' among a country of provincial 'hares') under an extended period with a single governing party has started to achieve gains, but still has a long way to go in creating a high-performing system.
	Political parties have so far not campaigned on, or achieved a political mandate for, a vision for a fully modernized health system that iteratively aligns incentives with 'triple aim' objectives and moves beyond silos in care, budgets and decision-making, while recognizing that citizens and health professionals need to be engaged in transitioning from a system built around hospitals and physicians more than 50 years ago, to a system that better meets their needs in the many sectors where they may obtain care, for the many conditions they may experience, and with the many treatments now available to them.
Performance	Existing approaches to monitoring and evaluation, which have both incomplete coverage and inconsistencies over time, leave significant imbalance in the health system's ability to identify and learn from where it is and is not achieving 'triple aim' objectives.
	Some performance indicators are improving, but the gains have rarely been significant either over time or compared to other comparable health systems.

of the health system are conducive to action at this time.

Unlike the books describing other health systems, our approach in this book has involved more fully delineating the building blocks that comprise the health system, dramatically expanding coverage of how care works in different sectors, for different conditions and treatments, and for a select population (Indigenous peoples), using robust frameworks for assessing reforms and performance, and attempting to engage a broader group of target audiences than the small group of health-system experts who typically read such books. If we haven't fully got it right this time, we will continue moving towards getting it right in the next and future editions.

A paragraph from the preface bears repeating here. We apologize for any errors in the text, tables or figures that escaped our scrutiny. We welcome corrections, updates and feedback, as well as suggestions for conditions, treatments and populations that we do not cover in the book, so that we can incorporate them when we create an eBook (which we plan to do in 2017), and when we update the print version of the book (which we plan to do periodically). Indeed we ask you the same questions we asked our 41 reviewers:

1) do the key messages appropriately highlight what each of engaged citizens, engaged professionals and engaged policymakers need to know (and if not, what would you recommend changing)?

2) do we get the 'big picture' right (and if not, what would you recommend emphasizing or de-emphasizing)?

3) do we get any of the details wrong (and if so, what would you recommend correcting and, if applicable, what citation(s) would you recommend be used to support the corrected content)?

4) do we present material in a fair and balanced way (and if not, what content or wording would you recommend be changed)?

5) do we use language that is appropriate for an audience comprised of engaged citizens, professionals and policymakers?

Please send your comments to mhf@mcmaster.ca.

81394706R00244

Made in the USA
Lexington, KY
16 February 2018